NEW EDITION

S0-BYJ-030

Teacher's Edition

WORKBOOK for New Progress in Mathematics

An innovative approach including *two* options:

- Pre-Algebra
- Algebra

Rose Anita McDonnell

Catherine D. LeTourneau

Anne Veronica Burrows

with

Dr. Elinor R. Ford

Sadlier-Oxford
A Division of William H. Sadlier, Inc.

Copyright ©1993 by William H. Sadlier, Inc. All rights reserved. This book, or any part thereof, may not be reproduced in any form, or by any means, including electronic, photographic, or mechanical, or by any sound recording system, or by any device for storage and retrieval of information, without the written permission of the publisher. Printed in the United States of America.

Home Office: 9 Pine Street,
New York, NY 10005
ISBN 0-8215-1758-9
5678910/1009080706

Table of Contents

Whole Numbers to Trillions*

Name ____________________

Date ____________________

Use the place value chart below to write the following numbers.

1. eleven million, six hundred forty thousand, eighteen
2. eighty-two billion, nine million, two thousand ten
3. ten trillion, five hundred million, two thousand

	Trillions period			Billions period			Millions period			Thousands period			Ones period		
	hundreds	tens	ones	hundreds	tens	ones	hundreds	tens	ones	hundreds	tens	ones	hundreds	tens	ones
1.								1	1	6	4	0	0	1	8
2.					8	2	0	0	9	0	0	2	0	1	0
3.		1	0	0	0	0	5	0	0	0	0	2	0	0	0

In what place is the underlined digit? What is its value?

4. 24,679 thousands; 4 thousands
5. 109,672,521 ten millions; 0 ten millions
6. 94,276,541,327 ten billions; 9 ten billions
7. 6,846,972,420 ten thousands; 7 ten thousands
8. 125,473,890,367 ten billions; 2 ten billions
9. 2,075,398,123 billions; 2 billions
10. 63,520,641 hundreds; 6 hundreds
11. 9,999,999,999,001 hundred billions; 9 hundred billions
12. 5,382,492,770 ten thousands; 9 ten thousands

Use these numbers to answer the following questions:
a. 8,752,461,304,001
b. 662,491,307,262,859

13. The value of 5 in **a** is how many times greater than the value of 5 in **b**? one billion times greater
14. The value of 3 in **a** is how many times less than the value of 3 in **b**? one thousand times less
15. The value of 8 in **a** is how many times greater than the value of 8 in **b**? 10 billion times greater

Solve.

16. About how old would you be if you lived until you were a billion hours old? 114,000 yr

    1,000,000,000 ÷ (24 × 365)

17. About how many years have passed since a trillion hours ago? Was America discovered yet? Were the pyramids built? 114,000,000 yr; No; No

    1,000,000,000,000 ÷ (24 × 365)

18. The current population of the United States is about 251,400,000 people. The annual budget is about $3 trillion. How much would this be per person in the country? about $12,000

    3,000,000,000,000 ÷ 251,400,000

*Use with Lesson 1-1, text pages 2–3.

Copyright © Sadlier-Oxford

Reading and Writing Whole Numbers and Decimals*

Name ______________________

Date ______________________

Read each number. Give the value of the circled digit.

1. 34.2⓪676 — 0 hundredths
2. 98.5050① — 1 hundred thousandths
3. 118.⑦4213 — 7 tenths
4. 2.②2222 — 2 tenths
5. 0.69138⑦ — 7 millionths
6. 442.922④26 — 4 ten thousandths

Write in standard form.

7. (8 × 10,000) + (4 × 100) + (2 × 1) — 80,402
8. (5 × 100,000) + (3 × 1000) + (6 × 1) — 503,006
9. (7 × 0.1) + (8 × 0.0001) — 0.7008
10. (5 × 0.1) + (9 × 0.0001) — 0.5009

Write the standard numeral.

11. 6 million — 6,000,000
12. 82 billion — 82,000,000,000
13. 7 billion — 7,000,000,000
14. 95 trillion — 95,000,000,000,000
15. 4.2 billion — 4,200,000,000
16. 5.1 million — 5,100,000
17. 3.8 trillion — 3,800,000,000,000
18. 7.75 billion — 7,750,000,000

Write the number that is named by the *scrambled* digits in exercises 19–21.

19. 8 millionths
0 thousandths
6 tenths
3 ones
5 ten thousandths
3.600508

20. 2 thousands
9 millionths
9 ones
5 tenths
1 ten thousandth
2009.500109

21. 2 hundredths
6 billionths
9 ten thousandths
8 millionths
2 thousandths
0.022908006

22. Write the *least* number using the digits 0,9,8,7,6 each once. 60,789
23. Write the *greatest* number using the digits 0,9,8,7,6 each once. 98,760
24. Write the number that is exactly 5,000,000 *less* than 9,125,799. 4,125,799
25. Write the number that is 0.012345 *greater* than 1.070707. 1.083052

*Use with Lesson 1-1, text pages 2–3.

Copyright © Sadlier-Oxford

Adding and Subtracting Whole Numbers and Decimals*

Name ______________________
Date ______________________

Find the sum or difference.

1.
$$\begin{array}{r} 0.3714 \\ 0.2401 \\ 0.096 \\ 0.4412 \\ +\ 0.55 \\ \hline 1.6987 \end{array}$$

2.
$$\begin{array}{r} 0.764 \\ 0.4036 \\ 0.5271 \\ 0.321 \\ +\ 0.908 \\ \hline 2.9237 \end{array}$$

3.
$$\begin{array}{r} 0.2 \\ 0.364 \\ 0.101 \\ 0.8964 \\ +\ 0.9 \\ \hline 2.4614 \end{array}$$

4.
$$\begin{array}{r} 0.48 \\ 0.6801 \\ 0.725 \\ 0.655 \\ +\ 0.861 \\ \hline 3.4011 \end{array}$$

5.
$$\begin{array}{r} 10.27 \\ -\ 4.38 \\ \hline 5.89 \end{array}$$

6.
$$\begin{array}{r} 27.82 \\ -\ 9.47 \\ \hline 18.35 \end{array}$$

7.
$$\begin{array}{r} 47.801 \\ -\ 9.38 \\ \hline 38.421 \end{array}$$

8.
$$\begin{array}{r} 702.08 \\ -\ 96.4 \\ \hline 605.68 \end{array}$$

9. $0.41 + 0.328 + 0.92 + 0.1435 =$ 1.8015

10. $38 - 4.921 =$ 33.079

11. $0.8654 + 0.9284 + 0.91 =$ 2.7038

12. $5.7 - 0.346 =$ 5.354

13. $5.1023 + 1.06 + 2.007 + 6.8 =$ 14.9693

14. $18.1 - 9.341 =$ 8.759

Estimate by rounding each number to the nearest tenth.

15.
$$\begin{array}{r} 0.324 \\ 0.9281 \\ 0.24 \\ +\ 0.8361 \\ \hline \end{array} \quad \begin{array}{r} 0.3 \\ 0.9 \\ 0.2 \\ +\ 0.8 \\ \hline 2.2 \end{array}$$

16.
$$\begin{array}{r} 1.207 \\ -\ 0.46 \\ \hline \end{array} \quad \begin{array}{r} 1.2 \\ -\ 0.5 \\ \hline 0.7 \end{array}$$

17.
$$\begin{array}{r} 0.24 \\ 0.3416 \\ 0.291 \\ 0.834 \\ +\ 0.33 \\ \hline \end{array} \quad \begin{array}{r} 0.2 \\ 0.3 \\ 0.3 \\ 0.8 \\ +\ 0.3 \\ \hline 1.9 \end{array}$$

Estimate by rounding each number to the nearest whole number.

18.
$$\begin{array}{r} 27.046 \\ -\ 13.9 \\ \hline \end{array} \quad \begin{array}{r} 27 \\ -\ 14 \\ \hline 13 \end{array}$$

19.
$$\begin{array}{r} 824.06 \\ -\ 421.73 \\ \hline \end{array} \quad \begin{array}{r} 824 \\ -\ 422 \\ \hline 402 \end{array}$$

20.
$$\begin{array}{r} 38.53 \\ -\ 18.49 \\ \hline \end{array} \quad \begin{array}{r} 39 \\ -\ 18 \\ \hline 21 \end{array}$$

*Use with Lessons 1-4, 1-5, text pages 8–11.

Copyright © Sadlier-Oxford

Multiplying Whole Numbers*

Name ______________________

Date ______________________

Multiply.

1. 8261 × 438
3,618,318

2. 9063 × 71
643,473

3. 6428 × 207
1,330,596

4. 3498 × 276
965,448

5. 4307 × 691
2,976,137

6. 8041 × 257
2,066,537

7. 5476 × 355
1,943,980

8. 6010 × 305
1,833,050

9. 2041 × 920
1,877,720

10. 5376 × 208
1,118,208

11. 9008 × 467
4,206,736

12. 3276 × 891
2,918,916

Estimate by rounding each number to its greatest place-value position.

13. 6041 × 935 5,400,000
6000 × 900

14. 888 × 222 180,000
900 × 200

15. 782 × 43 32,000
800 × 40

16. 8965 × 423 3,600,000
9000 × 400

17. 12,423 × 9 90,000
10,000 × 9

18. 53,219 × 452 25,000,000
50,000 × 500

19. 302,009 × 52 15,000,000
300,000 × 50

20. 87,526 × 347 27,000,000
90,000 × 300

21. 472,351 × 63 30,000,000
500,000 × 60

22. 92,718 × 586 54,000,000
90,000 × 600

*Use with Lesson 1-6, text pages 12–13.

Copyright © Sadlier-Oxford

Multiplying Decimals*

Name ______________________
Date ______________________

Find the product.

1. 23.4 × 8.6 = 201.24
2. 4.076 × 3.9 = 15.8964
3. 421.7 × 0.076 = 32.0492
4. 8.71 × 0.421 = 3.66691
5. 80.63 × 9.07 = 731.3141
6. 24.6 × 3.82 = 93.972
7. 5.071 × 0.34 = 1.72414
8. 7.031 × 2.7 = 18.9837
9. 4.075 × 3.12 = 12.714
10. 8.076 × 0.5 = 4.038
11. 4.071 × 3.7 = 15.0627
12. 72.51 × 0.08 = 5.8008
13. 8.055 × 9.3 = 74.9115
14. 84.75 × 1.05 = 88.9875
15. 3.067 × 9.1 = 27.9097
16. 6.934 × 0.8 = 5.5472

Estimate by rounding each number to its greatest place-value position.

17. 43.6 × 8.9 — 360 (40×9)
18. 59.09 × 21.6 — 1200 (60×20)
19. 0.086 × 3.5 — 0.36 (0.09×4)
20. 32.4 × 0.91 — 27 (30×0.9)
21. 80.6 × 1.7 — 160 (80×2)
22. 302.4 × 0.079 — 24 (300×0.08)

Solve.

23. Find the cost of 11.3 meters of plastic tubing if one meter costs $.72.

C = 11.3 × $.72; $8.14

24. Find the weight of 4.65 meters of copper tubing if one meter weighs 1.2 kg.

W = 4.65 × 1.2; 5.58 kg

*Use with Lesson 1-6, text pages 12–13.

Copyright © Sadlier-Oxford

Dividing Whole Numbers*

Name ______________________

Date ______________________

Divide.

1. 63)49,140 — 780	**2.** 54)24,300 — 450	**3.** 91)820,850 — 9 020 R30	**4.** 86)68,807 — 800 R7
5. 73)29,721 — 407 R10	**6.** 58)43,500 — 750	**7.** 92)55,209 — 600 R9	**8.** 65)63,245 — 973
9. 46)43,746 — 951	**10.** 75)73,650 — 982	**11.** 85)57,800 — 680	**12.** 76)63,769 — 839 R5
13. 103)3720 — 36 R12	**14.** 259)21,497 — 83	**15.** 481)32,708 — 68	**16.** 607)126,260 — 208 R4
17. 570)263,977 — 463 R67	**18.** 349)16,098 — 46 R44	**19.** 462)23,123 — 50 R23	**20.** 709)19,800 — 27 R657

Estimate by rounding each number to its greatest place-value position.

21. 2967 ÷ 62 — 50
3000 ÷ 60

22. 1904 ÷ 36 — 50
2000 ÷ 40

23. 38,416 ÷ 47 — 800
40,000 ÷ 50

24. 356,124 ÷ 18 — 20,000
400,000 ÷ 20

25. 423 ÷ 15 — 20
400 ÷ 20

26. 76,032 ÷ 413 — 200
80,000 ÷ 400

*Use with Lesson 1-7, text pages 14–15.

Copyright © Sadlier-Oxford

Dividing Decimals*

Name ______________________

Date ______________________

Find the quotient.

1. 9)1.44 — 0.16
2. 2)3.46 — 1.73
3. 24)81.6 — 3.4
4. 29)72.413 — 2.497
5. 0.9)18.27 — 20.3
6. 0.02)16.43 — 821.5
7. 1.5)25.305 — 16.87
8. 0.07)217.42 — 3106

Find the quotient to the nearest hundredth.

9. 2.3)46.07 — 20.03
10. 4.8)95.41 — 19.88
11. 3.4)6.317 — 1.86
12. 5.06)94.84 — 18.74

Estimate by rounding each number to its greatest place-value position.

13. 0.39 ÷ 8 = 0.05
    0.4 ÷ 8
14. 8.51 ÷ 2.71 = 3
    9 ÷ 3
15. 24.14 ÷ 0.41 = 50
    20 ÷ 0.4
16. 4.38 ÷ 0.95 = 4
    4 ÷ 1
17. 5.68 ÷ 2.94 = 2
    6 ÷ 3
18. 3.91 ÷ 0.39 = 10
    4 ÷ 0.4

Solve.

19. How much paint is required to paint one window frame if 18.45 L are needed for 45 frames?
    p = 18.45 ÷ 45
    0.41 L
20. Which costs less per kilogram: 3.25 kg of buttons for $2.11 or 4.45 kg of metal snaps for $3.65?
    b = $2.11 ÷ 3.25; s = $3.65 ÷ 4.45
    buttons

*Use with Lesson 1-8, text pages 16 – 17.

Copyright © Sadlier-Oxford

Estimating Whole Numbers and Decimals*

Name ______________________

Date ______________________

Compare. Use <, =, or >.

1. 400×90 __=__ 40×900
2. 6×600 __=__ 60×60
3. 300×700 __>__ 2.1×1000
4. 0.5×52.2 __<__ 1000×0.522
5. 0.487×500 __=__ 0.5×487
6. $9.09 \div 30$ __<__ $30 \div 9.09$

Estimate the sum or difference. Accept reasonable estimates.

7. 47,300 + 25,620 + 24,100 + 10,520 __107,500__
8. 6.96 + 12.22 + 8.65 + 9.01 + 3.25 __40__
9. 13.001 + 5.021 + 4.225 + 8.002 __30.2__

Estimate the product or quotient. Accept reasonable estimates.

10. 840×21 __16,000__
    800 × 20
11. $14{,}268 \times 39$ __560,000__
    14,000 × 40
12. 10.6×5.8 __66__
    11 × 6
13. $6448 \div 31$ __200__
    6000 ÷ 30
14. $51{,}416 \div 18$ __2,500__
    50,000 ÷ 20
15. $36.8 \div 4.2$ __9__
    36 ÷ 4

Find unreasonable answers. Write R for reasonable; U for unreasonable.
Estimate. Do not compute.

16. $1{,}411 + 3{,}656 + 7{,}722 \approx 13{,}000$ __R__
17. $4.8 + 3.9 + 7.2 + 0.8 \approx 16$ __R__
18. $72{,}328 \div 7.7 \approx 8200$ __U__
19. $426 \times 34.5 \approx 15{,}000$ __R__

Solve.

20. Create a division problem with whole numbers to fit these descriptions.
    a. A 5-digit number is divided by a 3-digit number. The remainder is 124. __Answers will vary.__
    b. A 4-digit number is divided by a 3-digit number. The remainder is 60. __Answers will vary.__
    c. A 6-digit number is divided by a 3-digit number. The remainder is 30. __Answers will vary.__

*Use with Lesson 1-9, text pages 18–19.

Copyright © Sadlier-Oxford

Number Properties*
(And Computational Shortcuts)

Name ______________________
Date ______________________

Match each example with the number property used to solve it. Use each example only once.

1. __e__ Identity for multiplication
2. __b__ Commutative for addition
3. __h__ Commutative and associative for multiplication
4. __f__ Associative for addition
5. __g__ Commutative and identity for addition
6. __c__ Distributive
7. __j__ Commutative for multiplication
8. __a__ Identity for addition
9. __i__ Commutative and associative for addition
10. __d__ Associative for multiplication

a. $341{,}296 + [49 - (7 \times 7)]$

b. $86 + 95 + 814 + 505 = 86 + 814 + 95 + 505$

c. $(8 \times 49) + (38 \times 49) = (8 + 38) \times 49$

d. $92 \times 10 \times 48 \times 2 = (94 \times 10) \times (48 \times 2)$

e. $(9 \div 9) \times 3247$

f. $12 + 8 + 24 + 64 = (12 + 8) + (24 + 64)$

g. $8.6 + 921 - 8.6 = 8.6 - 8.6 + 921$

h. $92 \times 43 \times 2 \times 20 = 92 \times 2 \times 43 \times 20 = (92 \times 2) \times (43 \times 20)$

i. $194 + 87 + 106 + 413 = 194 + 106 + 87 + 413 = (194 + 106) + (87 + 413)$

j. $8 \times 43 \times 21 = 8 \times 21 \times 43$

Solve. Use properties wherever possible.

11. $(7 \times 28) + (7 \times 42) =$ __490__
$7(28+42)$

12. $2.5 \times 813 \times 2 =$ __4065__
$(2.5 \times 2) \times 813$

13. $4.2 + 3.7 + 0.8 =$ __8.7__
$(4.2 + 0.8) + 3.7$

14. $4 \times 0.25 \times 847 =$ __847__
$(4 \times 0.25) \times 847$

15. $46 + 92 + 31 + 54 + 69 + 8 =$ __300__
$(46+54)+(92+8)+(31+69)$

16. $8.5 + [9.23 - (5.41 - 3.82)] =$ __16.14__

Compare. Write <, =, or >.

17. 20×20 __=__ 400

18. $(1.4 \times 0.4) + (1.4 \times 0.2)$ __<__ (1.4×0.9)

19. 2.83×2.61 __=__ 2.61×2.83

20. 3.41×100 __>__ 0.341×10

21. 3×120 __<__ 40×90

22. 470×50 __=__ 47×500

*Use with Lesson 1-10, text pages 20–21.

Copyright © Sadlier-Oxford

Fractions and Mixed Numbers*

Name ______________________

Date ______________________

Change each to a fraction.

1. $5\frac{1}{3} = \frac{16}{3}$	**2.** $7\frac{2}{5} = \frac{37}{5}$	**3.** $8\frac{1}{9} = \frac{73}{9}$	**4.** $6\frac{1}{4} = \frac{25}{4}$
5. $3\frac{2}{3} = \frac{11}{3}$	**6.** $4\frac{2}{9} = \frac{38}{9}$	**7.** $2\frac{1}{8} = \frac{17}{8}$	**8.** $12\frac{1}{10} = \frac{121}{10}$
9. $14\frac{1}{5} = \frac{71}{5}$	**10.** $2\frac{3}{7} = \frac{17}{7}$	**11.** $9\frac{3}{5} = \frac{48}{5}$	**12.** $3\frac{1}{4} = \frac{13}{4}$
13. $13\frac{2}{5} = \frac{67}{5}$	**14.** $8\frac{3}{11} = \frac{91}{11}$	**15.** $16\frac{2}{3} = \frac{50}{3}$	**16.** $8\frac{3}{9} = \frac{75}{9}$
17. $20\frac{5}{6} = \frac{125}{6}$	**18.** $9\frac{10}{11} = \frac{109}{11}$	**19.** $12\frac{4}{5} = \frac{64}{5}$	**20.** $10\frac{5}{13} = \frac{135}{13}$
21. $16\frac{4}{5} = \frac{84}{5}$	**22.** $8\frac{2}{7} = \frac{58}{7}$	**23.** $12\frac{3}{8} = \frac{99}{8}$	**24.** $20\frac{2}{3} = \frac{62}{3}$

Change each to a mixed number. (Show the fraction part in simplest form.)

25. $\frac{29}{3} = 9\frac{2}{3}$	**26.** $\frac{89}{5} = 17\frac{4}{5}$	**27.** $\frac{17}{3} = 5\frac{2}{3}$	**28.** $\frac{9}{7} = 1\frac{2}{7}$
29. $\frac{36}{7} = 5\frac{1}{7}$	**30.** $\frac{41}{9} = 4\frac{5}{9}$	**31.** $\frac{82}{7} = 11\frac{5}{7}$	**32.** $\frac{48}{5} = 9\frac{3}{5}$
33. $\frac{31}{6} = 5\frac{1}{6}$	**34.** $\frac{53}{10} = 5\frac{3}{10}$	**35.** $\frac{49}{5} = 9\frac{4}{5}$	**36.** $\frac{75}{8} = 9\frac{3}{8}$
37. $\frac{52}{7} = 7\frac{3}{7}$	**38.** $\frac{39}{4} = 9\frac{3}{4}$	**39.** $\frac{28}{3} = 9\frac{1}{3}$	**40.** $\frac{32}{5} = 6\frac{2}{5}$
41. $\frac{91}{4} = 22\frac{3}{4}$	**42.** $\frac{88}{6} = 14\frac{2}{3}$	**43.** $\frac{148}{12} = 12\frac{1}{3}$	**44.** $\frac{175}{13} = 13\frac{6}{13}$
45. $\frac{162}{4} = 40\frac{1}{2}$	**46.** $\frac{189}{10} = 18\frac{9}{10}$	**47.** $\frac{215}{15} = 14\frac{1}{3}$	**48.** $\frac{420}{22} = 19\frac{1}{11}$

Solve.

49. José worked for $3\frac{3}{4}$ hours. Change this mixed number to a fraction. $\frac{15}{4}$

50. Jessica pitched $\frac{10}{3}$ innings of the softball game. Change this fraction to a mixed number. $3\frac{1}{3}$

51. Heather used $2\frac{2}{3}$ cups of flour in her recipe. Change this mixed number to a fraction. $\frac{8}{3}$

52. Zach is $\frac{65}{12}$ feet tall. Change this fraction to a mixed number. $5\frac{5}{12}$

*Use with Lesson 2-1, text pages 32–33.

Copyright © Sadlier-Oxford

Equivalent Fractions*

Name ______________________

Date ______________________

Complete to show equivalent fractions for each.

1. $\frac{1}{5} = \frac{\boxed{2}}{10} = \frac{\boxed{4}}{20} = \frac{\boxed{6}}{30} = \frac{8}{\boxed{40}}$

2. $\frac{2}{7} = \frac{\boxed{4}}{14} = \frac{\boxed{6}}{21} = \frac{10}{\boxed{35}} = \frac{14}{\boxed{49}}$

3. $\frac{2}{9} = \frac{\boxed{4}}{18} = \frac{\boxed{10}}{45} = \frac{16}{\boxed{72}} = \frac{\boxed{18}}{81}$

4. $\frac{7}{10} = \frac{\boxed{14}}{20} = \frac{35}{\boxed{50}} = \frac{\boxed{70}}{100} = \frac{140}{\boxed{200}}$

5. $\frac{3}{13} = \frac{\boxed{6}}{26} = \frac{15}{\boxed{65}} = \frac{\boxed{24}}{104} = \frac{30}{\boxed{130}}$

6. $\frac{3}{4} = \frac{\boxed{15}}{20} = \frac{21}{\boxed{28}} = \frac{\boxed{27}}{36} = \frac{36}{\boxed{48}}$

Complete each equivalent fraction.

7. $\frac{8}{9} = \frac{\boxed{64}}{72}$

8. $\frac{4}{7} = \frac{\boxed{12}}{21}$

9. $\frac{3}{5} = \frac{\boxed{24}}{40}$

10. $\frac{2}{9} = \frac{\boxed{14}}{63}$

11. $\frac{42}{49} = \frac{6}{\boxed{7}}$

12. $\frac{3}{10} = \frac{6}{\boxed{20}}$

13. $\frac{10}{15} = \frac{2}{\boxed{3}}$

14. $\frac{12}{30} = \frac{2}{\boxed{5}}$

15. $\frac{25}{50} = \frac{\boxed{5}}{10}$

16. $\frac{4}{5} = \frac{28}{\boxed{35}}$

17. $\frac{12}{48} = \frac{\boxed{3}}{12}$

18. $\frac{55}{110} = \frac{1}{\boxed{2}}$

Write each fraction in simplest form.

19. $\frac{40}{56} = \frac{5}{7}$

20. $\frac{16}{24} = \frac{2}{3}$

21. $\frac{8}{20} = \frac{2}{5}$

22. $\frac{18}{72} = \frac{1}{4}$

23. $\frac{15}{45} = \frac{1}{3}$

24. $\frac{7}{11} = \frac{7}{11}$

25. $\frac{81}{108} = \frac{3}{4}$

26. $\frac{14}{21} = \frac{2}{3}$

27. $\frac{14}{56} = \frac{1}{4}$

28. $\frac{20}{56} = \frac{5}{14}$

29. $\frac{49}{70} = \frac{7}{10}$

30. $\frac{19}{29} = \frac{19}{29}$

31. $\frac{28}{36} = \frac{7}{9}$

32. $\frac{54}{78} = \frac{9}{13}$

33. $\frac{48}{144} = \frac{1}{3}$

34. $\frac{18}{48} = \frac{3}{8}$

35. $\frac{36}{42} = \frac{6}{7}$

36. $\frac{16}{48} = \frac{1}{3}$

37. $\frac{27}{42} = \frac{9}{14}$

38. $\frac{24}{28} = \frac{6}{7}$

*Use with Lesson 2-2, text pages 34–35.

Copyright © Sadlier-Oxford

Factors, Prime and Composite Numbers*

Name ____________________
Date ____________________

List the factors of each of the following numbers.

1. 14 1, 2, 7, 14
2. 21 1, 3, 7, 21
3. 35 1, 5, 7, 35
4. 25 1, 5, 25
5. 8 1, 2, 4, 8
6. 75 1, 3, 5, 15, 25, 75
7. 15 1, 3, 5, 15
8. 39 1, 3, 13, 39
9. 30 1, 2, 3, 5, 6, 10, 15, 30
10. 36 1, 2, 3, 4, 6, 9, 12, 18, 36
11. 60 1, 2, 3, 4, 5, 6, 10, 12, 15, 20, 30, 60
12. 72 1, 2, 3, 4, 6, 8, 9, 12, 18, 24, 36, 72
13. 120 1, 2, 3, 4, 5, 6, 8, 10, 12, 15, 20, 24, 30, 40, 60, 120

Find the prime numbers that complete each of these statements.

14. 2 + 3 = 5
15. 5 + 7 = 12
16. 2 + 59 = 61

Find the prime numbers between 100 and 200.

17. Use a calculator to find the numbers that are multiples of other numbers. Cross out these numbers on the chart. The numbers left are the prime numbers between 100 and 200. (Hint: You do not have to try a prime factor greater than 13.)

Prime Numbers

101	~~102~~	103	~~104~~	~~105~~	~~106~~	107	~~108~~	109	~~110~~
~~111~~	~~112~~	113	~~114~~	~~115~~	~~116~~	~~117~~	~~118~~	~~119~~	~~120~~
~~121~~	~~122~~	~~123~~	~~124~~	~~125~~	~~126~~	127	~~128~~	~~129~~	~~130~~
131	~~132~~	~~133~~	~~134~~	~~135~~	~~136~~	137	~~138~~	139	~~140~~
~~141~~	~~142~~	~~143~~	~~144~~	~~145~~	~~146~~	~~147~~	~~148~~	149	~~150~~
151	~~152~~	~~153~~	~~154~~	~~155~~	~~156~~	157	~~158~~	~~159~~	~~160~~
~~161~~	~~162~~	163	~~164~~	~~165~~	~~166~~	167	~~168~~	~~169~~	~~170~~
~~171~~	~~172~~	173	~~174~~	~~175~~	~~176~~	~~177~~	~~178~~	179	~~180~~
181	~~182~~	~~183~~	~~184~~	~~185~~	~~186~~	~~187~~	~~188~~	~~189~~	~~190~~
191	~~192~~	193	~~194~~	~~195~~	~~196~~	197	~~198~~	199	~~200~~

*Use with Lesson 2-3, text page 36.

Copyright © Sadlier-Oxford

Prime Factorization*

Name ______________________

Date ______________________

Draw a factor tree for each number. Then give the prime factorization for each.

1. 56 $2^3 \times 7$

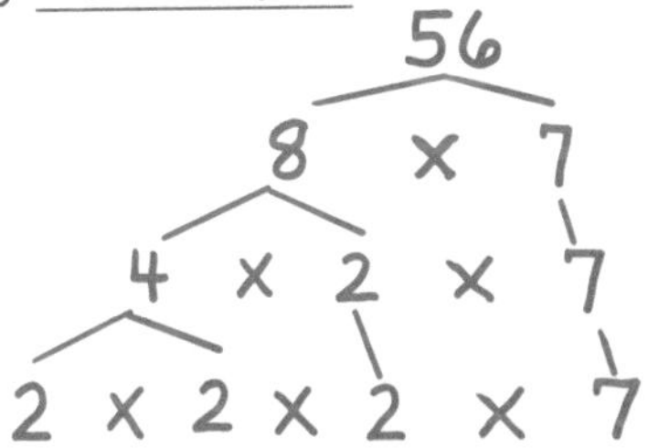

2. 42 $2 \times 3 \times 7$

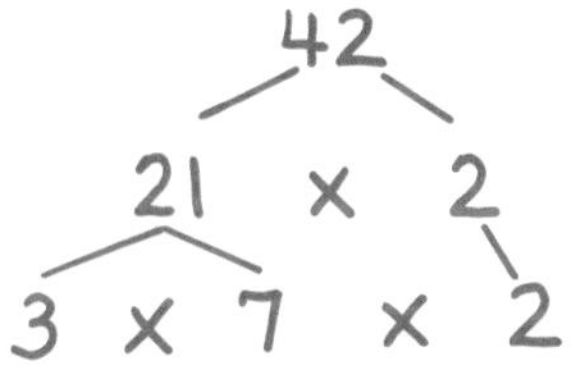

Write the prime factorization of each number using exponents.

3. 44 11×2^2

4. 32 2^5

5. 18 $3^2 \times 2$

6. 72 $2^3 \times 3^2$

7. 120 $2^3 \times 3 \times 5$

8. 105 $3 \times 5 \times 7$

9. 20 $2^2 \times 5$

10. 65 5×13

11. 90 $2 \times 3^2 \times 5$

12. 180 $2^2 \times 3^2 \times 5$

13. 48 $2^4 \times 3$

14. 78 $2 \times 3 \times 13$

Write the composite number for each prime factorization.

15. $2^3 \times 3^3$ 216

16. $2 \times 3^3 \times 7$ 378

17. $3^2 \times 11$ 99

18. $2^2 \times 5^2$ 100

19. $2^3 \times 3^3 \times 7$ 1512

20. $2^5 \times 5$ 160

21. $3 \times 7^2 \times 11$ 1617

22. $2^4 \times 3^2$ 144

23. 3×5^2 75

24. $3^2 \times 7^2$ 441

25. $3^2 \times 5 \times 13$ 585

26. $5 \times 11 \times 13$ 715

*Use with Lesson 2-4, text page 37.

Copyright © Sadlier-Oxford

Greatest Common Factor; Least Common Multiple*

Name ______________________

Date ______________________

Find the GCF.

1. 15 and 18 3

2. 56 and 16 8

3. 42 and 63 21

4. 70 and 28 14

5. 28 and 56 28

6. 35 and 15 5

7. 14 and 84 14

8. 30 and 45 15

9. 28 and 36 4

10. 14 and 49 7

Write the prime factorization in exponential form. Then write the GCF.

11. 9 3^2
12 $2^2 \times 3$
GCF: 3

12. 24 $2^3 \times 3$
18 2×3^2
GCF: 6

13. 8 2^3
20 $2^2 \times 5$
GCF: 4

14. 50 2×5^2
75 3×5^2
GCF: 25

Find the LCM.

15. 12 and 8 24

16. 3 and 8 24

17. 6 and 9 18

18. 4 and 10 20

19. 5 and 6 30

20. 2 and 7 14

21. 8 and 10 40

22. 18 and 3 18

23. 9 and 5 45

24. 36 and 9 36

Write the prime factorization in exponential form. Then write the LCM.

25. 6 2×3
8 2^3
LCM: 24

26. 20 $2^2 \times 5$
25 5^2
LCM: 100

27. 8 2^3
12 $2^2 \times 3$
40 $2^3 \times 5$
LCM: 120

28. 35 5×7
60 $2^2 \times 3 \times 5$
70 $2 \times 5 \times 7$
LCM: 420

*Use with Lessons 2-5, 2-6, text pages 38–39.

Copyright © Sadlier-Oxford

Renaming Fractions*

Name ______________________

Date ______________________

Use a power of ten to change each to a decimal.

1. $\frac{4}{50}$ = 0.08 **2.** $\frac{9}{25}$ = 0.36 **3.** $\frac{19}{20}$ = 0.95 **4.** $\frac{1}{10}$ = 0.1

5. $2\frac{1}{2}$ = 2.5 **6.** $4\frac{1}{25}$ = 4.04 **7.** $6\frac{1}{5}$ = 6.2 **8.** $7\frac{1}{20}$ = 7.05

Change each to a terminating or repeating decimal.

9. $\frac{2}{5}$ = 0.4 **10.** $\frac{7}{10}$ = 0.7 **11.** $\frac{5}{8}$ = 0.625 **12.** $\frac{3}{20}$ = 0.15

13. $\frac{5}{16}$ = 0.3125 **14.** $\frac{2}{11}$ = $0.\overline{18}$ **15.** $\frac{4}{25}$ = 0.16 **16.** $\frac{3}{10}$ = 0.3

17. $\frac{7}{9}$ = $0.\overline{7}$ **18.** $\frac{3}{50}$ = 0.06 **19.** $\frac{3}{4}$ = 0.75 **20.** $\frac{2}{9}$ = $0.\overline{2}$

21. $2\frac{1}{8}$ = 2.125 **22.** $6\frac{1}{4}$ = 6.25 **23.** $1\frac{1}{3}$ = $1.\overline{3}$ **24.** $8\frac{1}{2}$ = 8.5

25. $9\frac{2}{15}$ = $9.1\overline{3}$ **26.** $4\frac{3}{40}$ = 4.075 **27.** $7\frac{1}{6}$ = $7.1\overline{6}$ **28.** $4\frac{2}{3}$ = $4.\overline{6}$

29. $2\frac{1}{9}$ = $2.\overline{1}$ **30.** $5\frac{3}{11}$ = $5.\overline{27}$ **31.** $6\frac{4}{9}$ = $6.\overline{4}$ **32.** $3\frac{4}{5}$ = 3.8

Change the fraction to a decimal.

33. Two and seven-eighths truckloads were filled with coal. 2.875

34. The board measured $\frac{15}{4}$ inches. 3.75

35. The fabric measured $10\frac{3}{10}$ yards. 10.3

*Use with Lesson 2-7, text pages 40–41.

Copyright © Sadlier-Oxford

Comparing and Ordering Fractions*

Name ______________________

Date ______________________

Compare. Write $<$, $=$, or $>$.

1. $\frac{1}{5}$ $<$ $\frac{2}{9}$
2. $\frac{1}{3}$ $<$ $\frac{2}{5}$
3. $\frac{1}{6}$ $<$ $\frac{1}{5}$
4. $\frac{1}{8}$ $<$ $\frac{2}{11}$
5. $\frac{3}{7}$ $<$ $\frac{4}{9}$
6. $\frac{5}{8}$ $<$ $\frac{7}{10}$
7. $\frac{8}{15}$ $>$ $\frac{9}{20}$
8. $\frac{5}{6}$ $<$ $\frac{7}{8}$
9. $\frac{4}{5}$ $<$ $\frac{9}{10}$
10. $\frac{2}{11}$ $<$ $\frac{7}{9}$
11. $\frac{3}{4}$ $<$ $\frac{15}{19}$
12. $\frac{2}{3}$ $<$ $\frac{11}{12}$
13. $1\frac{2}{3}$ $>$ $1\frac{3}{5}$
14. $2\frac{1}{9}$ $<$ $2\frac{3}{11}$
15. $8\frac{1}{3}$ $>$ $8\frac{4}{15}$
16. $5\frac{1}{5}$ $<$ $5\frac{4}{18}$
17. $\frac{12}{20}$ $>$ $\frac{8}{15}$
18. $3\frac{1}{3}$ $=$ $2\frac{4}{3}$
19. $\frac{5}{18}$ $>$ $\frac{4}{15}$
20. $6\frac{1}{9}$ $<$ $6\frac{4}{25}$
21. $9\frac{1}{8}$ $<$ $9\frac{4}{7}$
22. $15\frac{2}{3}$ $>$ $15\frac{5}{9}$
23. $12\frac{5}{6}$ $=$ $10\frac{17}{6}$
24. $10\frac{3}{8}$ $>$ $10\frac{3}{16}$

Order from least to greatest.

25. $\frac{2}{3}, \frac{4}{5}, \frac{6}{7}$ — $\frac{2}{3}, \frac{4}{5}, \frac{6}{7}$
26. $\frac{1}{5}, \frac{3}{11}, \frac{4}{9}$ — $\frac{1}{5}, \frac{3}{11}, \frac{4}{9}$
27. $\frac{3}{4}, \frac{7}{10}, \frac{2}{3}$ — $\frac{2}{3}, \frac{7}{10}, \frac{3}{4}$
28. $\frac{8}{9}, \frac{11}{12}, \frac{3}{4}$ — $\frac{3}{4}, \frac{8}{9}, \frac{11}{12}$
29. $\frac{2}{7}, \frac{1}{5}, \frac{3}{10}$ — $\frac{1}{5}, \frac{2}{7}, \frac{3}{10}$
30. $\frac{1}{10}, \frac{3}{15}, \frac{4}{45}$ — $\frac{4}{45}, \frac{1}{10}, \frac{3}{15}$

Use a calculator to change each fraction to a decimal rounded to the nearest thousandth. Then compare.

31. $\frac{42}{89}, \frac{96}{112}$ — $0.472 < 0.857$
32. $\frac{68}{310}, \frac{59}{289}$ — $0.219 > 0.204$
33. $\frac{92}{140}, \frac{86}{130}$ — $0.657 < 0.662$
34. $\frac{123}{456}, \frac{208}{802}$ — $0.27 > 0.259$
35. $\frac{76}{218}, \frac{159}{551}$ — $0.349 > 0.289$
36. $\frac{482}{999}, \frac{651}{1000}$ — $0.482 < 0.651$

*Use with Lesson 2-8, text pages 42–43.

Copyright © Sadlier-Oxford

Adding and Subtracting Fractions and Mixed Numbers*

Name ______________________

Date ______________________

Write the sum in simplest form.

1. $\frac{7}{10} + \frac{4}{5} =$ $1\frac{1}{2}$

2. $\frac{3}{4} + \frac{3}{5} =$ $1\frac{7}{20}$

3. $\frac{4}{11} + \frac{1}{3} =$ $\frac{23}{33}$

4. $\frac{2}{5} + \frac{1}{7} =$ $\frac{19}{35}$

5. $\frac{4}{5} + \frac{3}{8} =$ $1\frac{7}{40}$

6. $\frac{5}{9} + \frac{7}{12} =$ $1\frac{5}{36}$

7. $\frac{5}{8} + \frac{5}{6} =$ $1\frac{11}{24}$

8. $\frac{3}{7} + \frac{4}{5} =$ $1\frac{8}{35}$

9. $7\frac{3}{10} + 9\frac{7}{10} =$ 17

10. $2\frac{3}{11} + 7\frac{5}{11} =$ $9\frac{8}{11}$

11. $4\frac{3}{8} + 4\frac{1}{4} =$ $8\frac{5}{8}$

12. $8\frac{2}{3} + 3\frac{4}{9} =$ $12\frac{1}{9}$

13. $10\frac{5}{9} + 6\frac{3}{4} =$ $17\frac{11}{36}$

14. $2\frac{2}{7} + 8\frac{1}{2} =$ $10\frac{11}{14}$

15. $12\frac{5}{6} + 6\frac{4}{5} =$ $19\frac{19}{30}$

16. $2\frac{1}{3} + 5\frac{4}{7} =$ $7\frac{19}{21}$

Write the difference in simplest form.

17. $\frac{5}{12} - \frac{1}{12} =$ $\frac{1}{3}$

18. $\frac{6}{7} - \frac{3}{7} =$ $\frac{3}{7}$

19. $\frac{7}{8} - \frac{5}{8} =$ $\frac{1}{4}$

20. $\frac{7}{9} - \frac{4}{9} =$ $\frac{1}{3}$

21. $15\frac{5}{8} - 3\frac{1}{8} =$ $12\frac{1}{2}$

22. $4\frac{2}{9} - 1\frac{2}{9} =$ 3

23. $16\frac{7}{8} - 4\frac{3}{4} =$ $12\frac{1}{8}$

24. $14\frac{1}{3} - 8\frac{5}{6} =$ $5\frac{1}{2}$

25. $17\frac{5}{7} - 5\frac{2}{3} =$ $12\frac{1}{21}$

26. $8\frac{1}{4} - 2\frac{1}{3} =$ $5\frac{11}{21}$

27. $10\frac{2}{9} - 5\frac{5}{6} =$ $4\frac{7}{18}$

28. $11\frac{3}{4} - 9\frac{1}{2} =$ $2\frac{1}{4}$

Solve.

29. Three boxes weigh $6\frac{1}{4}$ lb, $4\frac{3}{8}$ lb, and $5\frac{3}{16}$ lb. How much do they weigh together?

$6\frac{1}{4} + 4\frac{3}{8} + 3\frac{5}{16}$; $13\frac{15}{16}$ lb

30. The Gray family used $140\frac{5}{6}$ gallons of heating oil in January and $145\frac{3}{4}$ gallons in February. How many more gallons of oil did they use in February?

$145\frac{3}{4} - 140\frac{5}{6}$; $4\frac{11}{12}$ gal

31. A designer has a piece of lace that measures $\frac{5}{8}$ yard. He used a $\frac{1}{3}$-yd piece to trim a collar. How much lace does he have left?

$\frac{5}{8} - \frac{1}{3}$; $\frac{7}{24}$ yd

*Use with Lessons 2-9, 2-10, text pages 44–47.

Copyright © Sadlier-Oxford

Multiplying Fractions and Mixed Numbers*

Name ______________________

Date ______________________

Multiply. Cancel where possible.

1. $\frac{2}{3} \times \frac{4}{5} =$ $\frac{8}{15}$

2. $\frac{7}{8} \times \frac{2}{3} =$ $\frac{7}{12}$

3. $\frac{3}{5} \times \frac{1}{7} =$ $\frac{3}{35}$

4. $\frac{5}{6} \times \frac{3}{4} =$ $\frac{5}{8}$

5. $5 \times \frac{4}{15} =$ $1\frac{1}{3}$

6. $\frac{2}{3} \times 9 =$ 6

7. $\frac{7}{8} \times 14 =$ $12\frac{1}{4}$

8. $8 \times \frac{5}{6} =$ $6\frac{2}{3}$

9. $1\frac{3}{4} \times 2\frac{1}{3} =$ $4\frac{1}{12}$

10. $6\frac{1}{8} \times 1\frac{1}{7} =$ 7

11. $8\frac{1}{3} \times 2\frac{4}{5} =$ $23\frac{1}{3}$

12. $6\frac{1}{7} \times 3\frac{1}{2} =$ $21\frac{1}{2}$

13. $6\frac{1}{3} \times 4\frac{1}{5} =$ $26\frac{3}{5}$

14. $7\frac{1}{3} \times 9 =$ 66

15. $8 \times 4\frac{1}{2} =$ 36

Compute.

16. $(2\frac{1}{3} + 1\frac{5}{6}) \times \frac{4}{5} =$ $3\frac{1}{3}$

17. $(9\frac{1}{2} - 3\frac{3}{4}) \times \frac{8}{9} =$ $5\frac{1}{9}$

18. $(4\frac{3}{4} + 2\frac{3}{8}) \times 16 =$ 114

19. $(5\frac{3}{4} + 2\frac{1}{3}) \times \frac{4}{5} =$ $6\frac{7}{15}$

20. $(6\frac{2}{3} - \frac{4}{5}) \times \frac{1}{8} =$ $\frac{11}{15}$

21. $14 \times (5\frac{1}{3} + \frac{4}{7}) =$ $82\frac{2}{3}$

22. $6\frac{1}{3} \times 4\frac{1}{5} \times \frac{5}{6} =$ $22\frac{1}{6}$

23. $7\frac{1}{7} \times 4\frac{2}{3} \times \frac{9}{10} =$ 30

Solve.

24. Twenty-four students went to the museum. One sixth of these saw the biology exhibit. How many saw the biology exhibit?

$e = \frac{1}{6} \times 24$; 4 students

25. How many yards of fabric are needed to make 25 dolls if one doll requires $\frac{4}{5}$ yd of fabric?

$f = \frac{4}{5} \times 25$; 20 yd

26. Chris used $\frac{3}{5}$ of a $12\frac{1}{2}$-ft length of electrical wire. How much wire is left?

$\frac{5}{5} - \frac{3}{5} = \frac{2}{5}$; $n = \frac{2}{5} \times 12\frac{1}{2}$; 5 ft

*Use with Lesson 2-11, text pages 48–49.

Copyright © Sadlier-Oxford

Dividing Fractions, Complex Fractions, Mixed Numbers*

Name ______________________

Date ______________________

Write the reciprocal.

1. $\frac{3}{4}$ $\frac{4}{3}$
2. $\frac{2}{5}$ $\frac{5}{2}$
3. $\frac{1}{9}$ $\frac{9}{1}$
4. $\frac{2}{7}$ $\frac{7}{2}$
5. $\frac{4}{9}$ $\frac{9}{4}$
6. 4 $\frac{1}{4}$
7. $2\frac{1}{6}$ $\frac{6}{13}$
8. $3\frac{2}{3}$ $\frac{3}{11}$
9. $\frac{7}{11}$ $\frac{11}{7}$
10. 9 $\frac{1}{9}$
11. $8\frac{1}{3}$ $\frac{3}{25}$
12. $7\frac{2}{9}$ $\frac{9}{65}$
13. 18 $\frac{1}{18}$
14. $\frac{1}{12}$ 12
15. $5\frac{2}{5}$ $\frac{5}{27}$

Write the quotient in simplest form.

16. $\frac{3}{7} \div \frac{9}{10} =$ $\frac{10}{21}$
17. $\frac{4}{5} \div \frac{8}{9} =$ $\frac{9}{10}$
18. $\frac{3}{7} \div \frac{9}{14} =$ $\frac{2}{3}$
19. $\frac{4}{9} \div \frac{2}{3} =$ $\frac{2}{3}$
20. $\frac{5}{12} \div \frac{5}{6} =$ $\frac{1}{2}$
21. $\frac{2}{9} \div \frac{11}{18} =$ $\frac{4}{11}$
22. $18 \div \frac{6}{7} =$ 21
23. $\frac{4}{5} \div 16 =$ $\frac{1}{20}$
24. $21 \div \frac{7}{8} =$ 24
25. $3\frac{1}{3} \div 1\frac{1}{2} =$ $2\frac{2}{9}$
26. $5\frac{1}{8} \div \frac{1}{2} =$ $10\frac{1}{4}$
27. $7\frac{3}{5} \div \frac{2}{15} =$ 57
28. $6\frac{2}{5} \div 2\frac{2}{3} =$ $2\frac{2}{5}$
29. $5\frac{1}{4} \div 1\frac{2}{5} =$ $3\frac{3}{4}$
30. $15 \div 8\frac{1}{3} =$ $1\frac{4}{5}$

Simplify.

31. $\dfrac{3\frac{2}{3}}{1\frac{1}{2}} =$ $2\frac{4}{9}$
32. $\dfrac{2\frac{1}{8}}{\frac{1}{2}} =$ $4\frac{1}{4}$
33. $\dfrac{2\frac{1}{5}}{\frac{2}{15}} =$ $16\frac{1}{2}$
34. $\dfrac{1\frac{1}{7}}{\frac{4}{21}} =$ 6
35. $\dfrac{4\frac{3}{4}}{4\frac{1}{2}} =$ $1\frac{1}{18}$
36. $\dfrac{8\frac{2}{3}}{1\frac{2}{9}} =$ $7\frac{1}{11}$

Solve.

37. Stephanie bikes $82\frac{1}{2}$ miles in $6\frac{3}{4}$ hours. How many miles does she travel in one hour?

$d = 82\frac{1}{2} \div 6\frac{3}{4}$; $12\frac{2}{9}$ mi

Copyright © Sadlier-Oxford

Estimating Fractions*

Name ______________________

Date ______________________

Estimate each sum and difference. Use the estimation strategy that works best for you.

1. $5\frac{1}{15} + 6\frac{7}{30}$ 11
2. $3\frac{4}{7} + 9\frac{2}{11}$ 13
3. $4\frac{7}{10} + 5\frac{6}{35}$ 10
4. $11\frac{4}{5} + 9\frac{10}{11}$ 22
5. $8\frac{17}{18} - 4\frac{5}{8}$ 4
6. $7\frac{1}{7} - 5\frac{2}{5}$ 2
7. $14\frac{9}{10} - 9\frac{2}{31}$ 6
8. $16\frac{19}{20} - 7\frac{2}{5}$ 10
9. $\frac{7}{8} + 2\frac{5}{16} + \frac{2}{3} + 8\frac{5}{12} + 1\frac{3}{4}$ 14
10. $11\frac{4}{5} + 2\frac{8}{9} + 6\frac{2}{15} + 10\frac{3}{20} + \frac{5}{6}$ 32

Estimate each product.

11. $\frac{2}{3} \times 19$ 12
12. $\frac{5}{6} \times 31$ 25
13. $\frac{11}{12} \times 56$ 56
14. $\frac{9}{20} \times 41$ 18
15. $\frac{1}{6} \times 11$ 2
16. $\frac{1}{9} \times \frac{19}{20}$ $\frac{1}{10}$
17. $\frac{7}{8} \times \frac{31}{40}$ $\frac{2}{3}$
18. $\frac{1}{5} \times \frac{21}{23}$ $\frac{4}{23}$
19. $2\frac{2}{3} \times \frac{1}{15}$ $\frac{1}{6}$
20. $9\frac{1}{3} \times \frac{1}{13}$ $\frac{2}{3}$
21. $\frac{1}{4} \times 3\frac{4}{7}$ $\frac{6}{7}$
22. $\frac{7}{9} \times 2\frac{1}{5}$ 2

Solve mentally. (Remember: sometimes the *distributive property* can be used.)

23. $\frac{1}{2} \times 8\frac{2}{3}$ $4\frac{1}{3}$
24. $\frac{2}{5} \times 5\frac{1}{11}$ $2\frac{2}{55}$
25. $\frac{2}{7} \times 21\frac{2}{3}$ $6\frac{4}{21}$
26. $\frac{1}{8} \times 32\frac{3}{5}$ $4\frac{3}{40}$
27. $\frac{3}{4} \times 12\frac{1}{8}$ $9\frac{3}{32}$
28. $\frac{2}{3} \times 15\frac{4}{5}$ $10\frac{8}{15}$
29. $\frac{7}{9} \times 18\frac{3}{7}$ $14\frac{1}{3}$
30. $\frac{2}{11} \times 22\frac{1}{3}$ $4\frac{2}{33}$
31. $\frac{8}{9} \times 54\frac{4}{5}$ $48\frac{32}{45}$
32. $\frac{3}{16} \times 32\frac{1}{3}$ $6\frac{1}{16}$
33. $\frac{9}{10} \times 30\frac{2}{3}$ $27\frac{3}{5}$
34. $\frac{5}{8} \times 48\frac{1}{6}$ $30\frac{5}{48}$

Solve using estimation. Accept reasonable estimates.

35. An Amazon caterpillar grows $\frac{4}{15}$ of an inch each week. If it keeps growing at this rate, how long will it grow in $3\frac{2}{3}$ years? $\approx \frac{1}{4} \times 50 \times 4$; about 50 in.

36. A desert caravan carried $8\frac{3}{4}$ gallons of drinking water. If $\frac{2}{3}$ of the water was used on a trip, about how much was left? $\approx \frac{1}{3} \times 9$; about 3 gal

$1 - \frac{2}{3} = \frac{1}{3}$

*Use with Lesson 2-13, text pages 52–53.

Copyright © Sadlier-Oxford

Order of Operations*

Name ______________________

Date ______________________

Simplify. 20 ÷ 5 × 3 = 4 × 3 = 12

1. 14 + 3 − 7 = 10

2. 9 − 4 + 10 = 15

3. 7 + 3 − 2 = 8

4. 3 × 4 ÷ 2 = 6

5. 36 ÷ 9 × 5 = 20

6. 6 × 4 ÷ 12 = 2

7. 2 × 7 + 5 = 19

8. 4 × 3 + 6 = 18

9. 9 − 3 ÷ 3 = 8

10. 42 ÷ 7 − 6 = 0

11. 3 × 5 ÷ 5 + 1 = 4

12. 48 ÷ 3 × 2 + 5 = 37

13. [4(7 + 3)] − 5 = 35

14. 2[6(5 − 3)] = 24

15. [3(5 + 4) − 3] = 24

16. 5[4 + 3] + 10 = 45

17. 9(7 − 5) ÷ 3 = 6

18. 5(20 − 12) ÷ 4 = 10

Simplify.

19. [(5 × 8) + 9] ÷ [(10 − 6) + 3] = 7

20. [20 ÷ (30 − 26)] × [(56 + 48) ÷ 26] = 20

21. [2(6 × 2) ÷ 6] + [(24 + 11) ÷ 5] = 11

22. {3[2 × (37 − 12)] − 5} − (324 ÷ 9) = 109

23. [14 × 7 − 3(4 × 2) + 8] + 10 ÷ 2 = 87

24. 2(44) + [42 − 3(5 + 3)] − 21 = 85

25. [2(45 ÷ 5)] − [36 ÷ (3 × 3)] = 14

*Use with Lesson 3-1, text pages 64–65.

Copyright © Sadlier-Oxford

Mathematical or Algebraic Expressions*

Name ____________________
Date ____________________

Write a mathematical expression. Choose a letter for each variable.

1. 8 less than a number $n - 8$
2. a number divided by 3 $\frac{n}{3}$
3. 5 times a number $5n$
4. 4 more than a number $n + 4$
5. a number less 9 $n - 9$
6. 15 divided by a number $\frac{15}{n}$
7. 12 times a number $12n$
8. 2 less than a number $n - 2$
9. a number divided into 4 parts $\frac{n}{4}$
10. 7 more than twice a number $2n + 7$
11. 1 more than a number divided by 3 $\frac{n+1}{3}$ or $\frac{n}{3} + 1$
12. 30 less than a number $n - 30$
13. 9 more than 7 times a number $7n + 9$
14. 5 added to a number $n + 5$
15. the product of a number and 5 $5n$
16. 7 less than a number $n - 7$
17. half of a number $\frac{n}{2}$ or $\frac{1}{2}n$
18. 6 times a number $6n$
19. 4 less than 5 times a number $5n - 4$
20. a number divided by 3 increased by 2 $\frac{n}{3} + 2$

Write a word phrase for each. Answers will vary.

21. $7n + 9$ 9 more than 7 times a number.
22. $4a + 5$ 5 more than 4 times a number.

*Use with Lesson 3-2, text pages 66–67.

Copyright © Sadlier-Oxford

Mathematical or Algebraic Sentences*

Name ______________________

Date ______________________

Write a mathematical or algebraic sentence. Identify each as an equation or an inequality.

1. The sum of a number and 4 is 10. $n + 4 = 10$; equation
2. One fifth of a number is 20. $\frac{n}{5} = 20$ or $\frac{1}{5}n = 20$; equation
3. 5 less than a quarter of a number is greater than 1. $\frac{n}{4} - 5 > 1$ or $\frac{1}{4}n - 5 > 1$; inequality
4. The difference between a number and 3 is not 6. $n - 3 \neq 6$; inequality
5. The product of a number and 5 is less than 10. $5n < 10$; inequality
6. The quotient of a number and 10 is 5. $\frac{n}{10} = 5$; equation
7. 3 increased by a number is less than 6. $3 + n < 6$; inequality
8. 2 less than 3 times a number is less than or equal to 11. $3n - 2 \leq 11$; inequality
9. 5 less than half a number is greater than or equal to 6. $\frac{n}{2} - 5 \geq 6$ or $\frac{1}{2}n - 5 \geq 6$; inequality

Write a mathematical sentence to describe each problem situation.

10. The perimeter of a square is 24 cm. Find the length of one side. $4s = 24$
11. Jennifer is 6 years older than her sister Amanda. If Jennifer is 14, how old is Amanda? $A + 6 = 14$

Write an English sentence for each.

12. $2y - 1 = 1$ Answers will vary.
13. $\frac{z}{3} \geq 1$ Answers will vary.
14. $a + 2 \neq 7$ Answers will vary.
15. $\frac{x}{4} + 2 \leq 5$ Answers will vary.

*Use with Lesson 3-4, text pages 70–71.

Copyright © Sadlier-Oxford

Evaluating Expressions and Sentences*

Name ______________________

Date ______________________

Find the value when $a = 10$, $b = 25$, $c = 32$.

1. $4a$ 40

2. $b - 7$ 18

3. $a + 13$ 23

4. $a \div 2$ 5

5. $12 + c$ 44

6. $b - 17$ 8

7. $b \div 5$ 5

8. $4b$ 100

9. $c \div 16$ 2

10. $10a$ 100

11. $c \div 2$ 16

12. $14.2a$ 142

13. $c \div 4$ 8

14. $b + 5$ 30

15. $8a$ 80

16. $7 + c$ 39

17. $100 + b$ 125

18. $c - 21$ 11

Evaluate each expression when $r = 90$, $s = 50$, $t = 200$, $v = 3$.

19. $\frac{s}{2} + 6$ 31

20. $(r + 10) \div 5$ 20

21. $\frac{t}{4} \div 2$ 25

22. $\frac{t}{s} + 30$ 34

23. $(r - s) \div 8$ 5

24. $(70 - s) + r$ 110

25. $\frac{r}{v} + 9$ 39

26. $10v + r$ 120

27. $5s - t$ 50

28. $2r - \frac{3s}{v}$ 130

29. $(r + 7) - (s + 9)$ 38

30. $vt - vs$ 450

Evaluate each expression when $m = 40$, $n = 120$, $w = 100$, $x = 75$.

31. $\frac{m}{2} - (n - w)$ 0

32. $2(m + x) - w$ 130

33. $\frac{4n}{m} + w$ 112

34. $(2n - w) + 2x$ 290

35. $2(m + n) - w$ 220

36. $2m \div \frac{3w}{x}$ 20

37. $\frac{w}{4} + 3x$ 250

38. $2x - (n \div m)$ 147

*Use with Lesson 3-3, text pages 68–69.

Copyright © Sadlier-Oxford

Addition and Subtraction Equations*

Name ______________________

Date ______________________

Solve. $n + 6 = 9 \quad n + 6 - 6 = 9 - 6 \quad n = 3$

1. $n + 6 = 9$ $n =$ 3

2. $r + 8 = 14$ $r =$ 6

3. $v + 7 = 21$ $v =$ 14

4. $t + 2 = 10$ $t =$ 8

5. $x + 3 = 10$ $x =$ 7

6. $b + 4 = 20$ $b =$ 16

7. $a + 15 = 25$ $a =$ 10

8. $30 + c = 46$ $c =$ 16

9. $b + 12 = 21$ $b =$ 9

10. $42 = d + 11$ $d =$ 31

11. $19 = s + 6$ $s =$ 13

12. $9 + r = 14$ $r =$ 5

13. $n - 2 = 6$ $n =$ 8

14. $a - 3 = 12$ $a =$ 15

15. $r - 3 = 4$ $r =$ 7

16. $b - 8 = 16$ $b =$ 24

17. $s - 7 = 13$ $s =$ 20

18. $t - 21 = 30$ $t =$ 51

19. $b - 9 = 18$ $b =$ 27

20. $c - 17 = 41$ $c =$ 58

21. $d - 8 = 42$ $d =$ 50

22. $f - 9 = 6$ $f =$ 15

23. $h - 6 = 94$ $h =$ 100

24. $k - 12 = 7$ $k =$ 19

25. $a + 26 = 38$ $a =$ 12

26. $b - 40 = 20$ $b =$ 60

27. $c - 3 = 81$ $c =$ 84

28. $d + 14 = 30$ $d =$ 16

29. $21 + r = 38$ $r =$ 17

30. $50 = a + 7$ $a =$ 43

31. $t - 16 = 75$ $t =$ 91

32. $s + 16 = 80$ $s =$ 64

33. $r - 9 = 51$ $r =$ 60

34. $d - 32 = 140$ $d =$ 172

35. $f + 6 = 21$ $f =$ 15

36. $c - 7 = 48$ $c =$ 55

***Use with Lesson 3-6, text pages 74–75.**

Copyright © Sadlier-Oxford

Multiplication and Division Equations*

Name ______________________

Date ______________________

Solve.

1. $7x = 42$

   $x =$ 6

2. $9r = 36$

   $r =$ 4

3. $4n = 80$

   $n =$ 20

4. $6t = 24$

   $t =$ 4

5. $5y = 100$

   $y =$ 20

6. $3m = 96$

   $m =$ 32

7. $2a = 144$

   $a =$ 72

8. $9b = 288$

   $b =$ 32

9. $6c = 90$

   $c =$ 15

10. $600 = 12n$

    $n =$ 50

11. $7r = 112$

    $r =$ 16

12. $228 = 4y$

    $y =$ 57

13. $\frac{b}{6} = 12$

    $b =$ 72

14. $\frac{a}{9} = 10$

    $a =$ 90

15. $\frac{c}{4} = 21$

    $c =$ 84

16. $\frac{a}{3} = 25$

    $a =$ 75

17. $\frac{n}{7} = 14$

    $n =$ 98

18. $\frac{x}{5} = 32$

    $x =$ 160

19. $\frac{r}{27} = 3$

    $r =$ 81

20. $\frac{s}{10} = 13$

    $s =$ 130

21. $46 = \frac{t}{4}$

    $t =$ 184

22. $\frac{c}{3} = 27$

    $c =$ 81

23. $25 = \frac{a}{5}$

    $a =$ 125

24. $\frac{n}{14} = 14$

    $n =$ 196

25. $12a = 48$

    $a =$ 4

26. $\frac{a}{8} = 6$

    $a =$ 48

27. $5r = 300$

    $r =$ 60

28. $\frac{n}{12} = 10$

    $n =$ 120

29. $7c = 455$

    $c =$ 65

30. $\frac{d}{6} = 30$

    $d =$ 180

31. $\frac{j}{3} = 12$

    $j =$ 36

32. $9m = 405$

    $m =$ 45

33. $\frac{d}{4} = 48$

    $d =$ 192

*Use with Lesson 3-7, text pages 76–77.

Copyright © Sadlier-Oxford.

Equations*
(With More Than One Operation)

Name ____________________
Date ____________________

Solve. $3x + 1 = 13$ $3x + 1 - 1 = 13 - 1$ $3x = 12$ $x = 4$

1. $4a + 2 = 30$ $a =$ 7

2. $\frac{r}{7} + 5 = 10$ $r =$ 35

3. $\frac{b}{6} - 6 = 6$ $b =$ 72

4. $7c - 6 = 50$ $c =$ 8

5. $3n + 10 = 22$ $n =$ 4

6. $5x - 12 = 28$ $x =$ 8

7. $\frac{n}{9} + 4 = 12$ $n =$ 72

8. $9r - 14 = 67$ $r =$ 9

9. $2a + 53 = 67$ $a =$ 7

10. $\frac{s}{4} + 5 = 14$ $s =$ 36

11. $10a - 7 = 63$ $a =$ 7

12. $\frac{x}{11} + 6 = 10$ $x =$ 44

13. $\frac{4n + 4}{2} = 10$ $n =$ 4

14. $7n - 54 = 16$ $n =$ 10

15. $\frac{a}{5} + 7 = 20$ $a =$ 65

16. $\frac{n}{5} - 7 = 18$ $n =$ 125

17. $6x + 11 = 47$ $x =$ 6

18. $6b - 29 = 1$ $b =$ 5

19. $2a + 4 = 14$ $a =$ 5

20. $8x - 2 = 38$ $x =$ 5

21. $\frac{n}{4} + 5 = 9$ $n =$ 16

22. $\frac{a}{14} + 10 = 12$ $a =$ 28

23. $10x - 13 = 37$ $x =$ 5

24. $\frac{r}{12} + 21 = 24$ $r =$ 36

Solve.

25. The school science lab has 5 times as many microscopes now as it did last year. If there are now 75 microscopes, how many were there last year?

$75 = 5n$; 15 microscopes

*Use with Lesson 3-8, text pages 78–79.

Copyright © Sadlier-Oxford

Equations*
(With One or More Operations)

Name ____________________

Date ____________________

Solve and check.

1. $a + 19 = 46$ — $a =$ 27

2. $b - 38 = 10$ — $b =$ 48

3. $c - 4 = 96$ — $c =$ 100

4. $d + 15 = 130$ — $d =$ 115

5. $7n = 56$ — $n =$ 8

6. $\frac{r}{6} = 42$ — $r =$ 252

7. $\frac{2a}{3} + 2 = 8$ — $a =$ 9

8. $5(n + 3) - 5 = 40$ — $n =$ 6

9. $9 + \frac{a}{5} = 10$ — $a =$ 5

10. $42 + 3x = 54$ — $x =$ 4

11. $6c - 29 = 7$ — $c =$ 6

12. $\frac{5b}{2} + 7 = 17$ — $b =$ 4

13. $8n - 14 = 26$ — $n =$ 5

14. $\frac{7x + 9}{5} - 12 = 8$ — $x =$ 13

15. $6(n + 8) = 96$ — $n =$ 8

Solve.

16. On the first night of the science exhibit, 1427 people viewed projects. 369 fewer people came the second night. How many people came then?

$s = 1427 - 369$; 1058 people

17. There are 426 entries in the science fair. If this is 53 more than the last fair, how many entries were there in the earlier fair?

$426 = n + 53$; 373 entries

18. Mark read a book of 189 pages. If this is three times the number of pages in Adam's book, how many pages are there in Adam's book?

$189 = 3n$; 63 pages

19. Thirty-five students belong to the science club. This is $\frac{1}{4}$ the number in the 5 sections of the eighth grade. How many students are in the eighth grade? How many in each section if each section has the same number of students?

$35 = \frac{1}{4}e$; $e = 140$;
$140 = 5s$; $s = 28$

*Use with Lesson 3-8, text pages 78–79.

Copyright © Sadlier-Oxford

Equations with Grouping Symbols*

Name ______________________

Date ______________________

Solve each equation by using the distributive property.

$$5(n - 3) = 40$$
$$5n - 15 = 40$$
$$5n - 15 + 15 = 40 + 15$$
$$\frac{5n}{5} = \frac{55}{5}$$
$$n = 11$$

1. $4(a + 3) = 32$ a=5
2. $7(r - 7) = 49$ r=14
3. $5(y + 2) = 15$ y=1
4. $14(n - 9) = 42$ n=12
5. $8(s + 6) = 64$ s=2
6. $13(c + 8) = 143$ c=3

Solve each equation by using inverse operations.

7. $2(x + 8) = 48$ x=16
8. $12(h + 6) = 84$ h=1
9. $6(s - 8) = 30$ s=13
10. $(c + 5)25 = 600$ c=19
11. $(m - 9)8 = 64$ m=17
12. $9(k + 6) = 108$ k=6

Solve each equation.

13. $\frac{a - 6}{8} + 4 = 16$ a=102
14. $\frac{b + 9}{3} + 5 = 28$ b=60
15. $\frac{n + 4}{5} + 12 = 16$ n=16
16. $\frac{3x - 2}{4} + 5 = 15$ x=14
17. $\frac{n + 7}{2} + 2 = 11$ n=11
18. $\frac{8y - 2}{6} - 8 = 21$ y=22
19. $\frac{5d + 3}{4} - 1 = 18$ $d = 14\frac{3}{5}$
20. $\frac{t + 8}{2} - 6 = 3$ t=10
21. $\frac{d - 5}{6} - 3 = 10$ d=83
22. $\frac{8s + 14}{4} - 4 = 6$ $s = 3\frac{1}{4}$
23. $\frac{3r + 5}{2} + 2 = 12$ r=5
24. $\frac{7y + 2}{6} - 3 = 22$ $y = 21\frac{1}{7}$

Solve. Write an equation.

25. The product of 8 and the difference between a number and 9 is 96. What is the number? $8(n-9) = 96$; $n = 21$

26. When 12 is added to half the sum of a number and 8 the result is 40. What is the number? $\frac{n+8}{2} + 12 = 40$; $n = 48$

27. The difference between a number and 5, when multiplied by 3 is 36. What is the number? $(n-5)3 = 36$; $n = 17$

*Use with Lesson 3-9, text pages 80–81.

Copyright © Sadlier-Oxford

Solutions for Inequalities*

Name ____________________

Date ____________________

Complete the chart.

	Inequality	Replacement Set	Solution Set
1.	$r > 3$	{0, 1, 2, 3, 4}	{4}
2.	$s \leq 4$	{0, 1, 2, 3, 4}	{0, 1, 2, 3, 4}
3.	$9 < x$	{5, 6, 7, . . . , 25}	{10, 11, 12, . . . , 25}
4.	$11 \neq r$	{5, 6, 7, 8, 9}	{5, 6, 7, 8, 9}
5.	$b \geq 21$	{20, 25, 30, . . . , 50}	{25, 30, 35, . . . , 50}
6.	$c \leq 7$	{100, 99, 98, . . . , 0}	{7, 6, 5, 4, 3, 2, 1, 0}
7.	$19 \neq a$	{17, 19, 21, . . . , 33}	{17, 21, 23, . . . , 33}
8.	$26 \leq c$	{100, 200, 300}	{100, 200, 300}
9.	$3 \geq d$	{0, 1, 2, . . . , 10}	{0, 1, 2, 3}
10.	$x \neq 13$	{12, 14, 16, 18, 20}	{12, 14, 16, 18, 20}
11.	$c \leq 29$	{50, 40, 30, . . . , 10}	{20, 10}
12.	$y < 6$	{0, 1, 2, . . .}	{0, 1, 2, 3, 4, 5}

Write <, ≤, >, ≥, or = to form an inequality that matches the given solution set, S.
The replacement set is {0, 1, 2, 3, 4, 5, 6, 7, 8}

13. n __<__ 4 S: {0, 1, 2, 3}

14. r __>__ 4 S: {5, 6, 7, 8}

15. x __≥__ 4 S: {4, 5, 6, 7, 8}

16. a __≤__ 4 S: {0, 1, 2, 3, 4}

17. s __≠__ 4 S: {0, 1, 2, 3, 5, 6, 7, 8}

18. a __<__ 7 S: {0, 1, 2, 3, 4, 5, 6}

List the members of each set.

19. The set of whole numbers between 20 and 30 {21, 22, 23, 24, 25, 26, 27, 28, 29}

20. The set of odd numbers < 13 {1, 3, 5, 7, 9, 11}

21. The set of multiples of 3 less than 21 {0, 3, 6, 9, 12, 15, 18}

22. The set of multiples of 10 {0, 10, 20, 30, . . .}

*Use with Lesson 3-10, text pages 82–83.

Copyright © Sadlier-Oxford

Using Formulas*

Name ______________________

Date ______________________

What kind of problem does each formula solve?

1. $A = s^2$ Area of square
2. $A = \pi r^2$ Area of circle
3. $C = \pi d$ Circumference of circle
4. $P = 4s$ Perimeter of square
5. $A = \frac{1}{2}bh$ Area of triangle
6. $V = \ell wh$ Volume of rectangular prism

Solve for the missing variable.

7. $P = 4s$ when $P = 64$ — s = 16 units
8. $C = \pi d$ when $d = 42$ — C = 42π units
9. $V = \ell wh$ when $V = 75$ cubic feet, $w = 3'$, and $h = 5'$ — ℓ = 5′
10. $A = \frac{1}{2}bh$ when $b = 6'$, and $h = 21'$ — A = 63 ft²
11. $A = s^2$ when $A = 324$ square yards — s = 18 yd
12. $A = \pi r^2$ when $r = 9$ — A = 81 π square units

Write a formula for each.

13. Rate of Tax = Tax divided by Marked Price — R of T = T ÷ MP
14. Total Sales = Commission divided by Rate of Commission — TS = C ÷ R of C
15. Discount = List Price times Rate of Discount — D = LP × R of D
16. Commission = Total Sales times Rate of Commission — C = TS × R of C

Solve, using formulas.

17. The outside rim of a circular pool measures 68 ft. What is the radius of the pool?
    68 = 2× (3.14) × r
    r = $10\frac{9}{11}$ ft or 10.828 ft
18. A square board is 0.6 m long. Find its area.
    A= (0.6)²
    A = 0.36 m²
19. An aquarium is 20 feet long, 4 feet wide and 3 feet deep. How many cubic feet of water will it hold?
    V = 20 (4) (3)
    V = 240 ft³
20. How long will it take \$3200 to earn \$400 at 6% a year?
    400 = 3200 × 0.06 × t
    t = $2\frac{1}{12}$ yr

*Use with Lesson 3-11, text pages 84–85.

Copyright © Sadlier-Oxford

Integers*

Name ______________________

Date ______________________

Write the opposite of each integer.

1. $^{+}5$ $\underline{^{-}5}$ **2.** $^{-}6$ $\underline{^{+}6}$ **3.** $^{+}4$ $\underline{^{-}4}$ **4.** $^{+}102$ $\underline{^{-}102}$ **5.** $^{+}17$ $\underline{^{-}17}$

Compare. Write $<$, $=$, or $>$.

6. $^{+}3$ $\underline{>}$ $^{-}12$ **7.** $^{-}41$ $\underline{>}$ $^{-}50$ **8.** $^{+}1$ $\underline{>}$ $^{-}20$

9. $^{-}3$ $\underline{<}$ 0 **10.** $^{-}100$ $\underline{<}$ $^{+}1$ **11.** $^{-}16$ $\underline{<}$ $^{+}61$

12. $^{+}2$ $\underline{>}$ $^{-}5$ **13.** $^{+}21$ $\underline{>}$ $^{-}12$ **14.** $^{+}30$ $\underline{>}$ $^{+}3$

Arrange in order from least to greatest.

15. $^{+}5$, $^{+}2$, $^{-}20$, $^{-}15$, $^{+}20$ $\underline{^{-}20, ^{-}15, ^{+}2, ^{+}5, ^{+}20}$

16. $^{-}10$, $^{+}6$, $^{+}16$, $^{+}10$, $^{-}6$ $\underline{^{-}10, ^{-}6, ^{+}6, ^{+}10, ^{+}16}$

Arrange in order from greatest to least.

17. $^{-}19$, 0, $^{+}15$, $^{+}5$, $^{-}5$ $\underline{^{+}15, ^{+}5, 0, ^{-}5, ^{-}19}$

18. $^{-}10$, $^{+}20$, $^{-}30$, 0, $^{-}15$ $\underline{^{+}20, 0, ^{-}10, ^{-}15, ^{-}30}$

Write an integer for each expression.

19. a deduction of \$31.00 $\underline{^{-}\$31.00}$

20. a loss of 18 points $\underline{^{-}18}$

21. 500 meters above sea level $\underline{^{+}500}$

22. a 20° rise in temperature $\underline{^{+}20}$

Solve.

23. Last Monday the temperature was $^{-}12$°C. It rose 9°C this Monday. What is the temperature this Monday?

$^{-}12 + {}^{+}9 = t$; $^{-}3$°C

24. The temperature is 28°F but the wind chill makes it feel 18° colder. What is the wind chill temperature?

$^{+}28 - {}^{+}18 = t$; 10°F

25. How many integers are there between $^{-}13$ and $^{+}13$? Between $^{+}310$ and $^{-}300$? Between $^{-}15$ and 0?

25; 609; 14

*Use with Lesson 3-12, text pages 86–87.

Copyright © Sadlier-Oxford

Operations with Integers: Addition and Subtraction*

Name ______________________

Date ______________________

Add. $^{+}7 - {}^{+}10 = {}^{-}3$ $^{+}10 - {}^{+}7 = {}^{+}3$

1. $^{+}7 + {}^{+}2$ $^{+}9$
2. $^{-}6 + {}^{+}2$ $^{-}4$
3. $^{-}1 + {}^{+}8$ $^{+}7$
4. $^{+}9 + {}^{+}8$ $^{+}17$
5. $^{-}5 + 0$ $^{-}5$
6. $^{+}3 + {}^{-}3$ 0
7. $0 + {}^{+}10$ $^{+}10$
8. $^{-}8 + {}^{-}3$ $^{-}11$
9. $^{-}6 + {}^{+}6$ 0
10. $^{-}13 + 0$ $^{-}13$
11. $^{-}1 + {}^{-}1$ $^{-}2$
12. $^{+}7 + {}^{-}6$ $^{+}1$
13. $^{+}7 + 0$ $^{+}7$
14. $^{-}1 + {}^{+}6$ $^{+}5$
15. $0 + {}^{-}2$ $^{-}2$
16. $^{+}3 + {}^{-}10$ $^{-}7$

Subtract.

17. $^{+}3 - {}^{-}11$ $^{+}14$
18. $^{+}12 - {}^{-}12$ $^{+}24$
19. $^{-}8 - {}^{+}17$ $^{-}25$
20. $^{-}14 - {}^{-}24$ $^{+}10$
21. $^{+}30 - {}^{-}7$ $^{+}37$
22. $^{+}6 - {}^{+}18$ $^{-}12$
23. $0 - {}^{-}20$ $^{+}20$
24. $0 - {}^{+}32$ $^{-}32$
25. $^{-}13 - {}^{-}13$ 0
26. $0 - {}^{-}1$ $^{+}1$
27. $^{-}28 - {}^{+}5$ $^{-}33$
28. $^{+}8 - {}^{-}16$ $^{+}24$
29. $0 - {}^{+}22$ $^{-}22$
30. $^{+}15 - {}^{+}41$ $^{-}26$
31. $^{-}9 - {}^{+}9$ $^{-}18$
32. $^{+}2 - {}^{-}6$ $^{+}8$

Solve each addition or subtraction equation.

33. $^{-}4 + b = {}^{-}6$ $^{-}2$
34. $^{-}5 + d = {}^{+}4$ $^{+}9$
35. $x - {}^{+}3 = {}^{+}8$ $^{+}11$
36. $^{+}5 + c = {}^{+}13$ $^{+}8$
37. $c - {}^{+}3 = {}^{+}12$ $^{+}15$
38. $y - {}^{-}4 = {}^{-}7$ $^{-}11$
39. $a - {}^{-}8 = {}^{+}7$ $^{-}1$
40. $h - {}^{+}5 = {}^{+}9$ $^{+}14$
41. $x - {}^{-}10 = {}^{+}7$ $^{-}3$
42. $^{-}6 + x = {}^{-}8$ $^{-}2$
43. $c - {}^{-}8 = {}^{+}5$ $^{-}3$
44. $a + {}^{+}7 = {}^{-}3$ $^{-}10$

Solve.

45. Mike's checking account has a balance of $^{-}$\$44. If he deposits \$128, what will be the new balance?
$^{-}44 + 128 = {}^{+}84$; \$84

46. The temperature this morning was 2°F. It rose to 21° and then dropped by 15°. What was the final temperature?
$2 + 21 - 15 = 8$; 8°F

47. What number would you subtract from $^{-}31$ to give you a $^{+}19$?
$^{-}31 - n = {}^{+}19$; $n = {}^{-}50$

*Use with Lesson 3-13, text pages 88–89.

Copyright © Sadlier-Oxford

Operations with Integers: Multiplication and Division*

Name ______________________

Date ______________________

Multiply. $^{+}5 \times ^{-}8 = ^{-}40$

1. $^{+}6 \times ^{+}12$ $^{+}72$
2. $^{-}3 \times ^{+}13$ $^{-}39$
3. $^{-}9 \times 0$ 0
4. $^{+}8 \times ^{-}5$ $^{-}40$
5. $^{-}2 \times ^{-}2$ $^{+}4$
6. $^{+}9 \times ^{-}8$ $^{-}72$
7. $^{-}4 \times ^{-}7$ $^{+}28$
8. $^{-}2 \times ^{-}14$ $^{+}28$
9. $^{-}18 \times ^{-}5$ $^{+}90$
10. $^{-}22 \times ^{+}7$ $^{-}154$
11. $^{+}31 \times ^{-}3$ $^{-}93$
12. $^{-}100 \times ^{+}100$ $^{-}10{,}000$

Divide.

13. $\frac{^{-}40}{^{-}4}$ $^{+}10$
14. $\frac{^{-}144}{^{-}12}$ $^{+}12$
15. $\frac{^{-}45}{^{+}15}$ $^{-}3$
16. $\frac{^{+}54}{^{-}6}$ $^{-}9$
17. $\frac{^{+}63}{^{-}7}$ $^{-}9$
18. $\frac{^{-}300}{^{+}20}$ $^{-}15$
19. $\frac{^{+}225}{^{-}25}$ $^{-}9$
20. $\frac{^{-}72}{^{+}12}$ $^{-}6$
21. $\frac{^{-}119}{^{+}7}$ $^{-}17$
22. $\frac{^{+}315}{^{-}5}$ $^{-}63$
23. $\frac{^{-}135}{^{-}9}$ $^{+}15$
24. $\frac{^{-}168}{^{+}14}$ $^{-}12$

Solve each multiplication or division equation.

25. $^{+}12t = ^{-}144$ $t = ^{-}12$
26. $^{-}9d = ^{+}63$ $d = ^{-}7$
27. $^{+}20a = 0$ $a = 0$
28. $\frac{c}{^{+}12} = 0$ $c = 0$
29. $\frac{s}{^{-}6} = ^{-}6$ $s = ^{+}36$
30. $\frac{n}{^{+}9} = ^{-}14$ $n = ^{-}126$

Solve.

31. A number is multiplied by $^{+}2$, then multiplied by $^{-}4$. The result is $^{+}48$. What is the number?
    $(^{+}2n)(^{-}4) = ^{+}48;\ n = ^{-}6$
32. A number is divided by $^{-}9$, then by $^{+}3$. The result is $^{-}3$. What is the number?
    $\left(\frac{n}{^{-}9}\right) \div ^{+}3 = ^{-}3;\ n = ^{+}81$
33. A number is divided by $^{-}4$, then multiplied by $^{-}5$. The result is $^{+}40$. What is the number?
    $\left(\frac{n}{^{-}4}\right)(^{-}5) = ^{+}40;\ n = ^{+}32$
34. A number is multiplied by $^{-}8$, then divided by $^{-}4$. The result is $^{+}4$. What is the number?
    $(^{-}8n) \div ^{-}4 = ^{+}4;\ n = ^{+}2$

*Use with Lesson 3-13, text pages 88–89.

Copyright © Sadlier-Oxford

Equations with Integers*

Name ______________________

Date ______________________

Solve by writing and solving an equation.

1. Lisa has 14 coins. She has some quarters, 5 nickels, and one dime more than she has nickels. How many of each type of coin does she have? How much money does she have?

   Let q = quarters
   $q + 5 + (5+1) = 14$

   3 quarters, 5 nickels, 6 dimes; $1.60

2. The sum of a number and 98 is 150. What is the number?

   $n + 98 = 150$

   $n = 52$

3. The sum of eight and four times a number is forty. What is the number?

   $8 + 4n = 40$

   $n = 8$

4. The difference between 87 and a number is 31. Find the number.

   $87 - n = 31$

   $n = 56$

5. Six times a number increased by five is fifty-three. What is the number?

   $6n + 5 = 53$

   $n = 8$

6. Ten more than half a number is forty-eight. What is the number?

   $\frac{n}{2} + 10 = 48$

   $n = 76$

7. A race car is traveling at 120 mph. At this rate, how long will a race of 1500 miles take?

   $120t = 1500$

   $t = 12\frac{1}{2}$ hr

8. One number is nine times another. The greater number is 4950. What is the lesser number?

   $9n = 4950$

   $n = 550$

9. The length of a rectangle is four times its width. The length is 34 cm. Find the area.

   $4w = 34$; $w = 8.5$; $A = 34(8.5)$

   $A = 289\ cm^2$

10. The Tigers scored 16 more points in the second half than in the first half. They scored 86 points in all. How many points did they score in each half?

   1st half: 35 points
   2nd half: 51 points

   Let x = 1st half points; $x + (x+16) = 86$; $x = 35$

*Use with Lesson 3-15, text pages 92–93.

Copyright © Sadlier-Oxford

Rational Numbers*

Name ____________________

Date ____________________

Write the opposite of each rational number.

1. $^{-}0.2$ $\underline{^{+}0.2}$
2. $^{+}6.11$ $\underline{^{-}6.11}$
3. $^{-}\frac{5}{3}$ $\underline{^{+}\frac{5}{3}}$
4. $^{-}\frac{6}{4}$ $\underline{^{+}\frac{6}{4} = {}^{+}\frac{3}{2}}$
5. $^{-}8.1$ $\underline{^{+}8.1}$
6. $^{-}212$ $\underline{^{+}212}$
7. 0 $\underline{0}$
8. $^{-}3.0\overline{1}$ $\underline{^{+}3.0\overline{1}}$
9. $^{-}\frac{9}{2}$ $\underline{^{+}\frac{9}{2}}$
10. $^{+}\frac{8}{4}$ $\underline{^{-}\frac{8}{4} = {}^{-}2}$

Compare. Write <, =, or >.

11. $^{+}5 \ \underline{>} \ ^{-}6$
12. $^{-}4 \ \underline{<} \ ^{+}11$
13. $0 \ \underline{<} \ ^{+}7.2$
14. $^{+}0.9 \ \underline{>} \ ^{-}\frac{3}{4}$
15. $^{+}3.9 \ \underline{>} \ ^{+}1\frac{1}{2}$
16. $^{-}3.6 \ \underline{<} \ 0$
17. $^{-}\frac{1}{4} \ \underline{<} \ 0.1$
18. $^{+}10 \ \underline{>} \ ^{-}10.2$
19. $^{-}0.\overline{3} \ \underline{<} \ ^{-}\frac{1}{8}$
20. $^{-}\frac{2}{3} \ \underline{<} \ ^{+}0.7\overline{5}$
21. $^{-}\frac{4}{5} \ \underline{<} \ ^{-}0.6$
22. $^{-}0.\overline{1} \ \underline{<} \ ^{-}\frac{1}{10}$

Write each set of numbers in order from least to greatest.

23. $^{+}2\frac{1}{2}, {}^{-}\frac{7}{2}, {}^{-}0.1, {}^{+}3\frac{2}{3}, {}^{-}3$ $\underline{^{-}\frac{7}{2}, {}^{-}3, {}^{-}0.1, {}^{+}2\frac{1}{2}, {}^{+}3\frac{2}{3}}$
24. $^{-}\frac{11}{3}, {}^{-}5, {}^{-}2\frac{1}{4}, {}^{+}2.25, {}^{-}0.1$ $\underline{^{-}5, {}^{-}\frac{11}{3}, {}^{-}2\frac{1}{4}, {}^{-}0.1, {}^{+}2.25}$
25. $^{+}3.10, {}^{-}0.31, {}^{-}1.3, {}^{+}0.31, {}^{-}\frac{1}{3}$ $\underline{^{-}1.3, {}^{-}\frac{1}{3}, {}^{-}0.31, {}^{+}0.31, {}^{+}3.10}$

Write a rational number for each expression.

26. a deposit of \$141.15 $\underline{^{+}\$141.15}$
27. 5.03 km underwater $\underline{^{-}5.03}$
28. 20.4° below zero $\underline{^{-}20.4}$
29. down $4\frac{2}{3}$ points $\underline{^{-}4\frac{2}{3}}$
30. a gain of \$16.25 $\underline{^{+}\$16.25}$

*Use with Lesson 4-1, text pages 100–101.

Copyright © Sadlier-Oxford

Properties of Rational Numbers*

Name ______________________

Date ______________________

Name the property.

1. $^{-}7 \times {}^{+}4 = {}^{+}4 \times {}^{-}7$

Commutative of multiplication

2. $^{+}4 \times (^{-}1 + {}^{+}3) = (^{+}4 \times {}^{-}1) + (^{+}4 \times {}^{+}3)$

Distributive

3. $^{+}6 + {}^{-}6 = 0$

Inverse of addition

4. $(^{-}4 + {}^{+}5) + {}^{-}2 = {}^{-}4 + (^{+}5 + {}^{-}2)$

Associative of addition

5. $^{+}6 + {}^{-}3 = {}^{-}3 + {}^{+}6$

Commutative of addition

6. $^{-}8 \times -\frac{1}{8} = 1$

Inverse of multiplication

7. $^{+}9 + 0 = {}^{+}9$

Identity of addition

8. $^{-}3 \times 1 = {}^{-}3$

Identity of multiplication

Simplify. Use the number properties.

9. $^{-}12 + (^{+}3 + {}^{-}3) =$ $^{-}12$

10. $^{+}5 \times (^{-}6 + {}^{+}7) =$ $^{+}5$

11. $+\frac{24}{5} \times \frac{5}{(^{-}8 \times {}^{-}3)} =$ $^{+}1$

12. $(^{+}21 \times {}^{-}14) \times {}^{-}10 =$ $^{+}2940$

13. $(^{-}9 + {}^{-}6) - {}^{+}4 =$ $^{-}19$

14. $(^{+}19 + {}^{+}48 + {}^{-}67) =$ 0

15. $(^{+}6 + {}^{-}6) \times (^{-}4 + {}^{+}4) =$ 0

16. $^{-}246 \times {}^{+}308 \times -\frac{1}{246} =$ $^{+}308$

17. $^{-}48 + {}^{-}92 + {}^{+}48 =$ $^{-}92$

18. $(^{-}2 \times {}^{+}4) + (^{-}2 \times {}^{-}8) =$ $^{+}8$

19. $(^{+}17 + {}^{-}24) - {}^{-}16 =$ $^{+}9$

20. $+\frac{1}{3} \times -\frac{3}{4} \times -\frac{8}{9} =$ $+\frac{2}{9}$

21. $(^{-}3.4 - {}^{-}2.1) + {}^{-}2.1 =$ $^{-}3.4$

22. $^{+}6.2 \times (^{-}7 + {}^{+}1) =$ $^{-}37.2$

*Use with Lesson 4-2, text pages 102–103.

Copyright © Sadlier-Oxford

Adding Rational Numbers*

Name ____________________

Date ____________________

To add with *like* signs:

- Find the sum of the numbers.
- Use the sign of the addends.

To add with *unlike* signs:

- Find the difference of the numbers.
- Use the sign of the addend farther from zero (one with greater absolute value).

Find the sum.

1. ${}^{+}2.5 + {}^{+}5.6 =$ ${}^{+}8.1$

2. ${}^{+}6.1 + {}^{+}8.15 =$ ${}^{+}14.25$

3. ${}^{+}0.3 + {}^{+}7.2 =$ ${}^{+}7.5$

4. ${}^{+}7.5 + {}^{+}7.8 =$ ${}^{+}15.3$

5. ${}^{+}7.04 + {}^{+}8.7 =$ ${}^{+}15.74$

6. ${}^{-}0.43 + {}^{-}0.56 =$ ${}^{-}0.99$

7. ${}^{+}5.6 + {}^{-}0.01 =$ ${}^{+}5.59$

8. ${}^{+}2.2 + {}^{-}6.6 =$ ${}^{-}4.4$

9. ${}^{-}0.15 + {}^{-}1.8 =$ ${}^{-}1.95$

10. ${}^{+}7.8 + {}^{-}2.1 =$ ${}^{+}5.7$

11. ${}^{-}7.5 + {}^{+}2.5 =$ ${}^{-}5$

12. ${}^{+}0.15 + {}^{-}0.61 =$ ${}^{-}0.46$

13. ${}^{-}8.7 + {}^{+}7.8 =$ ${}^{-}0.9$

14. ${}^{+}0.16 + {}^{-}0.25 =$ ${}^{-}0.09$

15. ${}^{+}0.28 + {}^{-}0.35 =$ ${}^{-}0.07$

16. ${}^{-}10.1 + {}^{+}96.1 =$ ${}^{+}86$

17. ${}^{+}3.4 + {}^{-}0.8 =$ ${}^{+}2.6$

18. ${}^{-}0.6 + {}^{+}1 =$ ${}^{+}0.4$

19. ${}^{-}9.7 + {}^{+}8.9 =$ ${}^{-}0.8$

20. ${}^{+}1.9 + {}^{-}4.3 =$ ${}^{-}2.4$

21. ${}^{-}\frac{5}{8} + {}^{+}\frac{2}{3} =$ ${}^{+}\frac{1}{24}$

22. ${}^{+}3\frac{1}{2} + {}^{-}3\frac{1}{2} =$ 0

23. ${}^{-}7.81 + {}^{+}5.04 =$ ${}^{-}2.77$

24. ${}^{+}2\frac{1}{3} + {}^{-}\frac{1}{3} =$ ${}^{+}2$

25. ${}^{-}3.5 + {}^{+}2.7 + {}^{-}7 =$ ${}^{-}7.8$

26. ${}^{-}1.1 + {}^{-}5.7 + {}^{-}4 =$ ${}^{-}10.8$

27. ${}^{-}3.8 + {}^{-}2.6 + {}^{+}7.1 =$ ${}^{+}0.7$

28. ${}^{-}8.5 + {}^{-}4.9 + {}^{+}6.1 =$ ${}^{-}7.3$

29. ${}^{-}5.5 + {}^{+}8.8 + {}^{-}3.3 =$ 0

30. ${}^{+}1.4 + {}^{-}1.2 + {}^{+}0.08 =$ ${}^{+}0.28$

31. ${}^{-}13.1 + {}^{+}6.1 + {}^{+}1.2 =$ ${}^{-}5.8$

32. ${}^{+}1.1 + {}^{-}9.1 + {}^{+}5 =$ ${}^{-}3$

33. ${}^{-}8.2 + {}^{+}3.3 + {}^{+}5.6 =$ ${}^{+}0.7$

34. ${}^{-}3.5 + {}^{-}7.9 + {}^{+}11.8 =$ ${}^{+}0.4$

Solve.

35. A chemist is working with a certain metal. She changes the temperature as follows: ${}^{+}1.1$°C, ${}^{+}2.8$°C, ${}^{-}1.9$°C. What is the total net change in temperature?

${}^{+}1.1 + {}^{+}2.8 + {}^{-}1.9$; ${}^{+}2$°C

36. A hiker climbed 50 m from camp, then went down 21 m, then climbed up another 11 m. Find the net change in his position.

${}^{+}50 + {}^{-}21 + {}^{+}11$; ${}^{+}40$ m

*Use with Lesson 4-3, text pages 104–105.

Copyright © Sadlier-Oxford

Subtracting Rational Numbers*

Name ______________________

Date ______________________

To subtract a rational number, *add its opposite.* $^{+}7 - {}^{-}3 = \underline{?}$ $\quad {}^{+}7 + {}^{+}3 = {}^{+}10$

Subtract.

1. $^{+}5.1 - {}^{+}6.6 =$ $^{-}1.5$
2. $^{-}7.3 - {}^{+}3.7 =$ $^{-}11$
3. $^{-}8.1 - {}^{-}5.1 =$ $^{-}3$
4. $^{+}0.2 - {}^{-}8.01 =$ $^{+}8.21$
5. $^{-}1.3 - {}^{+}1.1 =$ $^{-}2.4$
6. $^{-}1.6 - {}^{-}4.6 =$ $^{+}3$
7. $^{+}14.5 - {}^{-}7.1 =$ $^{+}21.6$
8. $^{-}13.4 - {}^{+}6.1 =$ $^{-}19.5$
9. $^{-}10.2 - {}^{+}10.2 =$ $^{-}20.4$
10. $^{-}4.5 - {}^{+}4.5 =$ $^{-}9$
11. $^{-}2.8 - {}^{-}2.8 =$ 0
12. $^{+}9.8 - {}^{+}0.2 =$ $^{+}9.6$
13. $^{+}5 - {}^{-}2\frac{1}{2} =$ $^{+}7\frac{1}{2}$
14. $^{-}4\frac{2}{5} - {}^{-}5\frac{4}{5} =$ $^{+}1\frac{2}{5}$
15. $^{-}1\frac{1}{6} - {}^{+}3\frac{5}{6} =$ $^{-}5$
16. $^{+}3\frac{7}{10} - {}^{-}5\frac{1}{10} =$ $^{+}8\frac{4}{5}$
17. $^{+}4\frac{1}{2} - {}^{+}3 =$ $^{+}1\frac{1}{2}$
18. $^{-}10\frac{2}{7} - {}^{-}5\frac{1}{7} =$ $^{-}5\frac{1}{7}$

Simplify each expression. Use the rules for order of operations.

19. $^{-}3.1 - ({}^{+}0.4 - {}^{+}6.1) =$ $^{+}2.6$
20. $^{+}7.2 + (0 - {}^{+}8.6) =$ $^{-}1.4$
21. $^{-}1.1 + ({}^{-}8.7 - {}^{-}0.3) =$ $^{-}9.5$
22. $^{-}5.05 - ({}^{-}5.1 - {}^{-}5.1) =$ $^{-}5.05$
23. $({}^{+}0.39 - {}^{-}0.7) + {}^{-}4.1 =$ $^{-}3.01$
24. $({}^{+}6.1 - {}^{-}4.4) - ({}^{-}3.3 - {}^{-}2.2) =$ $^{+}11.6$
25. $({}^{-}11.1 - {}^{+}0.04) - ({}^{-}2.1 - {}^{+}3.3) =$ $^{-}5.74$
26. $({}^{+}7.9 + {}^{-}0.10) + ({}^{+}4.1 - {}^{-}6.4) =$ $^{+}18.3$

Solve.

27. Mrs. Moffet's special account has a balance of \$43.06. She writes a check for \$50. What is her new balance?

$^{+}43.06 - \$50 = n;\ {}^{-}\$6.94$

28. A chemist takes a liquid at $^{+}10.4$°C and cools it until its temperature is $^{-}1.5$°C. Find the change in temperature.

$^{+}10.4 - n = {}^{-}1.5;\ {}^{+}11.9$°C

*Use with Lesson 4-4, text pages 106–107.

Copyright © Sadlier-Oxford

Solving Equations*
(Addition and Subtraction)

Name ______________________
Date ______________________

Evaluate each expression.

1. $x - {}^{-}1$ when $x = {}^{+}3$ $\underline{{}^{+}4}$
2. $x + {}^{-}4$ when $x = {}^{-}2$ $\underline{{}^{-}6}$
3. $x + {}^{+}5$ when $x = 0$ $\underline{{}^{+}5}$
4. $x - {}^{+}3$ when $x = {}^{+}6$ $\underline{{}^{+}3}$
5. ${}^{-}2 + h$ when $h = {}^{+}3$ $\underline{{}^{+}1}$
6. $a - a$ when $a = {}^{-}2$ $\underline{0}$

Solve.

7. $s + {}^{+}4 = {}^{+}9$ — $s = \underline{{}^{+}5}$
8. $r + {}^{-}7 = {}^{+}14$ — $r = \underline{{}^{+}21}$
9. $t + {}^{+}12 = {}^{-}2$ — $t = \underline{{}^{-}14}$
10. $b - {}^{+}8 = {}^{-}16$ — $b = \underline{{}^{-}8}$
11. $c - {}^{+}11 = {}^{+}42$ — $c = \underline{{}^{+}53}$
12. $m - {}^{-}9 = {}^{+}6$ — $m = \underline{{}^{-}3}$
13. $c - {}^{-}10 = {}^{+}18$ — $c = \underline{{}^{+}8}$
14. $c - {}^{-}2 = {}^{-}1$ — $c = \underline{{}^{-}3}$
15. $b + {}^{-}4 = {}^{+}15$ — $b = \underline{{}^{+}19}$
16. $d + {}^{-}2.1 = {}^{-}3.4$ — $d = \underline{{}^{-}1.3}$
17. $x - {}^{+}4.1 = {}^{-}2.8$ — $x = \underline{{}^{+}1.3}$
18. $y + {}^{-}2.5 = {}^{-}2.5$ — $y = \underline{0}$
19. $a + {}^{+}5 = {}^{+}8$ — $a = \underline{{}^{+}3}$
20. $d - {}^{+}7 = {}^{+}21$ — $d = \underline{{}^{+}28}$
21. $g - {}^{-}2 = {}^{-}24$ — $g = \underline{{}^{-}26}$

Write a mathematical sentence for each. Then solve it.

22. Five less than a number is 26. $n - 5 = 26;\ n = {}^{+}31$
23. Seven more than a number is ${}^{-}12$. $n + 7 = {}^{-}12;\ n = {}^{-}19$
24. A number decreased by ${}^{-}8$ is ${}^{-}11$. $n - {}^{-}8 = {}^{-}11;\ n = {}^{-}19$
25. A number increased by 15 is 41. $n + 15 = 41;\ n = {}^{+}26$

*Use with Lesson 4-5, text pages 108–109.

Copyright © Sadlier-Oxford

Multiplying Rational Numbers*

Name ______________________

Date ______________________

The product of two rational numbers with *different* signs is negative; with the *same* sign is positive.

Find the product.

1. ${}^{+}3 \times {}^{+}2 =$ $^{+}6$

2. ${}^{+}6 \times {}^{+}2 =$ $^{+}12$

3. ${}^{+}3 \times {}^{+}12 =$ $^{+}36$

4. ${}^{-}1 \times {}^{-}3 =$ $^{+}3$

5. ${}^{-}8 \times {}^{-}2 =$ $^{+}16$

6. ${}^{-}7 \times {}^{-}5 =$ $^{+}35$

7. ${}^{-}4 \times {}^{-}7 =$ $^{+}28$

8. ${}^{-}8 \times {}^{+}3 =$ $^{-}24$

9. ${}^{+}3 \times {}^{-}4 =$ $^{-}12$

10. ${}^{+}5 \times {}^{+}9 =$ $^{+}45$

11. ${}^{-}10 \times {}^{+}2 =$ $^{-}20$

12. ${}^{+}6 \times {}^{-}6 =$ $^{-}36$

13. ${}^{-}7 \times {}^{-}9 =$ $^{+}63$

14. ${}^{-}8 \times {}^{-}4 =$ $^{+}32$

15. ${}^{+}3 \times {}^{-}9 =$ $^{-}27$

16. ${}^{-}3.2 \times {}^{-}0.4 =$ $^{+}1.28$

17. ${}^{-}0.08 \times {}^{-}0.3 =$ $^{+}0.024$

18. ${}^{+}5.1 \times {}^{-}7 =$ $^{-}35.7$

19. ${}^{+}5.14 \times {}^{-}2 =$ $^{-}10.28$

20. ${}^{-}4.3 \times {}^{-}0.09 =$ $^{+}0.387$

21. ${}^{+}6.07 \times {}^{-}0.01 =$ $^{-}0.0607$

22. ${}^{+}5.78 \times {}^{+}2.6 =$ $^{+}15.028$

23. $-\frac{3}{4} \times -\frac{1}{2} =$ $+\frac{3}{8}$

24. $+\frac{5}{6} \times -\frac{1}{3} =$ $-\frac{5}{18}$

25. $-\frac{1}{4} \times +\frac{3}{4} =$ $-\frac{3}{16}$

26. $-\frac{3}{4} \times -\frac{8}{9} =$ $+\frac{2}{3}$

27. $+\frac{2}{9} \times -\frac{5}{6} =$ $-\frac{5}{27}$

28. $+\frac{4}{5} \times -\frac{1}{8} =$ $-\frac{1}{10}$

29. $+2\frac{1}{2} \times -\frac{3}{4} =$ $-1\frac{7}{8}$

30. $-1\frac{1}{8} \times +\frac{1}{2} =$ $-\frac{9}{16}$

Compute.

31. ${}^{-}4 \times ({}^{-}2 + {}^{+}7) =$ $^{-}20$

32. ${}^{-}7 \times ({}^{-}3 - {}^{-}6) =$ $^{-}21$

33. $({}^{-}9 - {}^{-}4) \times ({}^{+}3 - {}^{-}1) =$ $^{-}20$

34. $({}^{+}6 + {}^{-}7) \times ({}^{-}4 + {}^{+}4) =$ 0

35. ${}^{-}5 \times ({}^{-}3 - {}^{-}10) =$ $^{-}35$

36. $({}^{-}8 \times {}^{-}2) + ({}^{-}4 \times {}^{+}2) =$ $^{+}8$

Evaluate.

37. $6y$ when $y = {}^{-}3$ $^{-}18$

38. ${}^{-}4t$ when $t = {}^{-}1$ $^{+}4$

39. ${}^{-}50m$ when $m = {}^{+}4$ $^{-}200$

40. ${}^{-}45s$ when $s = 0$ 0

*Use with Lesson 4-6, text pages 110–111.

Copyright © Sadlier-Oxford

Dividing Rational Numbers*

Name ______________________

Date ______________________

The quotient of two rational numbers with the *same sign* is positive; with *different signs* is negative.

Complete.

1. $^{+}5 \times \underline{\ ^{+}4\ } = {}^{+}20$
   $^{+}20 \div \underline{\ ^{+}4\ } = {}^{+}5$

2. $^{-}8 \times \underline{\ ^{-}7\ } = {}^{+}56$
   $^{+}56 \div \underline{\ ^{-}7\ } = {}^{-}8$

3. $^{-}9 \times {}^{-}7 = \underline{\ ^{+}63\ }$
   $\underline{\ ^{+}63\ } \div {}^{-}7 = {}^{-}9$

4. $^{+}48 \times \underline{\ ^{-}2\ } = {}^{-}96$
   $^{-}96 \div \underline{\ ^{-}2\ } = {}^{+}48$

5. $^{-}18 \times \underline{\ ^{+}3\ } = {}^{-}54$
   $^{-}54 \div \underline{\ ^{+}3\ } = {}^{-}18$

6. $^{+}12 \times {}^{-}9 = \underline{\ ^{-}108\ }$
   $\underline{\ ^{-}108\ } \div {}^{-}9 = {}^{+}12$

Divide.

7. $\frac{^{+}72}{^{-}9} = \underline{\ ^{-}8\ }$
8. $\frac{^{-}40}{^{+}8} = \underline{\ ^{-}5\ }$
9. $\frac{^{+}16}{^{-}4} = \underline{\ ^{-}4\ }$
10. $\frac{^{-}21}{^{-}7} = \underline{\ ^{+}3\ }$
11. $\frac{^{-}108}{^{-}12} = \underline{\ ^{+}9\ }$
12. $\frac{^{+}10}{^{+}5} = \underline{\ ^{+}2\ }$
13. $\frac{^{-}56}{^{-}7} = \underline{\ ^{+}8\ }$
14. $\frac{^{+}63}{^{-}7} = \underline{\ ^{-}9\ }$
15. $\frac{^{-}81}{^{+}9} = \underline{\ ^{-}9\ }$

Find the quotient.

16. $^{-}12 \div {}^{+}2 = \underline{\ ^{-}6\ }$
17. $^{-}18 \div {}^{-}9 = \underline{\ ^{+}2\ }$
18. $^{-}25 \div {}^{-}5 = \underline{\ ^{+}5\ }$
19. $^{+}2.3 \div {}^{-}2.3 = \underline{\ ^{-}1\ }$
20. $^{-}3.5 \div {}^{+}0.7 = \underline{\ ^{-}5\ }$
21. $^{+}2.8 \div {}^{-}4 = \underline{\ ^{-}0.7\ }$
22. $^{-}2\frac{3}{5} \div \frac{^{+}1}{10} = \underline{\ ^{-}26\ }$
23. $^{-}7\frac{1}{4} \div \frac{^{-}5}{8} = \underline{\ ^{+}11\frac{3}{5}\ }$
24. $^{+}5\frac{3}{5} \div {}^{+}7\frac{7}{15} = \underline{\ ^{+}\frac{3}{4}\ }$
25. $^{-}8\frac{3}{4} \div {}^{+}2\frac{1}{2} = \underline{\ ^{-}3\frac{1}{2}\ }$
26. $^{-}1\frac{1}{8} \div {}^{-}2\frac{3}{4} = \underline{\ ^{+}\frac{9}{22}\ }$
27. $^{-}6\frac{1}{3} \div {}^{-}4\frac{2}{9} = \underline{\ ^{+}1\frac{1}{2}\ }$
28. $(^{-}4 \times {}^{-}3) \div {}^{-}2 = \underline{\ ^{-}6\ }$
29. $(^{-}18 \times {}^{+}3) \div {}^{+}6 = \underline{\ ^{-}9\ }$
30. $(^{-}28 \times {}^{+}20) \div {}^{-}8 = \underline{\ ^{+}70\ }$

*Use with Lesson 4-7, text pages 112–113.

Copyright © Sadlier-Oxford

Solving Equations*
(Multiplication and Division)

Name ________________

Date ________________

Write an equation for each. Then solve it.

1. Four times a number is negative 55. $4n = {}^-55;\ n = {}^-13\frac{3}{4}$ or ${}^-13.75$
2. A number divided by negative 3 is positive 7. $\frac{n}{-3} = {}^+7;\ n = {}^-21$
3. A number times negative 9 is negative 36. $-9n = {}^-36;\ n = {}^+4$
4. Seven times a number is negative 56. $7n = {}^-56;\ n = {}^-8$

Solve.

5. $7x = {}^+49$ $x =$ +7
6. ${}^-5a = {}^-45$ $a =$ +9
7. $9r = {}^+81$ $r =$ +9
8. ${}^-3s = {}^-36$ $s =$ +12
9. ${}^-8t = {}^+0.64$ $t =$ −0.08
10. ${}^+1.4x = {}^-42$ $x =$ −30
11. $10y = {}^-350.1$ $y =$ −35.01
12. ${}^-0.12a = {}^+144$ $a =$ −1200
13. $21c = {}^-\frac{1}{3}$ $c =$ $\frac{-1}{63}$
14. $8d = \frac{4}{5}$ $d =$ $\frac{1}{10}$
15. ${}^-23b = {}^+20.7$ $b =$ −0.9
16. $9r = {}^-7.65$ $r =$ −0.85
17. $\frac{1}{4}t = {}^-400$ $t =$ −1600
18. $13n = {}^+91$ $n =$ +7
19. $8x = {}^-6$ $x =$ −0.75 or $-\frac{3}{4}$
20. $\frac{f}{{}^+4} = {}^+16$ $f =$ +64
21. $\frac{a}{{}^+9} = {}^-8$ $a =$ −72
22. $\frac{b}{{}^-3} = {}^+41$ $b =$ −123
23. $\frac{c}{{}^+8} = {}^-36$ $c =$ −288
24. $\frac{d}{{}^+20} = {}^-\frac{1}{5}$ $d =$ −4
25. $\frac{e}{{}^-1} = {}^+12.5$ $e =$ −12.5
26. $\frac{h}{{}^-1} = {}^-4.7$ $h =$ +4.7
27. $\frac{a}{{}^-0.7} = {}^-8$ $a =$ +5.6
28. $\frac{n}{{}^+10} = {}^-36\frac{1}{5}$ $n =$ −362
29. $\frac{t}{0.5} = {}^+26$ $t =$ +13
30. $\frac{c}{{}^-4} = {}^-10\frac{1}{2}$ $c =$ +42
31. $\frac{n}{{}^+3} = {}^+64$ $n =$ +192
32. $\frac{x}{{}^-2} = {}^+5.8$ $x =$ −11.6

*Use with Lesson 4-8, text pages 114–115.

Copyright © Sadlier-Oxford

Equations: Two-Step Solutions*

Name ______________________

Date ______________________

Find the LCM for each equation, when needed. Then solve.

1. $^{-}3.5 + 2x = {}^{-}13.5$
   LCM = 10
   $^{-}35 + 20x = {}^{-}135$; $x = {}^{-}5$

2. $2k - 6 = 8$
   $2k = 14$; $k = 7$

3. $24.1 + 6x = 38.5$
   LCM = 10
   $241 + 60x = 385$; $x = 2.4$

4. $\frac{n}{2} - 5 = 15$
   LCM = 2
   $n - 10 = 30$; $n = 40$

5. $\frac{y}{10} + 4 = 16$
   LCM = 10
   $y + 40 = 160$; $y = 120$

6. $\frac{y}{3.5} + 15 = 17$
   LCM = 3.5
   $y + 52.5 = 59.5$; $y = 7$

7. $\frac{s}{3} - 15 = 15$
   LCM = 3
   $s - 45 = 45$; $s = 90$

8. $0.5n + 3 = 8.5$
   LCM = 10
   $5n + 30 = 85$; $n = 11$

9. $3y - 11 = 25$
   $3y = 36$; $y = 12$

10. $4y + {}^{-}3 = {}^{-}25$
    $4y = {}^{-}28$; $y = {}^{-}7$

11. $3.6y + 3.2 = 15.8$
    LCM = 10
    $36y + 32 = 158$; $y = 3.5$

12. $\frac{^{-}s}{3} - 4 = {}^{-}10$
    LCM = 3
    $^{-}s - 12 = {}^{-}30$; $s = 18$

Combine like terms. Then solve.

13. $3c + 1\frac{1}{4} - 5c = {}^{-}5$
    $^{-}2c + 1\frac{1}{4} = {}^{-}5$; $c = 3\frac{1}{8}$

14. $3a + 2.1 + 4a = {}^{-}0.7$
    $7a + 2.1 = {}^{-}0.7$; $a = {}^{-}0.4$

15. $5r + 2r - 1 = {}^{-}36$
    $7r - 1 = {}^{-}36$; $r = {}^{-}5$

16. $2.1x - 6 + 1.6x = 12.5$
    $3.7x - 6 = 12.5$; $x = 5$

17. $5y - 1 - 3y = {}^{+}5\frac{1}{5}$
    $2y - 1 = {}^{+}5\frac{1}{5}$; $y = 3\frac{1}{10}$

18. $9d - 2.3 - 10d = 6$
    $^{-}d - 2.3 = 6$; $d = {}^{-}8.3$

19. $7x + 1.5 - 8x = {}^{-}2.1$
    $^{-}x + 1.5 = {}^{-}2.1$; $x = 3.6$

20. $10c - 20c = 90$
    $^{-}10c = 90$; $c = {}^{-}9$

21. $40t - 19t = 231$
    $21t = 231$; $t = 11$

Solve equations, using grouping symbols if needed.

22. $\frac{2x - 5 + x - 5}{10} = 8.3$
    $\frac{3x - 10}{10} = 8.3$; $3x - 10 = 83$
    $x = 31$

23. $\frac{n + 4}{4} = 3$
    $n + 4 = 12$; $n = 8$

24. $\frac{7}{2.1} = \frac{3}{a}$
    $7a = 6.3$; $a = 0.9$

25. $5x - 3x - 3 = 4.2$
    $2x - 3 = 4.2$; $x = 3.6$

*Use with Lesson 4-9, text pages 116–117.

Copyright © Sadlier-Oxford

Nonroutine Problems*

Name ______________________

Date ______________________

Solve. Strategies may vary.

1. Each of three cards contains one of the letters A, B, or C, and one of the numbers 1, 2, or 3. A is on the card to the right of C; 3 is on an end card. C and 3 are not on the same card. 2 is on the card to the left of A; 1 is on the card between B and 2. What number and letter are on each card?

   Logical reasoning: 2C, 1A, 3B

2. Carla, Brian, Sula, and Darryl were each born under a different sign of the zodiac. The signs are: Aquarius, Pisces, Leo, and Scorpio. Sula is neither a Scorpio nor a Pisces. Carla is not a Pisces. The name of the Aquarian does not start with the letter B. One of the four is a teacher who is a Leo. Sula, Carla, and Brian are students. What is each person's zodiac sign?

   Logical reasoning:
   Carla – Scorpio; Brian – Pisces;
   Sula – Aquarius; Darryl – Leo

	C	B	S	D
A	No	No	Yes	No
P	No	Yes	No	No
L	No	No	No	Yes
S	Yes	No	No	No

3. Maria, Megan, Ramon, and Jeff are to share in the Pot-O-Gold grand prize. Maria receives $\frac{1}{4}$ of the prize, Ramon $\frac{1}{3}$ of the prize, Jeff $\frac{1}{4}$ of the prize, and Megan receives \$72,000. Find each person's share.

   Finding hidden facts:
   Megan's share $= 1 - \left(\frac{1}{4} + \frac{1}{3} + \frac{1}{4}\right) = \frac{1}{6}$
   $\frac{1}{6}p = \$72{,}000$; $p = \$432{,}000$; Maria: \$108,000;
   Megan: \$72,000; Ramon: \$144,000; Jeff: \$108,000

4. The distance from town A to town B is 56 mi. Town C is halfway between town A and town B. Town D is $\frac{1}{4}$ of the way between towns A and C, but closer to town C. How far is town A from town D?

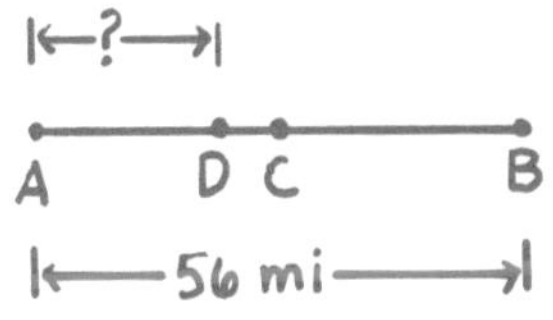

   Drawing a picture; finding hidden facts:
   distance from A to C $= \frac{1}{2}(56) = 28$
   $\frac{3}{4}(28) = 21$; 21 mi

5. Moya and Catherine each pick a number from a hat. The difference between 30 and Moya's number is 15. The difference between Catherine's number and 30 is $^{-}15$. Find each number.

   Using equations:
   $30 - M = 15$; Moya: 15
   $C - 30 = {}^{-}15$; Catherine: 15

*Use for Chapters 1 through 4.

Copyright © Sadlier-Oxford

Nonroutine Problems* (cont'd)

Name ____________________

Date ____________________

6. One carton of baseballs contains 10 more baseballs than a second carton. Together they contain 5 dozen baseballs. How many baseballs are in each carton?

Using equations; finding hidden facts: 1 doz = 12

$x + x + 10 = 5(12)$

35 baseballs; 25 baseballs

7. Juan bought a share of stock. The first week it doubled in value. The second week it decreased \$3.50 in value. The third week it increased \$5 in value. Juan then sold the share and received \$35.50 for it. What was the original cost?

Writing equations with rational numbers:

$2x - \$3.50 + \$5 = \$35.50$; \$17

8. Alicia wants to display five albums, equally spaced, on a 5-ft-wide rack. Each album is 9 in. wide. If she leaves no space at the ends, how much space should she allow between each album?

Drawing a picture; finding hidden facts;

Using equations: 1 ft = 12 in.

$[5(12) - 5(9)] \div 4$; $3\frac{3}{4}$ in.

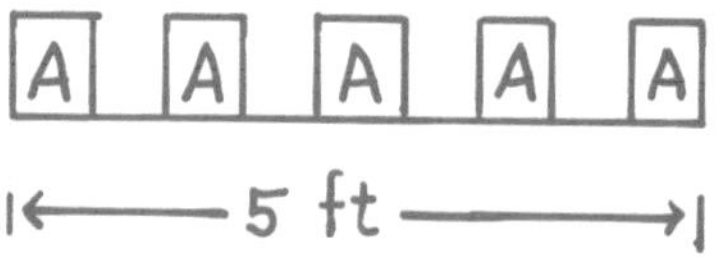

9. Three elephants are used to move some heavy logs blocking a road. Their owners are paid according to the number of tons of logs each elephant moves. The total cost of moving the logs is \$693.80. If Mighty Mo moves 5.8 T, Tiny Tim moves 7.3 T, and Sweet Pea moves 6.9 T, how much should each elephant (and owner) receive in payment?

Writing equations with rational numbers:

$5.8T + 7.3T + 6.9T = 20T$

$MM = \frac{5.8}{20}(\$693.80)$; $TT = \frac{7.3}{20}(\$693.80)$; $SP = \frac{6.9}{20}(\$693.80)$

MM: \$201.20; TT: \$253.24; SP: \$239.36

10. A number is divided by 7 and 11 is taken from the quotient. If the difference is 2, what is the number?

Using equations:

$\frac{n}{7} - 11 = 2$; $n = 91$

*Use for Chapters 1 through 4.

Copyright © Sadlier-Oxford

Powers of Ten*

Name ______________________

Date ______________________

Write each power of ten as a standard numeral.

1. 10^3 1000
2. 10^0 1
3. 10^4 10,000
4. 10^8 100,000,000
5. 10^{10} 10,000,000,000
6. 10^7 10,000,000

Write each as a power of ten (exponent form).

7. 10 × 10 × 10 × 10 × 10 10^5
8. 1,000,000,000,000 10^{12}
9. 1 10^0
10. 100 10^2
11. 10,000,000 10^7
12. one hundred billion 10^{11}

Find the product or quotient.

13. 8.4 × 10 = 84
14. 0.72 × 100 = 72
15. 9.48 × 100 = 948
16. 0.347 × 1000 = 347
17. 93 × 10^2 = 9300
18. 8.04 × 10^3 = 8040
19. 0.3841 × 10^3 = 384.1
20. 8.0315 × 10^4 = 80315
21. 6431.1 × 10^2 = 643,110
22. 0.3416 × 10^5 = 34160
23. 7.93 ÷ 100 = 0.0793
24. 3.621 ÷ 1000 = 0.003621
25. 50.63 ÷ 10^2 = 0.5063
26. 0.3141 ÷ 10^1 = 0.03141
27. 1.06 ÷ 10^5 = 0.0000106
28. 8032 ÷ 10^2 = 80.32
29. 4.2 ÷ 10^6 = 0.0000042
30. 215 ÷ 10^4 = 0.0215
31. 70.09 ÷ 10^4 = 0.007009
32. 5000 ÷ 10^7 = 0.0005

Arrange in order from greatest to least.

33. 5081.426 × 10^3; 42.21021 × 10^5; 6321.004 × 10^3; 4.321 × 10^6; 8.22 × 10^7

8.22 × 10^7; 6321.004 × 10^3; 5081.426 × 10^3; 4.321 × 10^6; 42.21021 × 10^5

34. 82.41 ÷ 10^2; 3.068 ÷ 10^1; 2800 ÷ 10^4; 438.61 ÷ 10^3; 0.9341 ÷ 10^0

0.9431 ÷ 10^0; 82.41 ÷ 10^2; 438.61 ÷ 10^3; 3.068 ÷ 10^1; 2800 ÷ 10^4

35. 8.4 ÷ 10^3; 8400 ÷ 10^5; 0.84 ÷ 10^6; 84 ÷ 10^2; 8400 ÷ 10^7

84 ÷ 10^2; 8400 ÷ 10^5; 8.4 ÷ 10^3; 8400 ÷ 10^7; 0.84 ÷ 10^6

*Use with Lesson 5-1, text pages 128–129.

Copyright © Sadlier-Oxford

Negative Exponents*

Name ______________________

Date ______________________

Standard Form →	1,000,000,000	100,000,000	10,000,000	1,000,000	100,000	10,000	1000	100	10	1		0.1	0.01	0.001	0.0001	0.00001	0.000001
Powers of Ten →	10^9	10^8	10^7	10^6	10^5	10^4	10^3	10^2	10^1	10^0		10^{-1}	10^{-2}	10^{-3}	10^{-4}	10^{-5}	10^{-6}
Number →	1	2	3	0	4	1	0	0	5	7	.	0	9	0	0	6	1

Write the standard numeral.

1. $(8 \times 10^2) + (4 \times 10^1) + (3 \times 10^0) + (7 \times \frac{1}{10^2}) + (4 \times \frac{1}{10^3})$ 843.074
2. $(3 \times 10^1) + (6 \times 10^{-1}) + (6 \times 10^{-2}) + (4 \times 10^{-3}) + (6 \times 10^{-4})$ 30.6646
3. $(1 \times 10^3) + (2 \times 10^2) + (4 \times 10^0) + (5 \times 10^{-1}) + (6 \times 10^{-2})$ 1204.56
4. $(2 \times 10^2) + (5 \times 10^0) + (3 \times 10^{-2}) + (6 \times 10^{-4}) + (1 \times 10^{-6})$ 205.030601

Give the value of the underlined digit.

5. 3481.2063 0 hundredths
6. 482.51006 5 tenths
7. 860.51427 2 ten thousandths
8. 3416.004 0 hundredths
9. 72,106.20071 1 hundred thousandth
10. 928.04165 1 thousandth
11. 3261.983 8 hundredths
12. 0.4268 8 ten thousandths

Write in expanded form using positive and negative exponents.

13. 0.09 (9×10^{-2})
14. 0.004 (4×10^{-3})
15. 0.0001 (1×10^{-4})
16. 0.000008 (8×10^{-6})
17. 66.3 $(6 \times 10^1) + (6 \times 10^0) + (3 \times 10^{-1})$
18. 276.8041 $(2 \times 10^2) + (7 \times 10^1) + (6 \times 10^0) + (8 \times 10^{-1}) + (4 \times 10^{-3}) + (1 \times 10^{-4})$
19. 838.00052 $(8 \times 10^2) + (3 \times 10^1) + (8 \times 10^0) + (5 \times 10^{-4}) + (2 \times 10^{-5})$
20. 6000.606 $(6 \times 10^3) + (6 \times 10^{-1}) + (6 \times 10^{-3})$
21. 4.000846 $(4 \times 10^0) + (8 \times 10^{-4}) + (4 \times 10^{-5}) + (6 \times 10^{-6})$
22. 203.01050907 $(2 \times 10^2) + (3 \times 10^0) + (1 \times 10^{-2}) + (5 \times 10^{-4}) + (9 \times 10^{-6}) + (7 \times 10^{-8})$

*Use with Lesson 5-2, text pages 130–131.

Copyright © Sadlier-Oxford

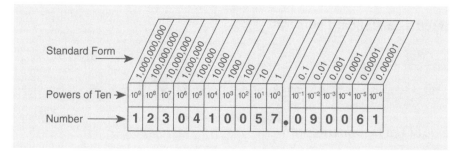

Scientific Notation*
(Multiplication and Division)

Name ______________________
Date ______________________

Complete with the correct power of ten.

1. $782 = 7.82 \times 10^?$ 2

2. $8469 = 8.469 \times 10^?$ 3

3. $0.000052 = 5.2 \times 10^?$ −5

4. $0.00073 = 7.3 \times 10^?$ −4

Write in scientific notation.

5. 62,000 6.2×10^4

6. 189,000 1.89×10^5

7. 0.000006 6×10^{-6}

8. 0.000065 6.5×10^{-5}

Compute. Express the answer in standard notation.

9. $(3.5 \times 10^5) \times (7.2 \times 10^4)$ 25,200,000,000

10. $(5.4 \times 10^3) \times (4.6 \times 10^6)$ 24,840,000,000

11. $(8.1 \times 10^8) \times (2.5 \times 10^2)$ 202,500,000,000

12. $(8.2 \times 10^4) \times (5.5 \times 10^8)$ 45,100,000,000,000

13. $(9.5 \times 10^2) \times (6.3 \times 10^{-4})$ 0.5985

14. $(1.7 \times 10^{-3}) \times (4.2 \times 10^{-2})$ 0.0000714

Divide.

15. $\frac{10^4}{10^1}$ 10^3

16. $\frac{10^{20}}{10^8}$ 10^{12}

17. $\frac{10^0}{10^{-3}}$ 10^3

18. $\frac{10^6}{10^{-3}}$ 10^9

19. $6^2 \div 6^{-2}$ 6^4

20. $5^4 \div 5^8$ 5^{-4}

21. $8^{-2} \div 8^{-3}$ 8^1

22. $5^6 \div 5^{-3}$ 5^9

Compute.

23. $\frac{1.2 \times 10^4}{6 \times 10^2}$ 2×10^1

24. $\frac{3.05 \times 10^{10}}{2.5 \times 10^2}$ 1.22×10^8

25. $\frac{6.2 \times 10^{-6}}{5 \times 10^{-3}}$ 1.24×10^{-3}

Solve.

26. The distance of Pluto from the Sun is about 5 910 000 000 km. Write this number in scientific notation. 5.91×10^9 km

27. The distance of Venus from the Sun is about 107 000 000 km. Write this number in scientific notation. 1.07×10^8 km

28. If a planet travels 8.9×10^4 mph in its orbit, how far will it travel in 8 days? $8 \times 24 \times 8.9 \times 10^4$
17,088,000 mi or 1.7088×10^7 mi

29. An outer bank rectangular island measures 65 000 m by 9 800 m. What is its area? 65 000 × 9800
637,000,000 m^2 or 6.37×10^8 m^2

30. A bird sanctuary in full season has a population of 9,500,000 and an area of 22.5 square miles. What is its population density? 9,500,000 ÷ 22.5
422,222.22 mi^2 or 4.2222222×10^5 mi^2

*Use with Lessons 5-3, 5-4, text pages 132–135.

Copyright © Sadlier-Oxford

Divisibility*

Name ______________________

Date ______________________

Circle the numbers in each row that are divisible by the first number.

1.	3	**168**	**2514**	826	43,025	**217,251**
2.	5	128	**450**	**2645**	**806,700**	324,106
3.	2	97	**948**	**66**	**27,684**	**18,630**
4.	10	**2460**	38,155	21,966	**34,100**	**2,671,050**
5.	9	**324**	**81,648**	**32,166**	821,940	**386,451**
6.	8	**29,648**	**321,032**	92,611	**43,824**	**592,560**
7.	4	**247,116**	**920,424**	**327,164**	807,199	**367,148**
8.	6	**19,800**	606,592	**408,906**	756,101	**125,910**
9.	11	1,210,117	**112,926**	**617,122**	320,693	**122,221**

Complete each chart. Write "Yes" or "No."

	Number	Divisible by 2	Divisible by 5	Divisible by 10
10.	820	Yes	Yes	Yes
11.	16,325	No	Yes	No
12.	73,240	Yes	Yes	Yes
13.	15,005	No	Yes	No
14.	144,240	Yes	Yes	Yes
15.	255,805	No	Yes	No

	Number	Divisible by 3	Divisible by 6	Divisible by 9
16.	1269	Yes	No	Yes
17.	5085	Yes	No	Yes
18.	1116	Yes	Yes	Yes
19.	387,189	Yes	No	Yes
20.	905,436	Yes	Yes	Yes
21.	539,514	Yes	Yes	Yes

22. Write the smallest number divisible by 2, 5, and 10. 10

23. Write the smallest number divisible by 3, 6, and 9. 18

24. Write the smallest number divisible by 2, 3, 4, 6, and 8. 24

25. Mr. Martin baked 688 fresh doughnuts. He wants to package them in boxes of 8. Will each box be filled with doughnuts? How many boxes will he use? Yes; 688 ÷ 8; 86

*Use with Lesson 5-5, text pages 136–137.

Copyright © Sadlier-Oxford

Patterns and Sequences*

Name ____________________

Date ____________________

Find the next three terms in each sequence.

1. 4, 9, 14, 19, 24, 29, 34

2. 1, 4, 7, 10, 13, 16, 19

3. 54, 52, 50, 48, 46, 44, 42

4. 2, 11, 20, 29, 38, 47, 56

5. 1, 2, 4, 8, 16, 32, 64

6. 1600, 1500, 1400, 1300, 1200, 1100, 1000

7. 8, 15, 22, 29, 36, 43, 50

8. 7, 13, 19, 25, 31, 37, 43

9. 10, 10.5, 11, 11.5 12, 12.5, 13

10. 27, 38, 49, 60, 71, 82, 93

11. $\frac{1}{3}$, $\frac{2}{3}$, 1, $\frac{4}{3}$, $\frac{5}{3}$, 2, $\frac{7}{3}$

12. 96, 93, 90, 87, 84, 81, 78

13. 1, 2, 4, 7, 11, 16, 22

14. 100, 95, 94, 89, 88, 83, 82

15. 12.3, 12.5, 12.7, 12.9, 13.1, 13.3, 13.5

16. 1, 3, 2, 4, 3, 5, 4

17. 5, 6, 11, 12, 17, 18, 23

18. 2, 7, 5, 10, 8, 13, 11, 16

19. 90, 80, 71, 63, 56, 50, 45

20. 1, $\frac{1}{2}$, $\frac{1}{4}$, $\frac{1}{8}$, $\frac{1}{16}$, $\frac{1}{32}$, $\frac{1}{64}$

21. 7, 10, 13, 16, 19, 22, 25

22. 92, 88, 84, 80, 76, 72, 68

23. 1, 3, 9, 27, 81, 243, 729

24. 2048, 1024, 512, 256, 128, 64, 32

25. 1, 1.3, 1.6, 1.9, 2.2, 2.5, 2.8

26. 7, 20, 33, 46, 59, 72, 85

27. 92, 91, 89, 86, 82, 77, 71

28. 2, 6, 5, 9, 8, 12, 11

29. 4, 5.5, 7, 8.5, 10, 11.5, 13

30. 13, 16, 11, 14, 9, 12, 7

31. 30, 15, 18, 9, 12, 6, 9

32. 70, 210, 110, 330, 230, 690, 590

33. 8, 32, 16, 64, 32, 128, 64

34. 10,000, 1000, 100, 10, 1, 0.1, 0.01

*Use with Lesson 5-6, text page 138.

Copyright © Sadlier-Oxford

Connectives*

Name ____________

Date ____________

Use *p*, *q*, and *r* to write each connective in symbols where:

***p*:** I seal the letter. ***q*:** You open the book. ***r*:** Nicki watches TV.

1. I seal the letter and you open the book. $p \wedge q$
2. You open the book or I seal the letter. $q \vee p$
3. If you open the book, Nicki watches TV. $q \rightarrow r$
4. I do *not* seal the letter and Nicki does *not* watch TV. $\sim p \wedge \sim r$
5. If Nicki watches TV, then I seal the letter and you open the book. $r \rightarrow (p \wedge q)$
6. It is not true that I seal the letter and you open the book. $\sim(p \wedge q)$

Use *r*, *s*, and *t* to write a statement in these exercises where:

***r*:** Love is everything. ***s*:** Silence gives consent. ***t*:** Time is a thief.

7. $r \wedge s$ Love is everything and silence gives consent.
8. $r \vee \sim t$ Love is everything or time is not a thief.
9. $s \rightarrow t$ If silence gives consent, then time is a thief.
10. $s \leftrightarrow t$ Silence gives consent if and only if time is a thief.
11. $t \vee r$ Time is a thief or love is everything.
12. $r \rightarrow (s \wedge t)$ If love is everything, then silence gives consent and time is a thief.

Complete these truth tables.

13.

p	q	$\sim p$	$\sim p \leftrightarrow q$
T	T	F	F
T	F	F	T
F	T	T	T
F	F	T	F

14.

p	q	$\sim q$	$p \wedge \sim q$
T	T	F	F
T	F	T	T
F	T	F	F
F	F	T	F

15.

p	q	$\sim p$	$\sim p \wedge q$
T	T	F	F
T	F	F	F
F	T	T	T
F	F	T	F

Construct a truth table for each.

16. $\sim p \vee \sim q$ ____________

p	q	~p	~q	~p∨~q
T	T	F	F	F
T	F	F	T	T
F	T	T	F	T
F	F	T	T	T

17. $\sim(p \vee q)$ ____________

p	q	p∨q	~(p∨q)
T	T	T	F
T	F	T	F
F	T	T	F
F	F	F	T

18. $(p \vee q) \rightarrow (p \wedge q)$ ____________

p	q	p∨q	p∧q	(p∨q)→(p∧q
T	T	T	T	T
T	F	T	F	F
F	T	T	F	F
F	F	F	F	T

*Use with Lessons 5-7, 5-8, text pages 139–141.

Copyright © Sadlier-Oxford

Converse, Inverse, Contrapositive*

Name ______________________

Date ______________________

Write the converse, inverse, and contrapositive for each conditional.

1. If a number is not divisible by one, it is zero.

Converse: If a number is zero, then it is not divisible by one.

Inverse: If a number is divisible by one, then it is not zero.

Contrapositive: If a number is not zero, then it is divisible by one.

2. If Killer is a dog, then Killer is a beagle.

Converse: If Killer is a beagle, then Killer is a dog.

Inverse: If Killer is not a dog, then Killer is not a beagle.

Contrapositive: If Killer is not a beagle, then Killer is not a dog.

3. If Stretch is a python, then Stretch is a snake.

Converse: If Stretch is a snake, then Stretch is a python.

Inverse: If Stretch is not a python, then Stretch is not a snake.

Contrapositive: If Stretch is not a snake, then Stretch is not a python.

Determine the truth value of each conditional, its converse, its inverse, and its contrapositive. The first one is done for you.

4. If water freezes at 0°C, then $2 + 3 = 5$. T, T, T, T

5. If the World Trade Center has 104 floors, then $2 \div 2 = 1$. T, F, F, T

6. If 1996 is a leap year, then February will have 29 days. T, T, T, T

7. If Boston is in Massachusetts, then the ice is hot. F, T, T, F

8. If sixteen is divisible by 5, then 7 is an even number. T, T, T, T

9. If $3 + 3 \neq 6$, then 109 is divisible by 3. T, T, T, T

Complete this truth table.

10.

p	q	$q \rightarrow p$	$\sim q$	$\sim p$	$(\sim p \rightarrow \sim q)$	$(q \rightarrow p) \rightarrow (\sim p \rightarrow \sim q)$
T	T	T	F	F	T	T
T	F	T	T	F	T	T
F	T	F	F	T	F	T
F	F	T	T	T	T	T

*Use with Lesson 5-9, text pages 142–143.

Copyright © Sadlier-Oxford

Ratios and Rates*

Name ______________________
Date ______________________

Write a ratio. Express it as a fraction in lowest terms. Change to like units where necessary.

1. 9 out of 10 people use Sure Glue $\frac{9}{10}$
2. 25¢ out of every dollar goes to entertainment $\frac{1}{4}$
3. 4 girls in a class of 9 students $\frac{4}{9}$
4. The number of even digits to the number of odd digits in 9,241,657 $\frac{3}{4}$
5. 8 apples in a basket of 2 dozen $\frac{1}{3}$
6. 6 inches out of a yard $\frac{1}{6}$

Write as a rate in simplest form.

7. 3 pages in 5 hours $\frac{3}{5}$
8. 7 books in 8 weeks $\frac{7}{8}$
9. $450 a month $\frac{\$450}{1}$
10. 6 cans for $1.29 $\frac{2}{\$.43}$
11. 2 shirts for $12.50 $\frac{1}{\$6.25}$
12. 12 guppies for $6.39 $\frac{4}{\$2.13}$
13. 500 yards in 40 seconds $\frac{25}{2}$
14. 6 bags for $3.50 $\frac{3}{\$1.75}$

Write an equal ratio in lowest terms.

15. 30 : 5 $\frac{6}{1}$
16. 7 : 49 $\frac{1}{7}$
17. 6 : 24 $\frac{1}{4}$
18. 40 : 8 $\frac{5}{1}$
19. 45 : 81 $\frac{5}{9}$
20. 24 : 72 $\frac{1}{3}$
21. 50 : 25 $\frac{2}{1}$
22. 36 : 54 $\frac{2}{3}$
23. 24 : 48 $\frac{1}{2}$
24. 42:12 $\frac{7}{2}$
25. $4\frac{1}{5} : 3\frac{1}{2}$ $\frac{6}{5}$
26. $\frac{2}{3} : \frac{6}{9}$ $\frac{1}{1}$
27. $1\frac{1}{3} : 2\frac{5}{6}$ $\frac{8}{17}$
28. $\frac{2}{3} : \frac{3}{4}$ $\frac{8}{9}$
29. $3\frac{1}{5} : 2\frac{2}{3}$ $\frac{6}{5}$
30. $3\frac{1}{3} : \frac{10}{15}$ $\frac{5}{1}$
31. 1.6 : 0.4 $\frac{4}{1}$
32. 8.1 : 1.8 $\frac{9}{2}$
33. 6.4 : 1.6 $\frac{4}{1}$
34. 2.5 : 6.25 $\frac{2}{5}$
35. 7.2 : 0.8 $\frac{9}{1}$

Solve.

36. Justin is 7 years old and his granddad is 77. What is the ratio of Justin's age to his granddad's age?

7:77; 1:11 or $\frac{1}{11}$

37. What is the ratio of the number of vowels to the number of consonants in this question?

27:43 or $\frac{27}{43}$

*Use with Lesson 6-1, text pages 154–155.

Copyright © Sadlier-Oxford

Proportions*

Name ______________________

Date ______________________

Write = or ≠.

1. $\frac{7}{9}$ = $\frac{21}{27}$
2. $\frac{28}{35}$ = $\frac{4}{5}$
3. $\frac{8}{7}$ ≠ $\frac{96}{49}$
4. $\frac{46}{58}$ = $\frac{23}{29}$
5. 6 : 138 = 4 : 92
6. 12 : 60 ≠ 4 : 24
7. 10 : 90 ≠ 45 : 5
8. 9 : 27 = 3 : 9
9. $\frac{4.2}{5.6}$ = $\frac{0.6}{0.8}$
10. $\frac{1.44}{1.32}$ = $\frac{1.2}{1.1}$
11. $\frac{8\frac{1}{2}}{5}$ ≠ $\frac{25\frac{1}{2}}{7\frac{1}{2}}$
12. $\frac{2\frac{1}{3}}{1\frac{2}{5}}$ = $\frac{11\frac{2}{3}}{7}$

Solve.

13. $\frac{27}{63} = \frac{n}{7}$ n = 3
14. $\frac{48}{x} = \frac{6}{12}$ x = 96
15. $\frac{a}{15} = \frac{18}{45}$ a = 6
16. $\frac{21}{b} = \frac{147}{105}$ b = 15
17. $\frac{42}{24} = \frac{a}{4}$ a = 7
18. $\frac{72}{64} = \frac{18}{r}$ r = 16
19. $\frac{\frac{5}{9}}{1\frac{1}{4}} = \frac{\frac{2}{3}}{s}$ s = $1\frac{1}{2}$
20. $\frac{b}{\frac{1}{3}} = \frac{4}{2}$ b = $\frac{2}{3}$
21. $\frac{4.8}{1.32} = \frac{c}{1.1}$ c = 4
22. $\frac{9.6}{a} = \frac{0.8}{0.6}$ a = 7.2
23. $\frac{n}{0.24} = \frac{0.05}{0.03}$ n = 0.4
24. $\frac{2.4}{3.7} = \frac{1.2}{t}$ t = 1.85
25. $\frac{r}{2\frac{1}{2}} = \frac{1}{2}$ r = $1\frac{1}{4}$
26. $\frac{2}{b} = \frac{\frac{5}{6}}{\frac{1}{3}}$ b = $\frac{4}{5}$
27. $\frac{s}{2\frac{1}{2}} = \frac{2\frac{1}{2}}{1\frac{1}{4}}$ s = 5
28. $\frac{\frac{3}{7}}{\frac{2}{3}} = \frac{\frac{1}{4}}{c}$ c = $\frac{7}{18}$
29. $\frac{a}{0.25} = \frac{0.8}{0.5}$ a = 0.4
30. $\frac{3.6}{c} = \frac{1.2}{2.1}$ c = 6.3

31. If 2.5 cm on a map represents 10 kilometers, how many kilometers will be represented by 4.8 cm? $\frac{2.5}{10} = \frac{4.8}{d}$; 19.2 km

Copyright © Sadlier-Oxford

Direct Proportion*

Name ____________________

Date ____________________

Solve by proportion. Round to the nearest cent where necessary.

1. An ad says that 6 lemons cost 94¢. What will 8 lemons cost?

   $\frac{6}{\$.94} = \frac{8}{c}$; \$1.25

2. Strawberries are marked 20 oz for \$1.29. How much will 15 oz cost?

   $\frac{20}{\$1.29} = \frac{15}{c}$; \$.97

3. A package of paper plates holding 150 plates costs \$3.29. At that rate, how many would be in a package that cost \$4.72?

   $\frac{150}{\$3.29} = \frac{p}{\$4.72}$; 215 plates

4. Hot dog rolls are priced at 2 packages for \$1.12. How many packages can be bought for \$3.86?

   $\frac{2}{\$1.12} = \frac{p}{\$3.86}$; 6 packages

5. A 30-oz can of lemonade drink mix costs \$1.80. At that rate, how much will a 21-oz can cost?

   $\frac{30}{\$1.80} = \frac{21}{c}$; \$1.26

6. If a 30-oz can of lemonade drink mix makes 8 quarts, how much mix is needed to make 10 quarts of the drink?

   $\frac{30}{8} = \frac{m}{10}$; 37.5 oz

7. Olives are 69¢ for $5\frac{3}{4}$ ounces. At this rate, what will $2\frac{1}{2}$ ounces of olives cost?

   $\frac{\$.69}{5\frac{3}{4}} = \frac{c}{2\frac{1}{2}}$; 30¢

8. A six pack of the store-brand cola cost \$1.64. How much must Denise pay for 14 cans of it?

   $\frac{6}{\$1.64} = \frac{14}{c}$; \$3.83

9. If a car travels 360 km in 5.4 hours, how far will it travel in 7.8 hours?

   $\frac{360}{5.4} = \frac{d}{7.8}$; 520 km

10. If 12 tickets for a football game cost \$98.40, how many can be bought for \$73.80?

    $\frac{12}{\$98.40} = \frac{t}{\$73.80}$; 9 tickets

11. If an office worker earns \$9460 in $\frac{4}{5}$ of a year, how much will he earn in $\frac{1}{5}$ of a year?

    $\frac{\$9460}{\frac{4}{5}} = \frac{x}{\frac{1}{5}}$; \$2365

12. Soup sells for 3 cans for 99¢. How much will 15 cans cost?

    $\frac{3}{\$.99} = \frac{15}{c}$; \$4.95

*Use with Lesson 6-3, text pages 158–159.

Copyright © Sadlier-Oxford

Scale Drawings*

Name ______________________

Date ______________________

Complete. Write and solve each proportion using the given scale.

	Scale: 2 cm = 5 km	
	Measures:	
	Scale	**Actual**
1.	4 cm	10 km
2.	4.8 cm	12 km
3.	30 cm	75 km
4.	1 cm	2.5 km
5.	16 cm	40 km
6.	0.5 cm	1.25 km
7.	44 cm	110 km

	Scale: 0.3 cm = 1.7 km	
	Measures:	
	Scale	**Actual**
8.	2.4 cm	13.6 km
9.	2.1 cm	11.9 km
10.	2.7 cm	15.3 km
11.	0.075 cm	0.425 km
12.	0.06 cm	0.34 km
13.	2.16 cm	12.24 km
14.	3 cm	17 km

15. **Find the scale used to make this plan. Then label all the sides with their actual measures. Write the actual measures in the boxes.** Scale: 2 cm = 1 m

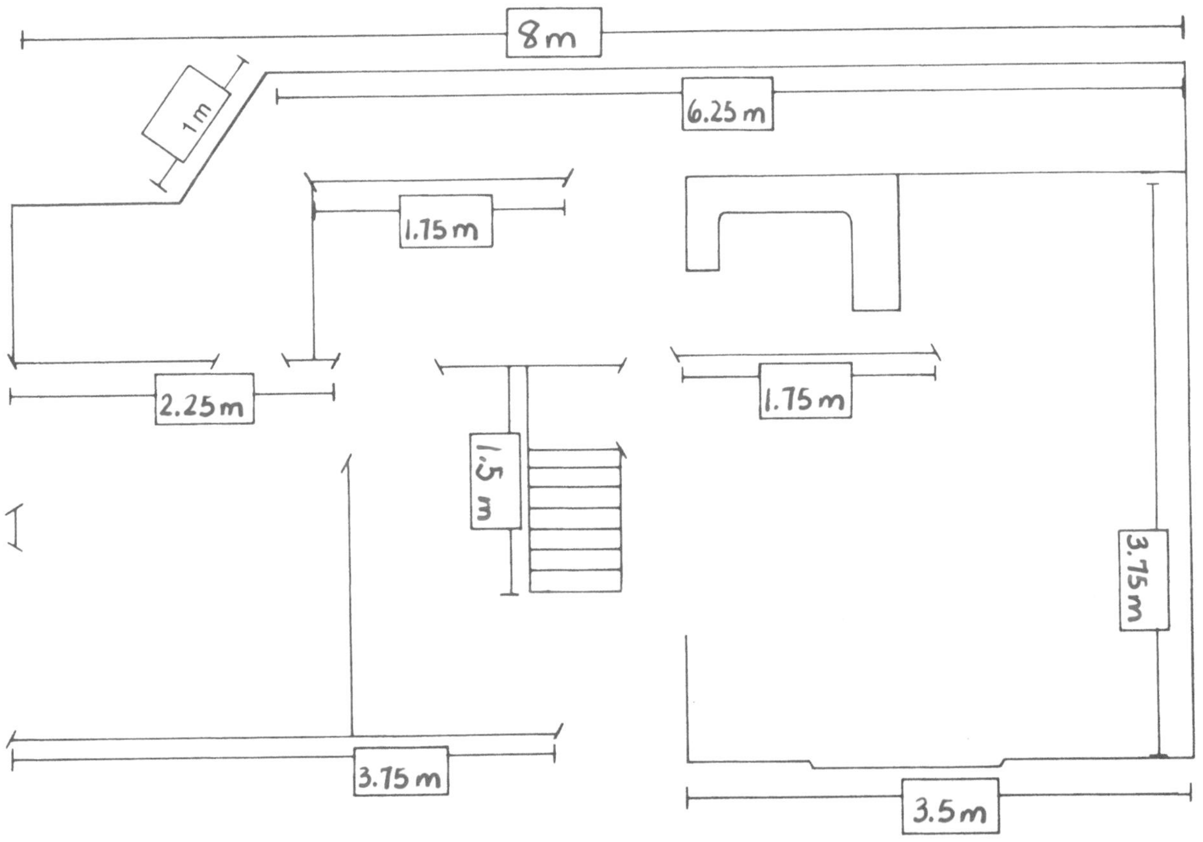

Copyright © Sadlier-Oxford

Inverse Proportion*

Name ______________________

Date ______________________

Write a proportion. Solve.

1. 4 bricklayers build a wall in 5 days.
   10 bricklayers build it in 2 days. $\frac{4}{10} = \frac{x}{5}$

2. 6 students decorate the gym in 3 hours.
   2 students do it in 9 hours. $\frac{6}{2} = \frac{x}{3}$

3. 8 workers plant a garden in 4 hours.
   16 workers plant it in 2 hours. $\frac{8}{16} = \frac{x}{4}$

4. 7 campers put up a tent in 45 minutes.
   4 campers put it up in $78\frac{3}{4}$ minutes. $\frac{7}{4} = \frac{x}{4}$

5. 5 people deliver the papers in $1\frac{1}{2}$ hours.
   10 people deliver the papers in $\frac{3}{4}$ hour.
   $\frac{5}{x} = \frac{\frac{3}{4}}{1\frac{1}{2}}$

6. 3 students made the scenery in 8 days.
   6 students can make it in 4 days. $\frac{3}{x} = \frac{4}{8}$

Solve.

7. If 8 people do a piece of work in 12 days, how many people will be needed to do the same work in 16 days?

   $\frac{8}{x} = \frac{16}{12}$; 6 people

8. If 3 workers can build a deck in $5\frac{2}{3}$ days, how many days will it take 5 workers to build the same deck?

   $\frac{3}{5} = \frac{x}{5\frac{2}{3}}$; $3\frac{2}{5}$ days

9. It took 7 hours for 12 doctors to give routine physical exams to 204 patients. How long would it have taken if 8 doctors gave the exams?

   $\frac{7}{8} = \frac{x}{12}$; $10\frac{1}{2}$ hr

10. How many students would be needed to distribute 780 advertisements in 2 hours if 9 students can distribute 540 ads in 2 hours?

    $\frac{9}{x} = \frac{540}{780}$; 13 students

11. Two people decorated 10 cakes in $2\frac{1}{2}$ hours. How many hours would it have taken if 5 people had been used to decorate the cakes?

    $\frac{2}{5} = \frac{x}{2\frac{1}{2}}$; 1 hr

12. Three workers can repave a driveway in 5 hours. How long will it take 8 workers to repave the driveway?

    $\frac{3}{8} = \frac{x}{5}$; $1\frac{7}{8}$ hr

13. It took 2 hours for 10 students to write 240 invitations to the school carnival. How long would it have taken if 5 students had done the writing?

    $\frac{10}{5} = \frac{x}{2}$; 4 hr

14. Four postal workers can sort 72 packages in $2\frac{1}{2}$ hours. If 2 extra workers are hired, how much time would be needed to sort the same number of packages?

    $\frac{4}{6} = \frac{x}{2\frac{1}{2}}$; $1\frac{2}{3}$ hr

*Use with Lesson 6-5, text pages 162–163.

Copyright © Sadlier-Oxford

Partitive Proportion*

Name ______________________

Date ______________________

Solve using partitive proportion.

1. Divide 64 into two parts with a ratio of 1 to 3. 16; 48
2. Divide 600 into two parts with a ratio of 10 to 20. 200; 400
3. Divide 270 into three parts with a ratio of 2 : 3 : 4. 60; 90; 120
4. Divide 300 into three parts with a ratio of 4 : 5 : 6. 80; 100; 120
5. Divide 450 into three parts with a ratio of 4 : 5 : 6. 120; 150; 180
6. Divide 810 into three parts with a ratio of 2 : 3 : 4. 180; 270; 360

Solve.

7. Three friends divided 165 baseball cards among themselves in a ratio of 1 : 4 : 6. How many cards did each receive?
   1m + 4m + 6m = 165
   15 cards; 60 cards; 90 cards
8. A toy manufacturer made 1424 stuffed animals. They made teddy bears, bunnies, and dogs in the ratio of 8 : 5 : 3. How many of each kind of stuffed animal did they make?
   8m + 5m + 3m = 1424
   712 bears; 445 bunnies; 267 dogs
9. John earned $6 for every $4 that Martin earned. How much did each earn if they earned $75 together?
   6m + 4m = 75
   John: $45; Martin: $30
10. The main library purchased 938 new books. They want to distribute the new books to three of their branch libraries in the ratio of 3 : 5 : 6. How many books will be given to each library?
    3m + 5m + 6m = 938
    201 books; 335 books; 402 books
11. A card store ordered 520 cards. They ordered birthday cards, anniversary cards, and get well cards in the ratio of 6 : 3 : 1. How many of each type of card did they order?
    6m + 3m + 1m = 520
    312 birthday cards
    156 anniversary cards
    52 get well cards
12. At a nursery, there are 1248 flowers. There are roses, orchids, and carnations in the ratio of 3 : 4 : 6. How many of each kind of flower are there?
    3m + 4m + 6m = 1248
    288 roses; 384 orchids; 576 carnations
13. In a local election, 2640 votes were cast for two candidates. Ms. Wayne received 7 votes for every 4 votes that Mr. Edwards received. How many votes did each candidate receive?
    7m + 4m = 2640
    Ms. Wayne: 1680 votes
    Mr. Edwards: 960 votes
14. A painter bought 96 L of paint. He bought blue, green, and yellow paint in the ratio of 4 : 3 : 1. How many liters of each color paint did he buy?
    4m + 3m + 1m = 96
    blue: 48 L; green: 36 L; yellow: 12 L

*Use with Lesson 6-6, text pages 164–165.

Copyright © Sadlier-Oxford

Similar Triangles and Trigonometric Ratios*

Name ______________________

Date ______________________

The figures below are similar. Write and solve proportions to find the indicated sides.

1.

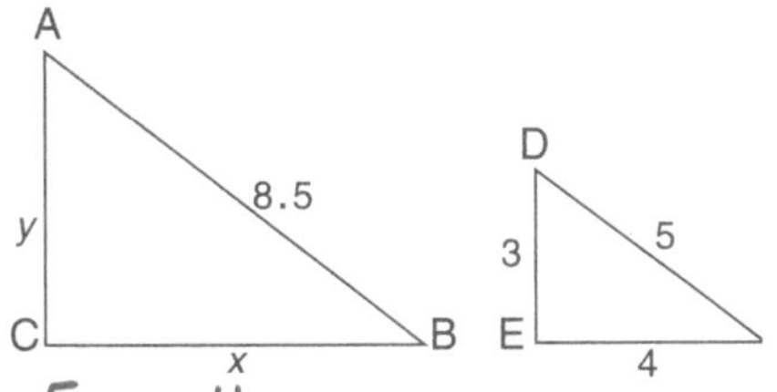

$\frac{5}{8.5} = \frac{4}{x}$; $x = 6.8$

$\frac{5}{8.5} = \frac{3}{y}$; $y = 5.1$

2.

$\frac{6}{12} = \frac{5}{w}$; $w = 10$

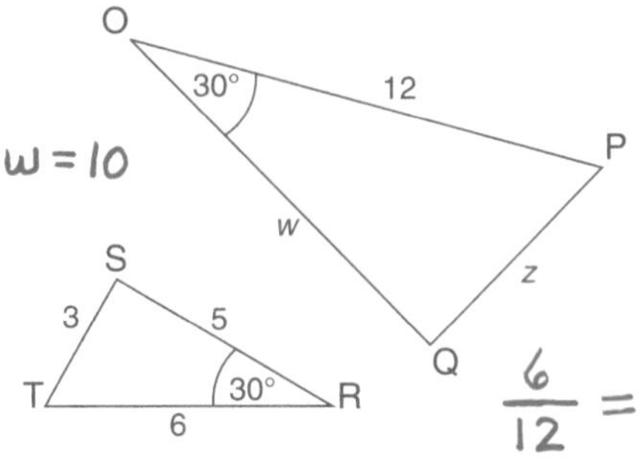

$\frac{6}{12} = \frac{3}{z}$; $z = 6$

Use similar triangles *EFG* and *HJK* to solve.

3. $\frac{\overline{FG}}{\overline{JK}} = \frac{\overline{EG}}{\overline{HK}}$

4. $\frac{\overline{HJ}}{\overline{EF}} = \frac{\overline{KH}}{\overline{GE}}$

5. $\angle F \cong \angle J =$ 73°

6. $\frac{x}{11} = \frac{7.5}{10}$

$x = 8.25$

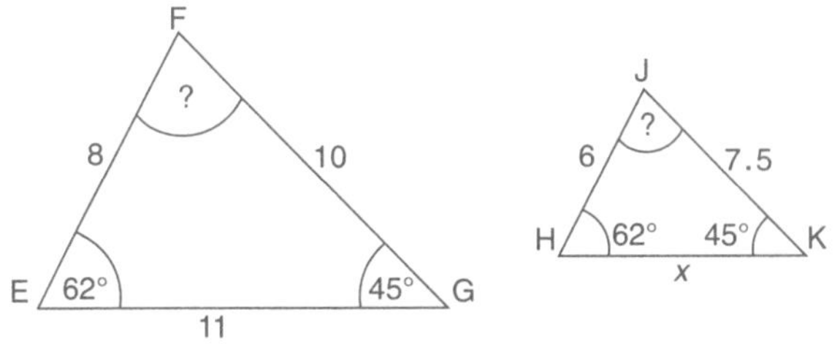

Find the value of each trigonometric ratio. Then use the table of trigonometric ratios (page 196) to find the measure of the angle.

7. tan *B*

$\frac{12}{16} = 0.75$; 37°

8. sin *A*

$\frac{16}{20} = 0.8$; 53°

9. cos *B*

$\frac{16}{20} = 0.8$; 37°

10. sin *B*

$\frac{12}{20} = 0.6$; 37°

11. cos *A*

$\frac{12}{20} = 0.6$; 53°

12. tan *A*

$\frac{16}{12} = 1.\overline{3}$; 53°

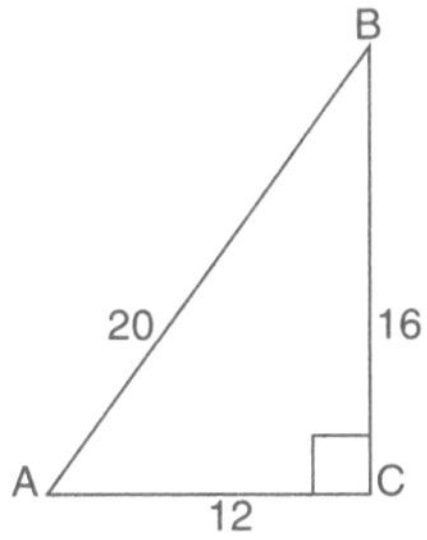

Solve, using a scientific calculator.

13. Find the length of side *s*.

$\sin 70° = \frac{s}{40}$

$s = 37.6$

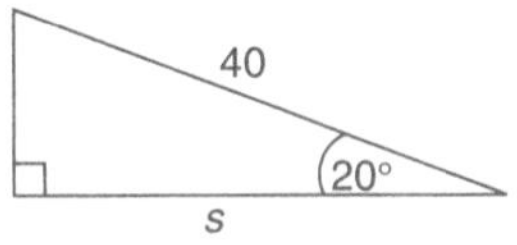

14. Find the length of side *r*.

$\sin 35° = \frac{r}{25}$

$r = 14.35$

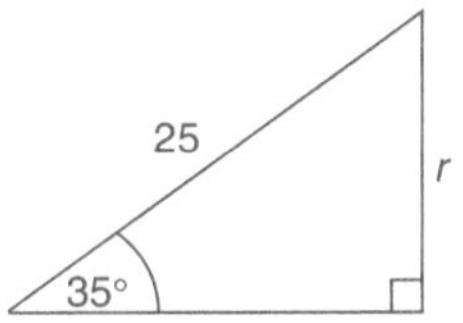

15. Find the length of side *h*.

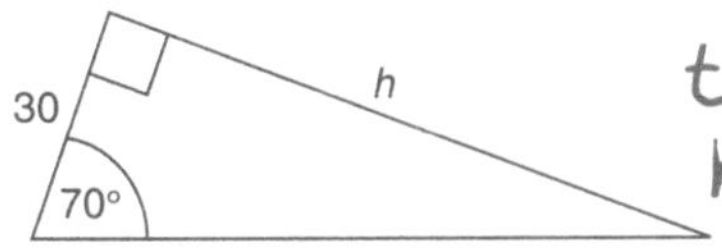

$\tan 70° = \frac{h}{30}$

$h = 82.41$

16. Find the length of side *t*.

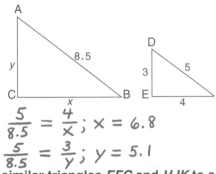

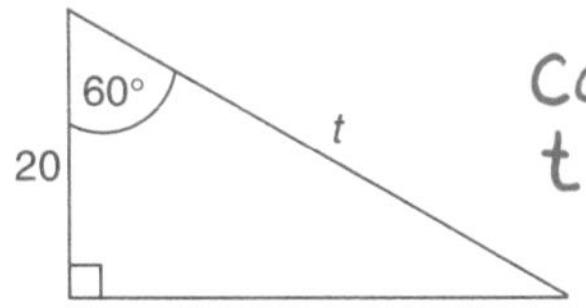

$\cos 60° = \frac{20}{t}$

$t = 40$

*Use with Lessons 6-7, 6-8, text pages 166–169.

Copyright © Sadlier-Oxford

Fractions and Decimals to Percents*

Name ______________________

Date ______________________

Complete the chart.

	Ratio	Fraction	Decimal	Percent
1.	30:100	$\frac{3}{10}$	0.3	30%
2.	50:100	$\frac{1}{2}$	0.5	50%
3.	25:100	$\frac{1}{4}$	0.25	25%
4.	$16\frac{2}{3}$:100	$\frac{1}{6}$	$0.16\frac{2}{3}$	$16\frac{2}{3}$%
5.	80:100	$\frac{4}{5}$	0.8	80%
6.	$33\frac{1}{3}$:100	$\frac{1}{3}$	$0.33\frac{1}{3}$	$33\frac{1}{3}$%
7.	42:100	$\frac{21}{50}$	0.42	42%
8.	90:100	$\frac{9}{10}$	0.9	90%
9.	5:8	$\frac{5}{8}$	0.625	62.5%
10.	7:9	$\frac{7}{9}$	$0.77\frac{7}{9}$	$77\frac{7}{9}$%
11.	6:10	$\frac{3}{5}$	0.6	60%
12.	175:100	$1\frac{3}{4}$	1.75	175%
13.	12.5:100	$\frac{1}{8}$	0.125	12.5%
14.	2:3	$\frac{2}{3}$	$0.66\frac{2}{3}$	$66\frac{2}{3}$%

Circle the percent, ratio, fraction, or decimal that does not belong in each exercise.

15. 2.5   25% $\frac{1}{4}$ 25:100

16. 13%   0.13 $\frac{13}{100}$ 1.3:100

17. 10:100 $\frac{70}{100}$ 70%   0.7

18. 1:2   50% $\frac{50}{100}$ 0.05

19. 45%   9:20 $\frac{45}{100}$ 4.5

20. 35%   35:100   0.35 $\frac{7}{10}$

21. 0.375 $37\frac{1}{2}$% $\frac{3}{8}$ 37:100

22. 1:3 $0.66\frac{2}{3}$ $\frac{2}{3}$ $66\frac{2}{3}$%

23. 2%   0.02   2:100 $\frac{2}{50}$

24. 48:100   48% $\frac{12}{50}$ 0.48

25. 0.15 $\frac{150}{100}$ 150%   150:100

26. 99%   99:100 $\frac{9}{10}$ 0.99

27. 0.875   87:100 $87\frac{1}{2}$% $\frac{7}{8}$

28. 0.3 $\frac{3}{10}$ 30:100   3%

***Use with Lesson 7-1, text pages 180–181.**

Copyright © Sadlier-Oxford

Percents to Fractions and Decimals*

Name ______________________
Date ______________________

Change to a fraction in lowest terms.

1. 40% = $\frac{2}{5}$	2. 80% = $\frac{4}{5}$	3. 32% = $\frac{8}{25}$	4. 48% = $\frac{12}{25}$
5. $12\frac{1}{2}$% = $\frac{1}{8}$	6. $83\frac{1}{3}$% = $\frac{5}{6}$	7. $16\frac{2}{3}$% = $\frac{1}{6}$	8. $22\frac{2}{9}$% = $\frac{2}{9}$
9. $14\frac{2}{7}$% = $\frac{1}{7}$	10. $8\frac{1}{3}$% = $\frac{1}{12}$	11. 62.5% = $\frac{5}{8}$	12. $66\frac{2}{3}$% = $\frac{2}{3}$
13. 125% = $1\frac{1}{4}$	14. 120% = $1\frac{1}{5}$	15. 275% = $2\frac{3}{4}$	16. 200% = 2
17. 4.5% = $\frac{9}{200}$	18. 2.25% = $\frac{9}{400}$	19. 3.5% = $\frac{7}{200}$	20. 6.25% = $\frac{1}{16}$
21. 0.4% = $\frac{1}{250}$	22. 0.25% = $\frac{1}{400}$	23. 105% = $1\frac{1}{20}$	24. 335% = $3\frac{7}{20}$

Change to a decimal.

25. 65% = 0.65	26. 46% = 0.46	27. 98% = 0.98	28. 72% = 0.72
29. 24% = 0.24	30. 6% = 0.06	31. 4% = 0.04	32. 8% = 0.08
33. 35.5% = 0.355	34. 86.2% = 0.862	35. 75.1% = 0.751	36. 13.2% = 0.132
37. 2.25% = 0.0225	38. 3.6% = 0.036	39. 7.4% = 0.074	40. 8.6% = 0.086
41. 100% = 1	42. 200% = 2	43. 250% = 2.5	44. 325% = 3.25
45. 0.6% = 0.006	46. 0.25% = 0.0025	47. 0.4% = 0.004	48. 0.15% = 0.0015

Solve.

49. The scouts sold 40 of the 4 dozen cakes baked for the fund-raising event. What percent of the cakes did they sell?

$\frac{40}{48}$; $83\frac{1}{3}$%

50. 0.85 of the seats for the 3:45 flight to Phoenix were filled. What percent of the seats were not filled?

1 − 0.85; 15%

*Use with Lesson 7-2, text pages 182–183.

Copyright © Sadlier-Oxford

Finding a Part or a Percentage*

Name ______________________

Date ______________________

Find the part or percentage of each number.

1. 10% of 40 = 4
2. 75% of 16 = 12
3. 50% of 42 = 21
4. 30% of 90 = 27
5. 5% of 70 = 3.5
6. 20% of 100 = 20
7. 80% of 10 = 8
8. 2% of 14 = 0.28
9. 36% of 78 = 28.08
10. 24% of 28 = 6.72
11. 1% of 34 = 0.34
12. 60% of 240 = 144
13. $12\frac{1}{2}$% of 56 = 7
14. $33\frac{1}{3}$% of 48 = 16
15. $16\frac{2}{3}$% of 246 = 41
16. 25% of 316 = 79
17. $87\frac{1}{2}$% of 32 = 28
18. $66\frac{2}{3}$% of 543 = 362
19. $3\frac{1}{4}$% of 620 = 20.15
20. 400% of 85 = 340
21. 0.75% of 30 = 0.225

Solve.

22. In order to determine the need for traffic signals at a suburban intersection, a 48-hour watch was kept. During that time, $12\frac{1}{2}$% of the 8424 cars recorded made left-hand turns. How many cars was this?

    $12\frac{1}{2}\% \times 8424$; 1053 cars

23. During the same watch, it was noted that $16\frac{2}{3}$% of the cars made right-hand turns. How many cars made right-hand turns?

    $16\frac{2}{3}\% \times 8424$; 1404 cars

24. Last summer, Julie earned \$145. This summer, she earned 25% more. How much did she earn this summer?

    \$145 + 25% (145); \$181.25

25. 30% of 50 students play a musical instrument. How many students play musical instruments?

    30% × 50; 15 students

*Use with Lesson 7-3, text pages 184–185.

Copyright © Sadlier-Oxford

Finding Percent*

Name ______________________

Date ______________________

Find the percent. Round to the nearest tenth, if necessary.

1. What percent of 8 is 2? 25%
2. What percent of 9 is 3? $33\frac{1}{3}$% or 33.3%
3. What percent of 25 is 5? 20%
4. 8 is what percent of 40? 20%
5. 12 is what percent of 50? 24%
6. What percent of 16 is 48? 300%
7. What percent of 120 is 80? $66\frac{2}{3}$% or 66.7%
8. What percent of 9 is 72? 800%
9. 11 is what percent of 99? $11\frac{1}{9}$% or 11.1%
10. What percent of 48 is 36? 75%
11. What percent of 14 is 49? 350%
12. 54 is what percent of 90? 60%
13. What percent of 24 is 2? $8\frac{1}{3}$% or 8.3%
14. What percent of 500 is 600? 120%
15. 81 is what percent of 36? 225%
16. What percent of 963 is 642? $66\frac{2}{3}$% or 66.7%
17. What percent of 455 is 182? 40%
18. What percent of 224 is 140? $62\frac{1}{2}$% or 62.5%

Solve.

19. A team won 18 games and lost 9 games. The number of games won is what percent of the total games played?

$\frac{18}{18+9}$; $66\frac{2}{3}$%

20. Bob earned $810 last summer. He spent $540. What percent of his earnings did he save?

$\frac{\$810-\$540}{\$810}$; $33\frac{1}{3}$%

*Use with Lesson 7-4, text pages 186–187.

Copyright © Sadlier-Oxford

Finding the Original Number*

Name ____________________

Date ____________________

75% of n = 27 75% × n = 27 n = 27 ÷ 75% n = 36

Find the original number.

1. 3% of a = 42

a = 1400

2. 10% of b = 9

b = 90

3. 50% of c = 16

c = 32

4. 20% of d = 10

d = 50

5. 80% of e = 12

e = 15

6. 25% of f = 20

f = 80

7. 75% of g = 18

g = 24

8. 12% of h = 3.6

h = 30

9. $33\frac{1}{3}$% of i = 17

i = 51

10. 45% of j = $20\frac{1}{4}$

j = 45

11. 16% of k = 8.32

k = 52

12. 2% of l = 8.4

l = 420

13. $16\frac{2}{3}$% of m = 44

m = 264

14. $12\frac{1}{2}$% of n = 70

n = 560

15. 2.5% of o = $12\frac{1}{2}$

o = 500

16. 1.8% of p = 0.9

p = 50

17. 150% of q = 7.5

q = 5

18. 300% of r = 12

r = 4

Complete the table.

a = rate; b = percentage; c = original number or base

	a	b	c
19.	14%	0.84	6
20.	30%	4.5	15
21.	$14\frac{2}{7}$%	3	21
22.	25%	100	400
23.	$66\frac{2}{3}$%	54	81
24.	20%	9	45
25.	80%	24	30
26.	$16\frac{2}{3}$%	6	36

***Use with Lesson 7-5, text pages 188–189.**

Copyright © Sadlier-Oxford

Estimating with Percents*

Name ______________________

Date ______________________

Use your Table of Common Percents (p. 562) to estimate each percent.

1. 32% $\frac{1}{3}$ 2. 48% $\frac{1}{2}$ 3. 13% $\frac{1}{8}$ 4. 19% $\frac{1}{5}$ 5. 33% $\frac{1}{3}$

6. $9\frac{2}{3}\%$ $\frac{1}{10}$ 7. 41.5% $\frac{2}{5}$ 8. 76.1% $\frac{3}{4}$ 9. $18\frac{2}{3}\%$ $\frac{1}{5}$ 10. 81.9% $\frac{5}{6}$

Estimate the percentage. Accept reasonable estimates.

11. 9% of 71 7 12. 53% of 98.6 49 13. 42% of 38.9 16

14. $6\frac{7}{8}\%$ of 16 1 15. 92% of 30 27 16. 14.5% of 76 11

Choose the best ratio and then estimate each percent.

17. $33\frac{1}{3}$ % of 22 is 8. a. $\frac{9}{15}$ (b.) $\frac{7}{21}$ c. $\frac{22}{8}$

18. $12\frac{1}{2}$ % of 89 is 11.6. (a.) $\frac{11}{88}$ b. $\frac{10}{100}$ c. $\frac{90}{100}$

19. 60 % of 14.4 is 9.2. a. $\frac{8}{15}$ (b.) $\frac{9}{15}$ c. $\frac{10}{20}$

Estimate the original number. Accept reasonable estimates.

20. 9% of 70 is 7.
10% 7

21. 36.5% of 112 is 42.
$37\frac{1}{2}\%$ 42

22. 7.8% of 216 is 18.
$8\frac{1}{3}\%$ 18

23. 14% of 147 is 21.
$14\frac{2}{7}\%$ 21

Solve. Accept reasonable estimates.

24. Of 526 students taking a high school entrance exam, 6.5% scored in the top percentile. About how many students were in that percentile? 35 students
7% of 500

25. A survey of 12,212 people in four states showed that 3.6% were not able to read. About how many people is that? 480 people
4% of 12,000

*Use with Lesson 7-6, text pages 190–191.

Copyright © Sadlier-Oxford

Percent of Increase or Decrease*

Name ______________________

Date ______________________

Complete. (Round each answer to the nearest tenth of a percent.)

Percent of Change in Car Sales

		Car Sales		Increase		Decrease	
	Month	1981	1982	Number	%	Number	%
1.	March	45	50	5	11.1%		
2.	April	64	53			11	17.2%
3.	May	60	52			8	13.3%
4.	June	59	62	3	5.1%		
5.	July	58	65	7	12.1%		
6.	August	60	51			9	15%
7.	September	74	80	6	8.1%		
8.	October	61	51			10	16.4%
9.	November	56	62	6	10.7%		
10.	December	30	34	4	13.3%		

Solve. (Round each answer to the nearest tenth of a percent.)

11. Last year, 11 students tried out for the debating team. This year, 15 students tried out. What was the percent of increase?

$\frac{15-11}{11}$; 36.4%

12. 11 inches of rain fell last month. This month, 10 inches fell. What was the percent of decrease?

$\frac{11-10}{11}$; 9.1%

13. Sales of radios decreased one month from 150 to 100. What was the percent of decrease?

$\frac{150-100}{150}$; 33.3%

14. Joan worked 28 hours last week and 34 hours this week. What is the percent of increase in her work time?

$\frac{34-28}{28}$; 21.4%

15. In last year's graduating class, 75 students went to college. From this year's class, 80 students will go to college. Find the percent of change.

$\frac{80-75}{75}$; 6.7% increase

16. 1450 new texts have been purchased for this school year. Last year, 1600 were purchased. What was the percent of change?

$\frac{1600-1450}{1600}$; 9.4% decrease

*Use with Lesson 7-7, text pages 192–193.

Copyright © Sadlier-Oxford

Progress Test: Chapters 1–7*

Name ______________________

Date ______________________

Write each answer on the numbered line. Do all computations on a separate sheet of paper.

Choose the correct answer. Write the letter.

Answers

1. One hundred billion, four hundred million, fifty-five thousand four is:
   a. 50,004,004 **b.** 100,400,055,004 **c.** 100,055,004 **d.** 554,000,400
   — 1. b (1–1)

2. Rounded to the nearest thousandth, 624.0729 is:
   a. 624.1 **b.** 62.507 **c.** 624.073 **d.** 624.072
   — 2. c (1–3)

3. The best estimate for $461 + 1739 + 23{,}104$ is:
   a. 24,200 **b.** 25,000 **c.** 25,300 **d.** 24,000
   — 3. c (1–9)

4. $31.213 \div 4.9$ rounded to the nearest tenth is:
   a. 0.6 **b.** 6.3 **c.** 6.4 **d.** 6.37
   — 4. c (1–7)

5. If $n = 9$, then the value of $n - 9$ is:
   a. 18 **b.** 1 **c.** 0 **d.** 81
   — 5. c (3–3)

6. 3 more than 4 times a number (a) is 27. To solve for a, use the equation:
   a. $3a + 4 = 27$ **b.** $3a - 4 = 27$ **c.** $4a + 3 = 27$ **d.** $4a - 3 = 27$
   — 6. c (3–2)

7. The decimal equivalent of $\frac{7}{8}$ is:
   a. 0.78 **b.** 0.785 **c.** 0.875 **d.** 0.87
   — 7. c (2–7)

8. $\frac{7}{12}$ of 15 means:
   a. $\frac{7}{12} + 15$ **b.** $\frac{7}{12} - 15$ **c.** $\frac{7}{12} \times 15$ **d.** $\frac{7}{12} \div 15$
   — 8. c (2–11)

9. $4\frac{5}{9} - 2\frac{2}{3}$ equals:
   a. $2\frac{1}{3}$ **b.** $2\frac{8}{9}$ **c.** $2\frac{1}{9}$ **d.** $1\frac{8}{9}$
   — 9. d (2–10)

10. $\frac{3}{5} \times \frac{1}{6} + \frac{2}{5}$ equals:
    a. $1\frac{1}{6}$ **b.** $\frac{1}{2}$ **c.** $\frac{1}{3}$ **d.** 4
    — 10. b (2–11)

11. The reciprocal of $2\frac{2}{3}$ is:
    a. $\frac{8}{3}$ **b.** $2\frac{1}{2}$ **c.** $\frac{3}{8}$ **d.** $\frac{3}{22}$
    — 11. c (2–12)

12. If $n - {}^{-}4 = 6$, then n equals:
    a. ${}^{-}2$ **b.** ${}^{+}2$ **c.** ${}^{-}10$ **d.** ${}^{+}10$
    — 12. b (3–13)

13. To solve $\frac{3}{4} \times n = 30$:
    a. divide both sides by 30 **b.** multiply both sides by 30
    c. divide both sides by $\frac{3}{4}$ **d.** multiply both sides by $\frac{3}{4}$
    — 13. c (3–7)

14. Choose the composite number equal to $2^3 \times 5 \times 7$.
    a. 125 **b.** 96 **c.** 280 **d.** 210
    — 14. c (2–4)

15. The fraction equivalent to $14\frac{2}{7}\%$ is:
    a. $\frac{4}{7}$ **b.** $\frac{2}{7}$ **c.** $\frac{1}{14}$ **d.** $\frac{1}{7}$
    — 15. d (7–2)

***Next to each item is given the lesson number in the text where the item was taught.**

Copyright © Sadlier-Oxford

Progress Test: Chapters 1–7*

Name ______________________

Date ______________________

Compare. Write <, =, or >.

16. 0.023 __?__ 0.23
17. 12(1.6 − 0.6) __?__ 2 + 2 · 5
18. $\frac{3}{4}$ __?__ 0.752

Compute.

19. 0.89 × 7.5
20. 31.5% of 42
21. $^{-}8 + {}^{+}0.6$
22. $^{-}6 \times {}^{-}\frac{2}{3}$

Write an equation and solve.

23. 15 more than *n* is equal to 41. Find the value of *n*.
24. Alicia's age divided by 3, minus 6, is 18. Find Alicia's age.
25. 4 times a number, increased by 5, is 17. What is the number?

Solve.

26. Jan worked 4 hours on a job and Ted worked 5 hours. Together they earned $31.50. How much did each receive?
    4e + 5e = $31.50
27. Last week Martin's Newstand sold 325 newspapers, 120 magazines, and 79 paperbacks. This week total sales increased approximately 6%. About how many of the three items combined were sold this week?
    325 + 120 + 79 + 0.06(325 + 120 + 79)
28. The average distance of the earth from the sun is 93,000,000 mi. Express this distance in scientific notation.
29. Write the converse of this statement: If it is raining, then it is spring.
    If it is spring, then it is raining.
30. Halley's Comet appears every 76 years. How many times will it be seen in 692 years?
    692 ÷ 76

Answers

16. < (1–2)
17. = (3–1)
18. < (2–8)
19. 6.675 (1–6)
20. 13.23 (7–3)
21. $^{-}7.4$ (4–3)
22. $^{+}4$ (4–6)
23. n + 15 = 41; n = 26 (3–6)
24. $\frac{a}{3} - 6 = 18$; a = 72 (3–8)
25. 4n + 5 = 17; n = 3 (3–8)
26. Jan: $14, Ted: $17.50 (6–6)
27. 555 (7–10)
28. 9.3×10^7 (5–3)
29. ______ (5–9)
30. 9 (1–13)

*Next to each item is given the lesson number in the text where the item was taught.

Copyright © Sadlier-Oxford

Profit and Loss*

Name ______________________

Date ______________________

Find the profit or loss to the nearest cent. Use a formula. $P = C \times R$ $L = C \times R$

1. Cost: $80
   Rate of Profit: $12\frac{1}{2}$%
   $10

2. Cost: $32.64
   Rate of Profit: 25%
   $8.16

3. Cost: $196
   Rate of Loss: $33\frac{1}{3}$%
   $65.33

4. Cost: $624
   Rate of Loss: 10%
   $62.40

5. Cost: $575.25
   Rate of Loss: 3.5%
   $20.13

6. Cost: $99.98
   Rate of Profit: 3.4%
   $3.40

Find the profit or loss to the nearest cent. Use proportion.

7. Cost: $82.95
   Rate of Loss: $8\frac{1}{3}$%
   $6.91

8. Cost: $172.40
   Rate of Profit: 15%
   $25.86

9. Cost: $412.50
   Rate of Loss: 8.2%
   $33.83

10. Cost: $615.45
    Rate of Loss: 4.5%
    $27.70

11. Cost: $272.62
    Rate of Loss: $6\frac{1}{4}$%
    $17.04

12. Cost: $95.98
    Rate of Loss: 2.6%
    $2.50

Find the selling price. (Gain: $SP = C + P$; Loss: $SP = C - L$)

13. Cost: $86.50
    Gain: $12.90
    $99.40

14. Cost: $114.20
    Loss: $26.10
    $88.10

15. Cost: $320.25
    Loss: $4.32
    $315.93

16. Cost: $156.40
    Gain: $22.15
    $178.55

17. Cost: $681.11
    Gain: $47.90
    $729.01

18. Cost: $587.62
    Loss: $37.40
    $550.22

Solve.

19. A house was originally priced at $132,515. It was sold at a 12% loss. How much money was lost on the sale?
    L = 132,515 × 0.12
    $15,901.80

20. A florist made a profit of 15% on holiday sales. The flowers cost him $7800. What was the total selling price?
    SP = 7800 + 7800 × 0.15
    $ 8970

*Use with Lesson 8-1, text pages 204–205.

Copyright © Sadlier-Oxford

Discount and Sale Price*

Name ______________________

Date ______________________

Find the discount and the sale price. $D = LP \times R$ $SP = LP - D$

1. Regular price: $156.99
   $33\frac{1}{3}$% off
   Discount: $52.33
   Sale price: $104.66

2. Original price: $24.75
   4% off
   Discount: $.99
   Sale price: $23.76

3. List price: $32
   16% off
   Discount: $5.12
   Sale price: $26.88

4. List price: $44.99
   12% discount
   Discount: $5.40
   Sale price: $39.59

5. Regular price: $56
   8% discount
   Discount: $4.48
   Sale price: $51.52

6. Original price: $145
   10% discount
   Discount: $14.50
   Sale price: $130.50

7. Regular price: $14.95
   Rate: 7%
   Discount: $1.05
   Sale price: $13.90

8. List price: $25.50
   Rate: 2.5%
   Discount: $.64
   Sale price: $24.86

9. List price: $77.20
   Rate: 16%
   Discount: $12.35
   Sale price: $64.85

10. Original price: $95.25
    Rate: 8%
    Discount: $7.62
    Sale price: $87.63

11. Regular price: $80
    Rate: 25%
    Discount: $20
    Sale price: $60

12. List price: $45.60
    Rate: 18%
    Discount: $8.21
    Sale price: $37.39

13. List price: $186.25
    Rate: 20%
    Discount: $37.25
    Sale price: $149

14. Regular price: $350
    Rate: 12%
    Discount: $42
    Sale price: $308

15. Original price: $1400
    Rate: 15%
    Discount: $210
    Sale price: $1190

*Use with Lesson 8-2, text pages 206–207.

Copyright © Sadlier-Oxford

Rate of Discount and List Price*

Name ______________________

Date ______________________

$$D = LP \times R \textbf{ or } \frac{D}{LP} = \frac{R \text{ of } D}{R \text{ of } LP}$$

Find the rate of discount.

1. List price: $96.50
   Discount: $28.95
   Rate: 30%

2. List price: $33.60
   Discount: $6.72
   Rate: 20%

3. List price: $124.00
   Discount: $17.36
   Rate: 14%

4. List price: $89.98
   Discount: $44.99
   Rate: 50%

5. List price: $63.18
   Discount: $42.12
   Rate: $66\frac{2}{3}$%

6. List price: $453.00
   Discount: $67.95
   Rate: 15%

Find the list price.

7. Discount: $225
   Rate: 5%
   List price: $4500

8. Discount: $5.67
   Rate: 9%
   List price: $63

9. Discount: $7.56
   Rate: 12%
   List price: $63

10. Discount: $72.80
    Rate: 14%
    List price: $520

11. Discount: $12.75
    Rate: 15%
    List price: $85

12. Discount: $241
    Rate: $33\frac{1}{3}$%
    List price: $723

Solve.

13. Steve bought a book with a list price of $9.80. He received a discount of 49¢. Find the rate of discount.

    $R = 0.49 \div 9.80$

    5%

14. Laura bought a bike on sale for $7.16 off the list price. The discount was 8%. What was the list price?

    $LP = 7.16 \div 0.08$

    $89.50

*Use with Lesson 8-3, text pages 208–209.

Copyright © Sadlier-Oxford

Sales Tax*

Name ______________________

Date ______________________

$$T = MP \times R \text{ or } \frac{T}{MP} = \frac{R \text{ of } T}{R \text{ of } MP}$$

Find the sales tax.

1. Price: $89.45
Tax: 5%
Sales tax: $4.47

2. Price: $593.80
Tax: 6%
Sales tax: $35.63

3. Price: $210.70
Tax: 5%
Sales tax: $10.54

4. Price: $56.49
Tax: $2\frac{1}{2}$%
Sales tax: $1.41

5. Price: $152.00
Tax: 4%
Sales tax: $6.08

6. Price: $75.99
Tax: 6%
Sales tax: $4.56

7. Price: $138.40
Tax: 7%
Sales tax: $9.69

8. Price: $29.75
Tax: 3%
Sales tax: $.89

9. Price: $48.21
Tax: 5.8%
Sales tax: $2.80

Complete the chart. (Round tax to the nearest cent.)

	Price	Tax	Amount of Tax	Total Cost
10.	$23.95	5%	$1.20	$25.15
11.	$348.60	5%	$17.43	$366.03
12.	$72.20	5%	$3.61	$75.81
13.	$99.50	5%	$4.98	$104.48
14.	$559.25	5%	$27.96	$587.21
15.	$279.85	5%	$13.99	$293.84

Find the total cost including 6% sales tax.

16. Regular price: $4.95
Discount: 20%
Total cost: $4.20

17. Regular price: $12.50
Discount: 14%
Total cost: $11.40

18. Original price: $10.90
Discount: 10%
Total cost: $10.40

*Use with Lesson 8-4, text pages 210–211.

Copyright © Sadlier-Oxford

Commission*

Name ____________________

Date ____________________

$$C = TS \times R \text{ or } \frac{C}{TS} = \frac{R \text{ of } C}{R \text{ of } TS}$$

Find the commission.

1. Total sales: $4800
   Rate: 2.5%
   Commission: $120

2. Total sales: $2400
   Rate: 2%
   Commission: $48

3. Total sales: $6000
   Rate: 1.5%
   Commission: $90

4. Total sales: $8276.20
   Rate: 5%
   Commission: $413.81

5. Total sales: $8730
   Rate: 3%
   Commission: $261.90

6. Total sales: $548
   Rate: 32%
   Commission: $175.36

7. Total sales: $4725
   Rate: 3%
   Commission: $141.75

8. Total sales: $976
   Rate: 4%
   Commission: $39.04

9. Total sales: $490
   Rate: 4%
   Commission: $19.60

10. Total sales: $3550
    Rate: 5%
    Commission: $177.50

11. Total sales: $649
    Rate: 6%
    Commission: $38.94

12. Total sales: $9632
    Rate: 3.5%
    Commission: $337.12

Solve.

13. Mrs. Deno earns a weekly salary of $250 plus a 1.5% commission on all sales she makes. If her sales for one week totaled $7841.56, what was her total income for the week?

    TI = 250 + 7841.56 × 0.015;
    $367.62

14. During a sale Mr. White sold a piano for $1560. He received a commission of 4.5%. What was the amount of commission?

    C = 1560 × 0.045;
    $70.20

15. Nicole is paid $200 a week plus a 6% commission on all sales over $1000. What were here earnings for a week in which she sold $3400 worth of goods?

    E = 200 + 2400 × 0.06;
    $344

*Use with Lesson 8-5, text pages 212–213

Copyright © Sadlier-Oxford

Rate of Commission and Total Sales*

Name ______________________

Date ______________________

Find the rate of commission.

1. Commission: $40
   Total sales: $500

   Rate: 8%

2. Commission: $120
   Total sales: $2000

   Rate: 6%

3. Commission: $1275
   Total sales: $8500

   Rate: 15%

4. Commission: $63.75
   Total sales: $1275

   Rate: 5%

5. Commission: $3650.75
   Total sales: $73,015

   Rate: 5%

6. Commission: $3436
   Total sales: $85,900

   Rate: 4%

Find the total sales.

7. Commission: $27.00
   Rate: 12%

   Total sales: $225

8. Commission: $48.00
   Rate: 2%

   Total sales: $2400

9. Commission: $162
   Rate: 4%

   Total sales: $4050

10. Commission: $139
    Rate: 10%

    Total sales: $1390

11. Commission: $250.25
    Rate: 5.5%

    Total sales: $4550

12. Commission: $195
    Rate: $3\frac{1}{4}$%

    Total sales: $6000

Solve.

13. An agent earned $200 for collecting rents at 4%. How much rent did he collect?

    $5000

    R = 200 ÷ 0.04

14. An electrician received $45 for installing a security system in a building. If the system cost $225, what rate of commission did he earn?

    20%

    R of C = 45 ÷ 225

15. Bob works in a music store. One day he earned $40 for selling 5 stereo cassette recorders at $80 each. What was his rate of commission on these sales?

    10%

    R of C = 40 ÷ (5 × 80)

Copyright © Sadlier-Oxford

Simple Interest*

Name ____________________

Date ____________________

Find the interest.

1. p = \$1600
r = 5%
t = 6 yr
I = \$480

2. p = \$1260
r = 6%
t = 5 yr
I = \$378

3. p = \$300
r = 3%
t = 7 yr
I = \$63

4. p = \$2400
$r = 2\frac{1}{2}\%$
t = 4 yr
I = \$240

5. p = \$960
r = 4%
t = 8 yr
I = \$307.20

6. p = \$200
r = 6%
t = 2 yr
I = \$24

7. p = \$150
r = 5%
t = 3 yr
I = \$22.50

8. p = \$400
$r = 4\frac{1}{2}\%$
t = 1 yr
I = \$18

9. p = \$1260
$r = 2\frac{1}{4}\%$
t = 4 yr
I = \$113.40

Solve.

10. On Dec. 6, 1990, Mr. Dixon borrowed \$3600. The time of the loan was 3 years. How much interest did he pay if the bank charged $14\frac{1}{2}\%$ interest?

3600 × 0.145 × 3

\$1566

11. Mrs. Helin secured a loan of \$1860 from the bank. How much money will she have to pay back on a 3-year loan at a 6% interest rate?

1860 + 1860 × 0.06 × 3

\$2194.80

12. What will be the mount due on a loan of \$960 at the rate of $6\frac{1}{2}\%$ for 3 years?

960 + 960 × 0.065 × 3

\$1147.20

13. Miss Ennis deposited \$450 on June 1, 1990. If the bank paid 5.4% interest, how much did she have in the bank on June 1, 1994?

450 + 450 × 0.054 × 4

\$547.20

14. A club borrowed \$3000 for 2 years at $4\frac{1}{2}\%$ interest. What was the amount due on the loan?

3000 + 3000 × 0.045 × 2

\$3270.00

*Use with Lesson 8-7, text pages 216–217.

Copyright © Sadlier-Oxford

Compound Interest*

Name _____

Date _____

Complete each chart.

1. Find the compound interest on $5000 at 6% for 2 years compounded annually.

Time Period	Principal	Interest
1 year	$5000	$300
2 years	$5300	$318

2. Find the compound interest on $5000 at 6% for 2 years compounded semiannually.

Time Period	Principal	Interest
$\frac{1}{2}$ year	$5000	$150
1 year	$5150	$154.50
$1\frac{1}{2}$ years	$5304.50	$159.14
2 years	$5463.64	$163.91

Solve.

3. A customer took out a loan of $7500 at 15% interest compounded quarterly for 15 months. How much did he have to pay back?

7500 × 0.15 × 0.25,
and so on.

$I = \$1515.75; \ T = \$9015.75$

4. A family deposited $500 in a savings account to prepare for a trip. If their money earns $12\frac{1}{2}$% interest compounded quarterly, how much will they earn in one year?

500 × 0.125 × 0.25,
and so on.

$65.50

5. Ms. Salta deposited $2000 in a savings account for one year at $2\frac{1}{2}$% simple interest. Mr. Mendoza deposited the same amount in a savings bank which pays $2\frac{1}{2}$% interest compounded semiannually. Who receives the greater interest after one year?

1) 2000 × 0.025 × 1
2) 2000 × 0.025 × 5, and so on.

1) Ms. Salta : $50
2) Mr. Mendoza: $50.31
Mr. Mendoza : $.31 more.

6. What is the difference in interest on $2500 at 6% compounded annually for 3 years and the same amount invested at 6% simple interest for 3 years?

1) 2500 × 0.06 × 1, and so on.
2) 2500 × 0.06 × 3

1) Compound: $477.54
2) Simple : 450.00
Difference $ 27.54

Use with Lesson 8-8, text pages 218–219.

Copyright © Sadlier-Oxford

Buying on Credit *

Name ______________________

Date ______________________

Find the monthly finance charge on the unpaid balance. Round to the nearest cent.

1. Bill: $200
   Paid: $75
   Rate: 2%
   Charge: $2.50

2. Bill: $62.85
   Paid: $12.85
   Rate: $1\frac{1}{2}$%
   Charge: $.75

3. Bill: $50.75
   Paid: $15
   Rate: 2.5%
   Charge: $.89

4. Bill: $365.50
   Paid: $100
   Rate: $1\frac{1}{2}$%
   Charge: $3.98

5. Bill: $126.80
   Paid: $40
   Rate: $2\frac{1}{4}$%
   Charge: $1.95

6. Bill: $288.90
   Paid: $75
   Rate: $1\frac{3}{4}$%
   Charge: $3.74

Find the total finance charge. Round to the nearest cent.

	Bill	Down Payment	Monthly Payment	Number of Months	Finance Charge
7.	$450	$150	$35	10	$50
8.	$96	$30	$20	4	$14
9.	$125	$25	$25	5	$25
10.	$260	$50	$40	6	$30
11.	$800	$250	$50	12	$50
12.	$80	25%	$20	4	$20
13.	$150	25%	$25	5	$12.50
14.	$500	10%	$40	12	$30
15.	$365	$65	$40	8	$20
16.	$76	$26	$10	6	$10

Solve:

17. A real estate broker used her credit card to buy an answering machine for $180. She paid $40 a month for two months and the balance the third month. If there was a $1\frac{1}{2}$% finance charge after the first month, how much did she actully pay for the machine?

($180−40) × 0.015 = $2.10;
($142.10 − 40) × 0.015 = $1.53;
$180 + 2.10 + 1.53 = $183.63

*Use with Lesson 8-9, text pages 220–221.

Copyright © Sadlier-Oxford

Probability of a Single Event*

Name ____________________

Date ____________________

Find the probability.

Experiment A: Toss a cube with sides marked 1, 2, 3, 4, 5, and 6.

1. P(3) $\frac{1}{6}$

2. P(odd number) $\frac{1}{2}$

3. P(multiple of 3) $\frac{1}{3}$

4. P(4) $\frac{1}{6}$

5. P(2-digit number) 0

6. P(1-digit number) 1

7. $P(< 5)$ $\frac{2}{3}$

8. P(2 or 3) $\frac{1}{3}$

9. $P(\geq 6)$ $\frac{1}{6}$

Experiment B: Spin the dial.

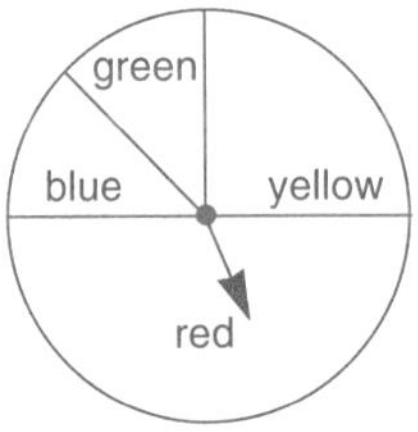

10. P(red) $\frac{1}{2}$

11. P(green) $\frac{1}{8}$

12. P(yellow) $\frac{1}{4}$

13. P(blue) $\frac{1}{8}$

14. P(yellow or red) $\frac{3}{4}$

15. P(black) 0

Experiment C: Choose a card from an envelope containing 10 cards numbered 1 to 10.

16. P(5) $\frac{1}{10}$

17. P(even) $\frac{1}{2}$

18. P(greater than 2) $\frac{4}{5}$

19. P(multiple of 4) $\frac{1}{5}$

20. P(divisible by 5) $\frac{1}{5}$

21. P(less than 1) 0

22. P(5 or 7) $\frac{1}{5}$

23. P(odd) $\frac{1}{2}$

24. P(less than 9) $\frac{4}{5}$

25. Project: Complete the chart by flipping a coin for the number of flips given. Each time find the probability of getting heads. Answers will vary.

Number of Flips	Number of heads	Number of tails	*P* (heads)
10			
20			
30			
40			
50			

*Use with Lesson 9-1, text pages 240–241.

Copyright © Sadlier-Oxford

Independent, Dependent and Compound Events*

Name ____________________

Date ____________________

Find the probability.

Experiment A: Spin the dial twice.

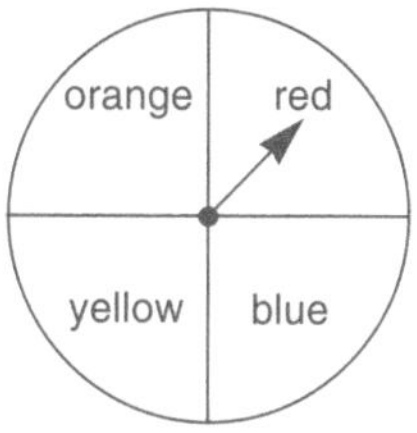

1. P (red, blue) $\frac{1}{16}$
2. P (orange, yellow) $\frac{1}{16}$
3. P (blue, red) $\frac{1}{16}$
4. P (red, blue or orange) $\frac{1}{8}$

Experiment B: Spin the dial twice.

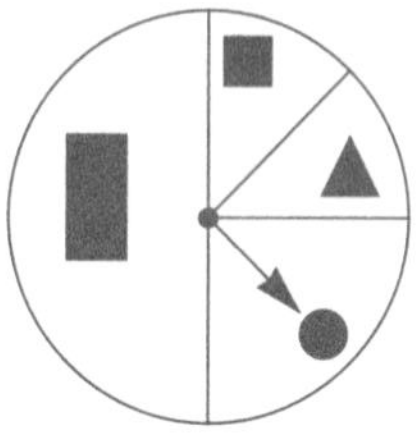

5. P (■, ●) $\frac{1}{32}$
6. P (▲, ●) $\frac{1}{32}$
7. P (▮, ▲) $\frac{1}{16}$
8. P (■, ▲) $\frac{1}{64}$
9. P (●, ▮) $\frac{1}{8}$
10. P (▮, ● or ▲) $\frac{3}{16}$

Find each probability. Complete the chart.

Experiment C: Pick two cards.

1 2 3 4 5 6 7 8

		Replacing first card	Not replacing first card
11.	P (1, 2)	$\frac{1}{64}$	$\frac{1}{56}$
13.	P (4, 8)	$\frac{1}{64}$	$\frac{1}{56}$
15.	P (odd, even)	$\frac{1}{4}$	$\frac{2}{7}$
17.	P (even, even)	$\frac{1}{4}$	$\frac{3}{14}$
19.	P (2, odd)	$\frac{1}{16}$	$\frac{1}{14}$

		Replacing first card	Not replacing first card
12.	P (3, even)	$\frac{1}{16}$	$\frac{1}{14}$
14.	P (4, prime)	$\frac{1}{16}$	$\frac{1}{14}$
16.	P (3, prime)	$\frac{1}{16}$	$\frac{3}{56}$
18.	P (4, even)	$\frac{1}{16}$	$\frac{3}{56}$
20.	P (1, 10)	0	0

*Use with Lesson 9-2, text pages 242–243.

Copyright © Sadlier-Oxford

Permutations*

Name ______________________

Date ______________________

Find the value of each factorial expression.

1. 6! 720
2. 3! 6
3. 8! 40320
4. 4! · 2! 48
5. (5 · 2)! 3628800
6. 6! + 3! 726
7. 8! − 3! 40314
8. 9! − 6! 362160
9. 7! ÷ (6 − 2)! 210

Solve.

10. There are 10 entries in the local dog show. Three ribbons will be awarded. In how many ways can the ribbons be awarded?

$$\frac{10!}{(10-3)!} = 720$$

11. The swimming relay team has 4 members. How many ways can the coach set the order in which they will swim?

$$4! = 24$$

12. You have 7 cards. In how many ways can they be arranged?

$$7! = 5040$$

13. In how many ways can the letters M, E, D, A, R be arranged? What is the probability that a random arrangement of these letters will form the word DREAM?

$$5! = 120 \; ; \; \frac{1}{120}$$

14. Four skydivers were entered in a target-landing contest. How many different orders of finish are possible?

$$4! = 24$$

*Use with Lesson 9-3, text pages 244–245.

Copyright © Sadlier-Oxford

Random Samples*

Name ______________________

Date ______________________

Complete each chart. Then find the estimates.

Question asked of 60 people: What is your favorite TV station for sports?

	Responses	Number	% of Sample
1.	Channel 3 卌 卌 卌	15	25%
2.	Channel 6 卌 卌 卌 卌 卌	25	$41\frac{2}{3}$%
3.	Channel 9 卌 卌 卌 卌	20	$33\frac{1}{3}$%

Estimate the number of people in a population of 240 who would prefer these stations:

4. Channel 3 60
5. Channel 6 100
6. Channel 9 80

Estimate the number of people in a population of 600 who would prefer these stations:

7. Channel 3 150
8. Channel 6 250
9. Channel 9 200

Question asked of 95 high school seniors: What is the maximum level of schooling you plan to complete?

	Responses	Number	% of Sample
10.	High School 卌 I	6	6%
11.	Junior College 卌 卌 卌 卌 II	22	23%
12.	Trade School 卌 卌 IIII	14	15%
13.	College 卌 卌 卌 卌 卌 卌 I	31	33%
14.	Post Graduate 卌 卌 卌 卌 II	22	23%

Estimate the number of high school seniors in a class of 300 who expect to complete the following:

15. High School 18
16. Junior College 69
17. Trade School 45
18. College 99
19. Post Graduate 69

*Use with Lesson 9-4, text pages 246–247.

Copyright © Sadlier-Oxford

Pictographs*

Name ______________________
Date ______________________

Answer these questions about the pictographs below.

Attendance at Sports Events

(stick figure) = 100 fans

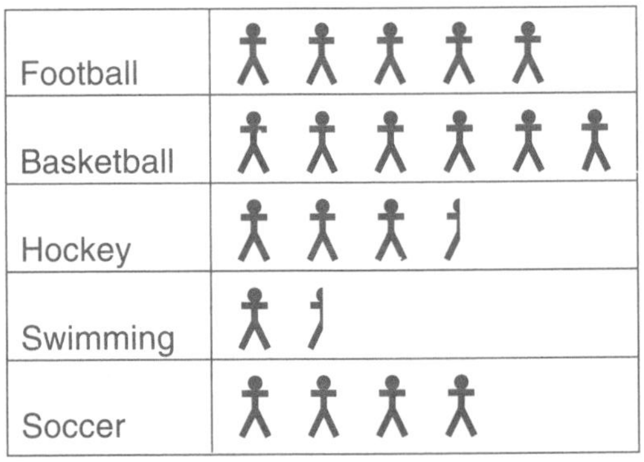

1. About how many fans attend basketball games? 600
2. About how many fans attend swimming meets? 150
3. What two sports have almost the same attendance?
   hockey and soccer
4. What is the difference in attendance at football games and hockey games?
   150

Branch Libraries Circulations

January – February ☐ = 1000 Books

5. What is the circulation at the busiest branch? 7000 books
6. What is the circulation at Bayside? 5500 books
7. What is the difference in circulation between Pawmont and Moreland?
   2500 books
8. What is the total circulation at these six branches?
   26250 books

9. **Construct a pictograph for this chart.**
   Favorite Ice-Cream Flavors

Flavors	Number
Chocolate	25 people
Vanilla	22 people
Mint Chip	20 people
Strawberry	12 people
Butterscotch	16 people

Pictograph

Answers will vary depending on the scale chosen.

*Use with Lesson 9-5, text page 248.

Copyright © Sadlier-Oxford

Bar Graphs*

Name ____________

Date ____________

Complete this frequency table and the bar graph for it.

1.

Baskets Scored in Free-Throw Contest		
Contestant	**Tally**	**Number**
Rob	𝍸 𝍸 I	11
Kate	𝍸 𝍸 III	13
Agnes	𝍸 III	8
Scott	𝍸 𝍸	10
Manuel	𝍸 II	7
Chen	𝍸 𝍸	10

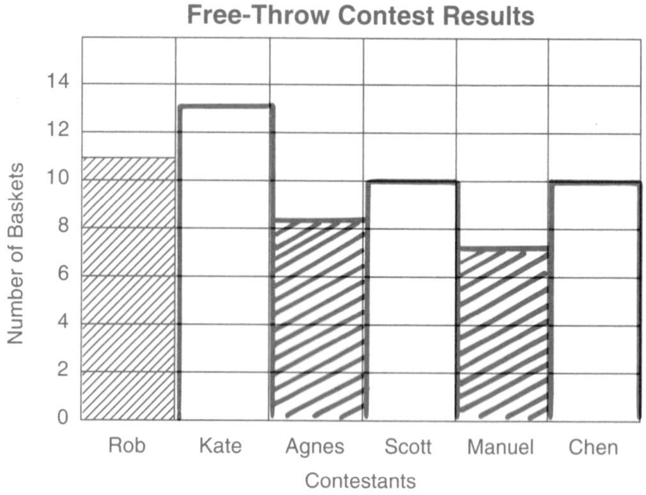

Construct a bar graph for each chart.

2.

Totals in Fund-Raiser	
Grade	**Amount**
Grade 4	$100
Grade 5	$200
Grade 6	$150
Grade 7	$225
Grade 8	$300
Grade 9	$250

Answers to ex. 2–3 will vary depending on the scale chosen.

3.

Oceans of the Earth	
Ocean	**Area**
Atlantic	82 million km^2
Pacific	166 million km^2
Indian	66 million km^2
Arctic	14 million km^2

*Use with Lesson 9-6, text page 249.

Copyright © Sadlier-Oxford

Histograms*

Name ______________________________

Date ______________________________

Answer the questions about the histograms.

Final Examination Scores – Social Studies

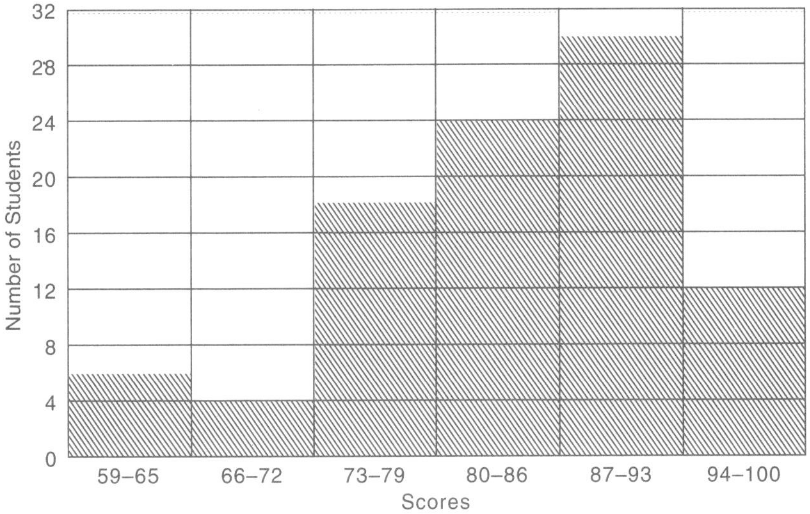

Grade Chart
A = 94–100
B = 87–93
C = 80–86
D = 73–79
F = below 73

1. How many students scored between 87 and 93 on the exam? 30
2. Which group is larger and by how much: those who scored 80 or more or those who scored less than 80? The group of those who scored 80 or more is larger by 38 students
3. How many students took the examination? 94
4. Letter grades were given according to the grade chart shown above. How many students received A or B? 42
5. How many students received C or D? 42
6. How many students received F? 10

Survey Responses–Annual Income, Drendel Hill Township

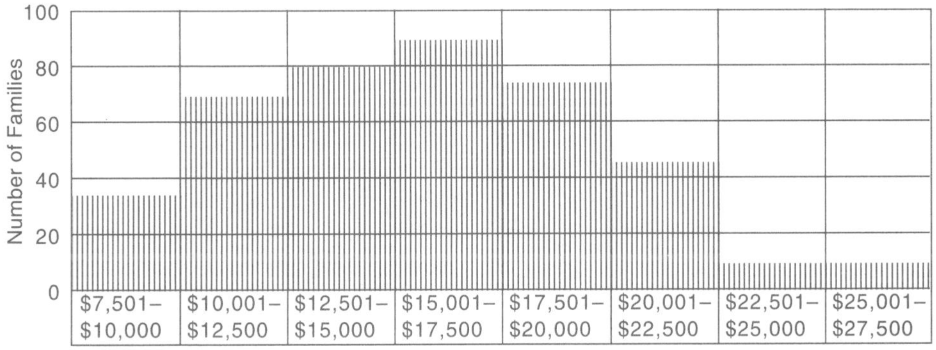

7. About how many families have an income between $10,001 and $12,500? 70
8. About how many families have an income between $12,501 and $20,000? 245
9. About how many families answered the survey? 415

*Use with Lesson 9-7, text page 250.

Copyright © Sadlier-Oxford

Line Graphs*

Name ______________________

Date ______________________

1. Complete the line graph for the information in the chart.

Week's High Temperatures	
Day	**Temperature, °C**
Sunday	20°
Monday	22°
Tuesday	26°
Wednesday	30°
Thursday	28°
Friday	28°
Saturday	32°

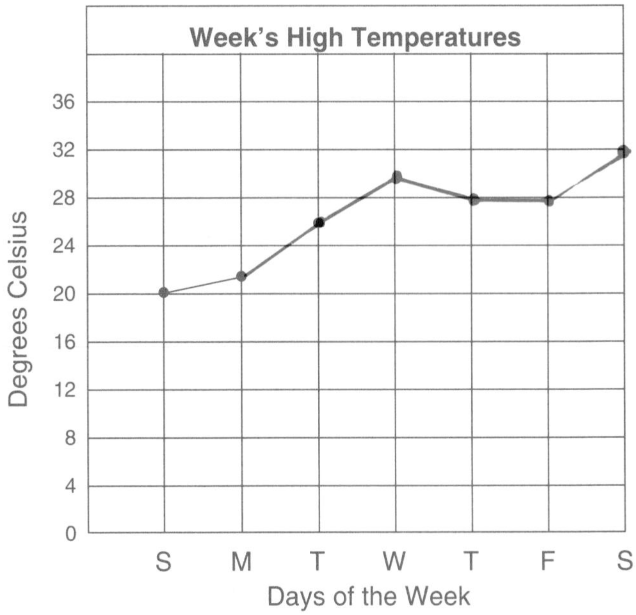

2. Complete the double line graph.

Monthly High Temperatures		
	Temperature, °F	
Month	Los Angeles	San Francisco
Jan	65°	56°
Feb	66°	59°
Mar	69°	61°
Apr	71°	63°
May	74°	65°
Jun	77°	69°
July	83°	69°
Aug	84°	70°
Sept	82°	72°
Oct	77°	69°
Nov	73°	64°
Dec	67°	57°

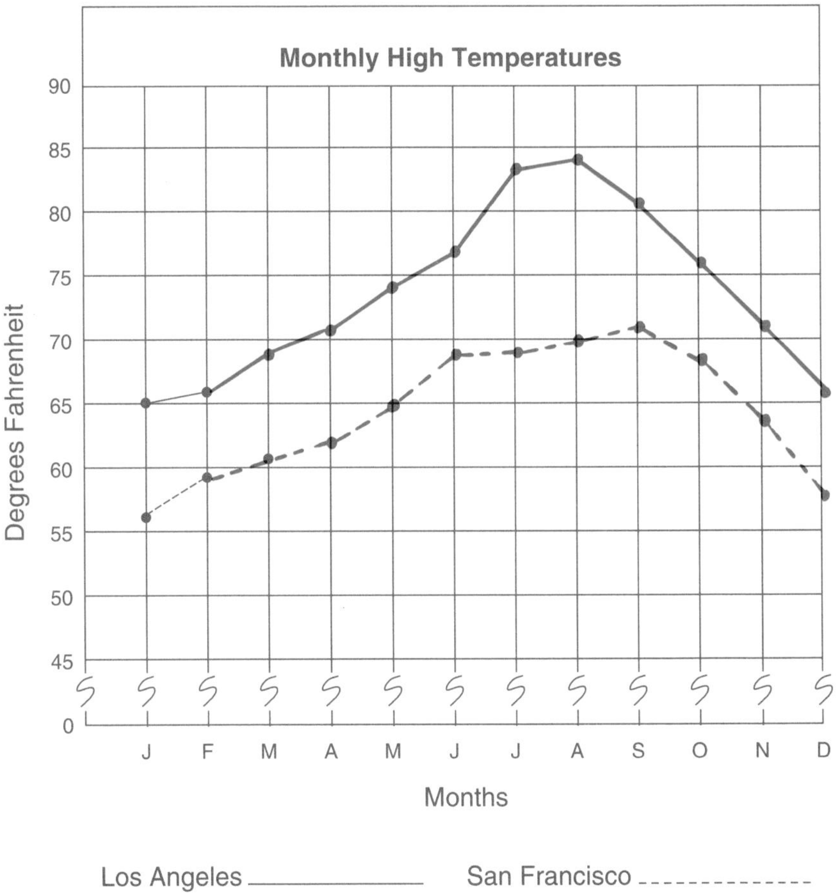

*Use with Lessons 9-8, 9-9, text pages 251–253.

Copyright © Sadlier-Oxford

Circle Graphs*

Name ____________________
Date ____________________

How many degrees in a circle graph are needed to show each?

1. 5 out of 20 people 90°
2. 4 out of 40 doctors 36°
3. 8 out of 24 hours 120°
4. 150 out of 200 books 270°
5. 20 out of 30 days 240°
6. 45 out of 54 children 300°
7. 60 out of 100 dollars 216°
8. 21 out of 56 votes 135°

Find each percent.

9. John spends his allowance as follows:

Books: $3.75 $37\frac{1}{2}$ %

Lunches: $2.50 25 %

Records: $2.50 25 %

Savings: $1.25 $12\frac{1}{2}$ %

10. Kate spends her leisure time each week as follows:

Reading: 8 hours $33\frac{1}{3}$ %

Jogging: 8 hours $33\frac{1}{3}$ %

Movies or TV: 4 hours $16\frac{2}{3}$ %

Others: 4 hours $16\frac{2}{3}$ %

Complete the chart. Then construct a circle graph for it.

11.

Major Uses of Energy in the U.S.		
Use	**Percent**	**Degrees**
Heat for industry	35	126
Transportation	24	86.4 (86)
Heat for buildings	18	64.8 (65)
Electricity for industry	12	43.2 (43)
Water heating	4	14.4 (14)
Air conditioning	2.3	8.28 (8)
Refrigeration	2.1	7.56 (8)
Lighting	1.3	4.68 (5)
Cooking	1.3	4.68 (5)

(Have students round the number of degrees to the nearest whole number before constructing the graph.)

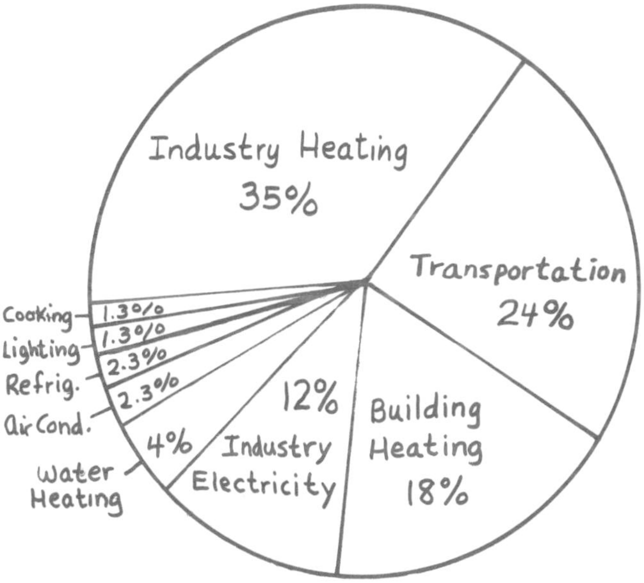

Copyright © Sadlier-Oxford

Central Tendency*

Name ______________________

Date ______________________

Find the range, mean, median, and mode for each set of data.

1. Savings for the past 10 months:
$25, $56, $97, $38, $50
$46, $49, $52, $61, $75

range: $72 **median:** $51

mean: $54.90 **mode:** none

2. Expenses for the past 10 months:
$91, $107, $82, $98, $91
$49, $86, $55, $51, $66

range: $58 **median:** $84

mean: $77.60 **mode:** $91

3. Number of people on 8 tours:
60, 42, 48, 35
51, 28, 39, 64

range: 36 **median:** 45

mean: 45.875 **mode:** none

4. Test scores for 8 students:
72, 79, 91, 84
96, 88, 81, 70

range: 26 **median:** 82.5

mean: 82.625 **mode:** none

Solve.

5. The softball team won the league batting title. The individual averages were 0.325, 0.380, 0.298, 0.308, 0.312, 0.300, 0.292, 0.288, 0.316. Compute the team average, the range, and the median.

average: 0.313 **range:** 0.092 **median:** 0.308

6. At summer camp, a record number of campers were enrolled in 8 fields of activity: 38, 47, 26, 52, 59, 65, 53, 32. Compute the average number, the range, and the median.

average: 46.5 **range:** 39 **median:** 49.5

7. A cyclist kept a record of the distance she biked each day for a week. The record was as follows: 14.5 mi, 9.6 mi, 5.6 mi, 10.7 mi, 15.1 mi, 4.3 mi, and 5.6 mi. Find the mean and the mode.

mean: 9.34 **mode:** 5.6

8. The track team's times in the 200-meter dash were 26.1, 27.5, 27.2, 26.2, 25.0, 24.3, and 24.9. How many runners' times were above the team average?

above average: 25.89; 4 runners

***Use with Lesson 9-11, text pages 256–257.**

Copyright © Sadlier-Oxford

Geometric Concepts*

Name ______________________

Date ______________________

Match each symbol with the corresponding figure.

1. a $\overrightarrow{CT}$
2. g $\overrightarrow{SR}$
3. b $\overleftrightarrow{QS}$
4. f *PQR*
5. c $\angle RWM$
6. d $\angle MRW$
7. e $\overline{TP}$
8. i *M*

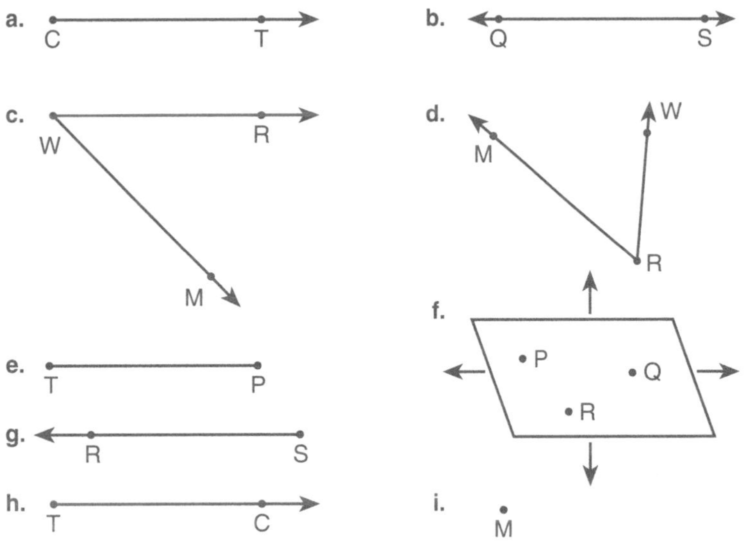

Draw the figure.

9. $\overrightarrow{AB}$ 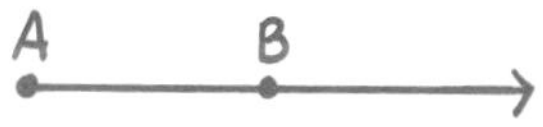	10. $\angle BML$ 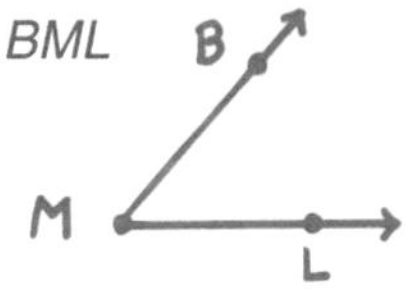	11. *J* 
12. $\overline{MN}$ 	13. $\overleftrightarrow{RT}$ 	14. $\angle TRS$ 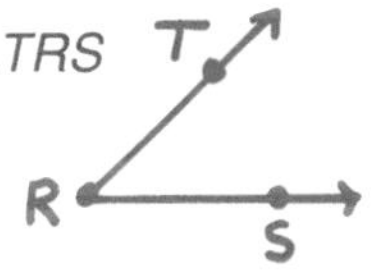

Write "True" or "False."

15. A line can contain a point. True
16. A ray contains a line. False
17. $\overleftrightarrow{AB}$ and $\overline{AB}$ name the same set of points. False
18. The vertex of $\angle CBA$ is the point *C*. False
19. $\overrightarrow{BA}$ and $\overrightarrow{AB}$ are different rays. True
20. $\overrightarrow{RS}$ is one of the sides of $\angle SRA$. True
21. $\angle TMN$ contains $\overrightarrow{TM}$. False
22. A side of an angle contains a segment. True

*Use with Lesson 10-1, text pages 272–273.

Copyright © Sadlier-Oxford

Measuring and Classifying Angles*

Name ______________________

Date ______________________

Measure each angle. Then label it as right, straight, obtuse, or acute.

1.

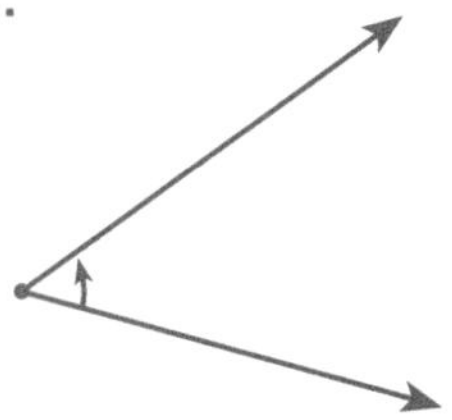

Measure: 50°

Kind: acute

2.

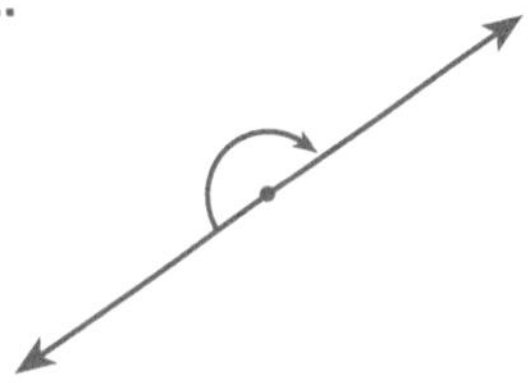

Measure: 180°

Kind: straight

3.

Measure: 120°

Kind: obtuse

4.

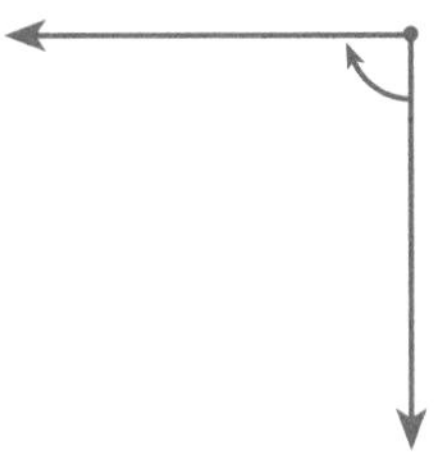

Measure: 90°

Kind: right

Draw an angle whose measure is: Check students' drawings.

5. 100°

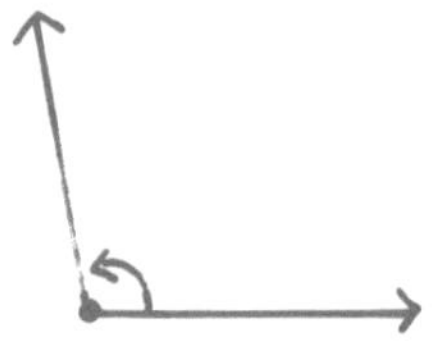

6. 30°

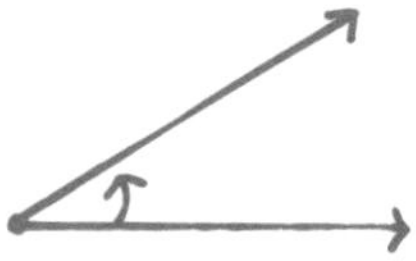

7. 120°

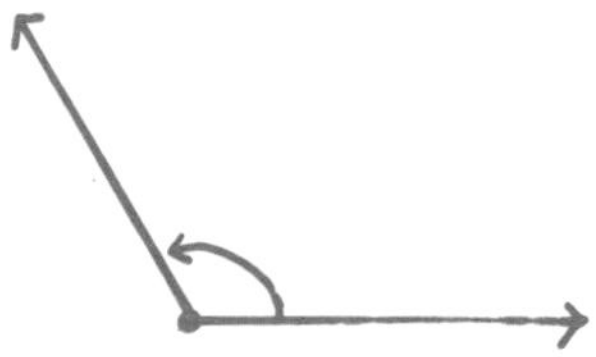

Complete each chart.

	Measure of ∠A	Complement
8.	75°	15°
9.	88°	2°
10.	47°	43°
11.	13°	77°

	Measure of ∠B	Supplement
12.	144°	36°
13.	14°	166°
14.	51°	129°
15.	92°	88°

Circle the correct answer.

16. If two angles are congruent and complementary, they each measure: **a.** 90° **(b.)** 45° **c.** 30°

17. Another name for ∠*BON* is: **(a.)** ∠*NOB* **b.** ∠*OBN* **c.** ∠*NBO*

18. An acute angle has a supplement that is: **a.** acute **(b.)** obtuse **c.** right

*Use with Lesson 10-2, text pages 274–275.

Copyright © Sadlier-Oxford

Constructions with Angles*

Name ______________________

Date ______________________

Check students' constructions for ex. 1–7.

Using a compass and straightedge, construct an angle congruent to each.

1.

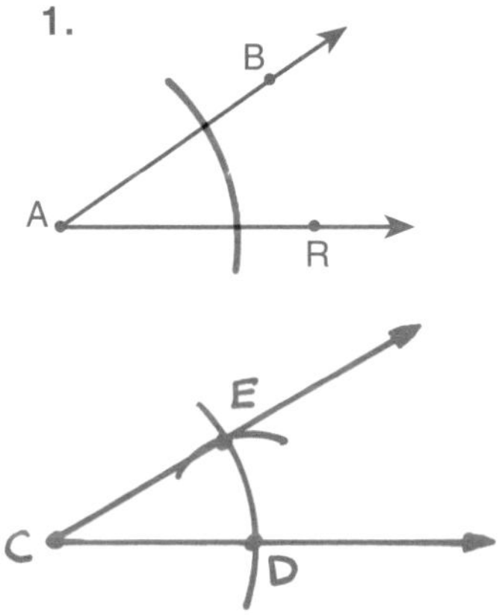

2.

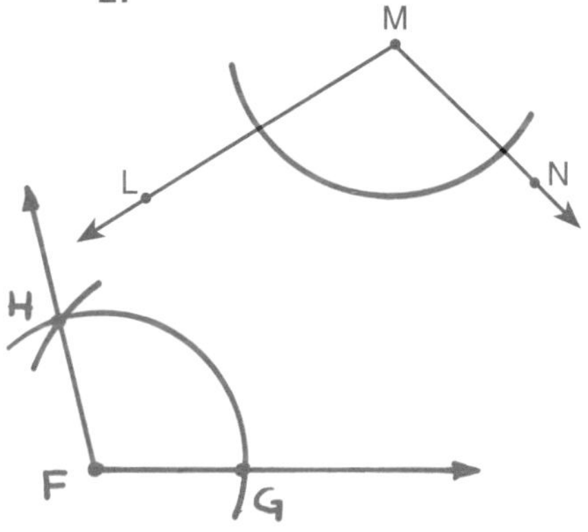

3.

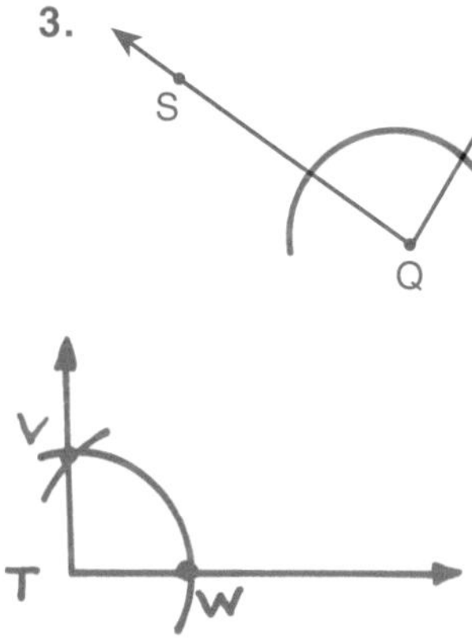

Bisect each angle, using a compass and straightedge.

4.

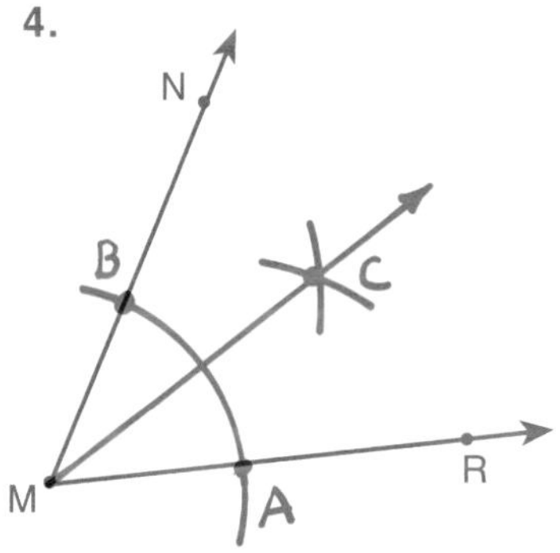

5.

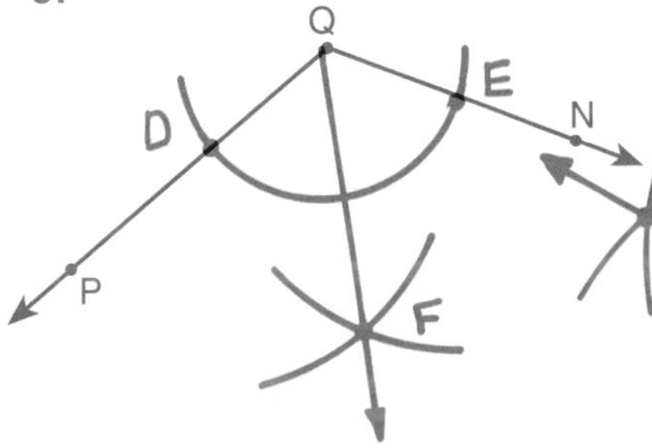

6.

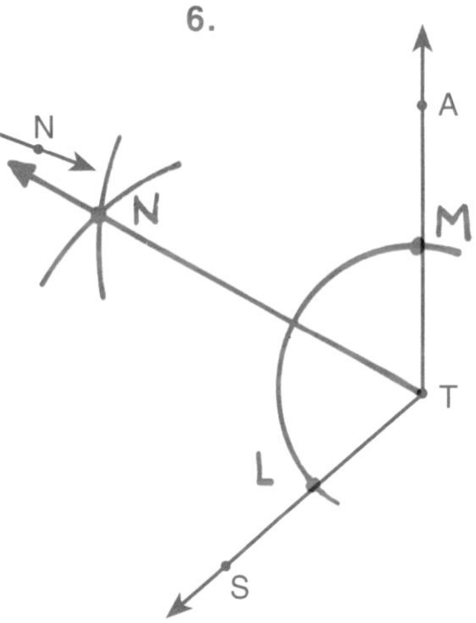

7. Follow the directions.

a. Construct an angle congruent to $\angle PNR$ having $\overrightarrow{NR}$ as one side. Label it $\angle RNS$.

b. Bisect the two congruent angles.

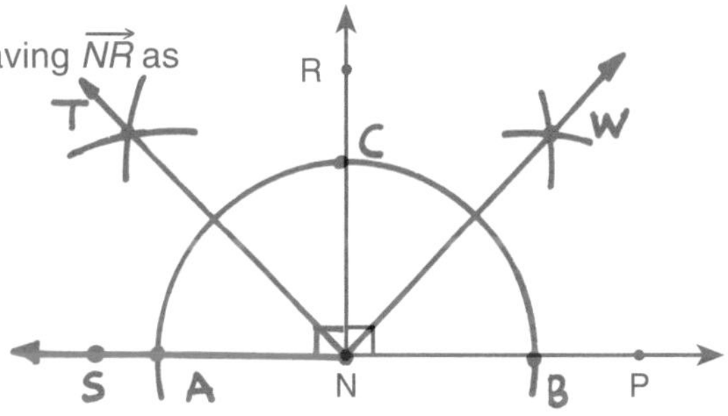

8. Measure each of the four angles formed. What do you find?

The four angles are congruent; each measures 45°.

Copyright © Sadlier-Oxford

Parallel, Intersecting, and Perpendicular Lines*

Name ______________________

Date ______________________

Use the figure at the right to answer exercises 1-5.

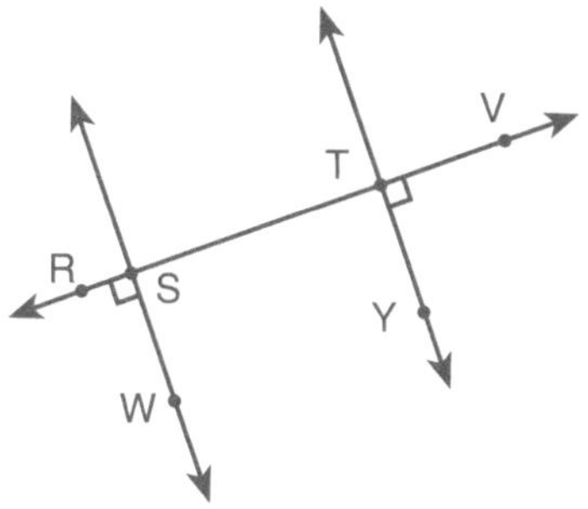

1. Name a pair of parallel lines. $\overleftrightarrow{SW} \parallel \overleftrightarrow{TY}$
2. Name a pair of perpendicular lines. $\overleftrightarrow{RS} \perp \overleftrightarrow{SW}$ or $\overleftrightarrow{TY} \perp \overleftrightarrow{TV}$
3. What is the measure of $\angle VTY$? 90°
4. How many right angles are shown? 8
5. What is the measure of $\angle TSW$? 90°

Use the figure at the left to answer exercises 6-10.

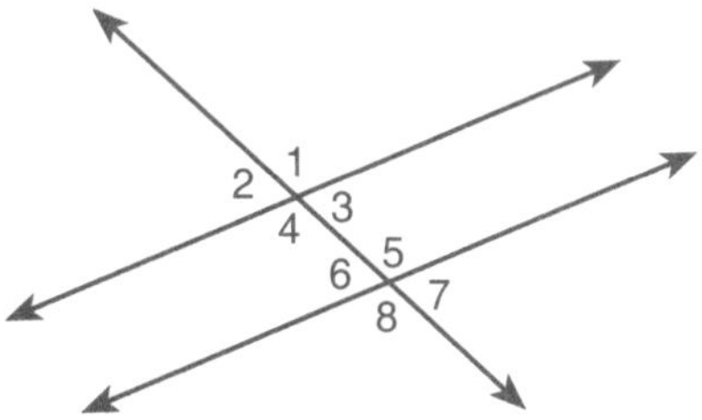

6. Name all pairs of vertical angles. $\angle 1, \angle 4; \angle 2, \angle 3; \angle 6, \angle 7; \angle 5, \angle 8$
7. Name all pairs of adjacent angles. $\angle 1, \angle 2; \angle 2, \angle 4; \angle 1, \angle 3; \angle 3,$ $\angle 5, \angle 7; \angle 5, \angle 6; \angle 6, \angle 8; \angle 7, \angle 8$
8. Name all pairs of alternate interior angles. $\angle 3, \angle 6; \angle 4, \angle 5$
9. Name all pairs of corresponding angles. $\angle 2, \angle 6; \angle 4, \angle 8;$ $\angle 1, \angle 5; \angle 3, \angle 7$
10. Name all pairs of alternate exterior angles. $\angle 2, \angle 7; \angle 1, \angle 8$

Use the figure at the right to answer exercises 11-16.

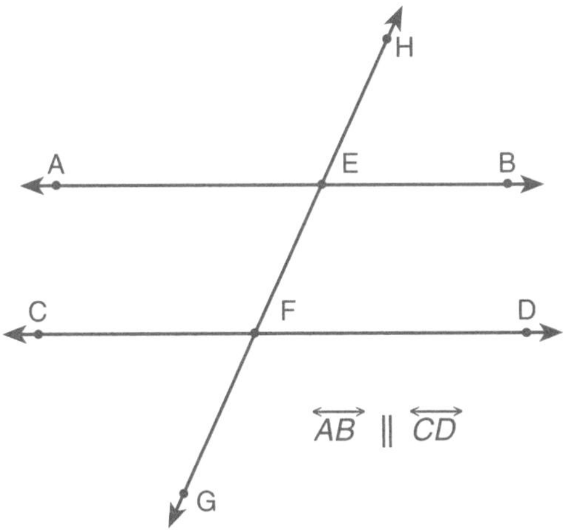

11. Name a pair of parallel lines. $\overleftrightarrow{AB} \parallel \overleftrightarrow{CD}$
12. Name a transversal. $\overleftrightarrow{GH}$
13. Name the corresponding angle to $\angle AEH$. $\angle CFH$
14. Name the alternate interior angle to $\angle BEF$. $\angle EFC$
15. Name the alternate exterior angle to $\angle GFD$. $\angle AEH$
16. Name two angles adjacent to $\angle EFD$. $\angle EFC; \angle DFG$

*Use with Lesson 10-4, text pages 278–279.

Copyright © Sadlier-Oxford

Classifying Triangles*

Name ______________________

Date ______________________

Supply the missing angle measure for each triangle. Then classify the triangle.

	∠*a*	∠*b*	∠*c*	Type of Triangle
1.	40°	70°	70°	acute isosceles
2.	65°	25°	90°	right scalene
3.	72°	61°	47°	acute scalene
4.	20°	90°	70°	right scalene
5.	12°	80°	88°	acute scalene
6.	15°	75°	90°	right scalene
7.	42°	66°	72°	acute scalene
8.	69°	60°	51°	acute scalene
9.	100°	15°	65°	obtuse scalene
10.	70°	50°	60°	acute scalene
11.	60°	60°	60°	acute equilateral
12.	40°	100°	40°	obtuse isosceles
13.	90°	45°	45°	right isosceles

Answer each question about triangles. Write each letter of the answer on a line. Use the letters in the boxes to answer the riddle below.

14. A triangle with no congruent sides. S C A L E [N] E

15. A triangle with two congruent sides. [I] S O S C E L E S

16. A triangle with three congruent sides. E Q U I L A [T] E [R] A L

17. A triangle with one angle greater than 90°. [O] B T U S E

18. A triangle formed by 30°, 60°, 90° angles. R I [G] [H] T

What did the triangle say to the green light? [R] [I] [G] [H] [T] [O] [N] !

16 15 18 18 16 17 14

Copyright © Sadlier-Oxford

Congruent Triangles*

Name ______________________

Date ______________________

Complete exercises 1-6 for these congruent triangles.

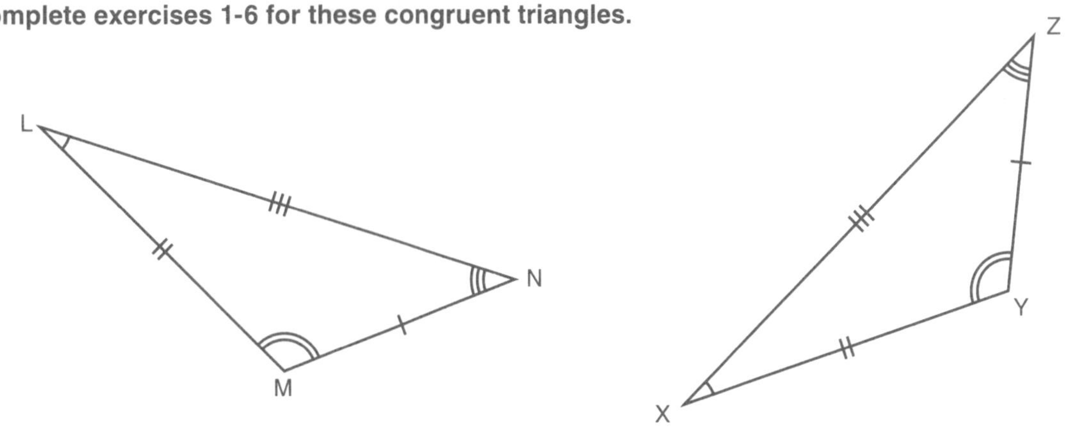

1. $\overline{LN} \cong$ $\overline{XZ}$

2. $\overline{XY} \cong$ $\overline{LM}$

3. $\overline{MN} \cong$ $\overline{YZ}$

4. $\angle L \cong$ $\angle X$

5. $\angle Y \cong$ $\angle M$

6. $\angle Z \cong$ $\angle N$

Tell which rule, SSS, ASA, or SAS, states why the pairs of triangles are congruent.

7.

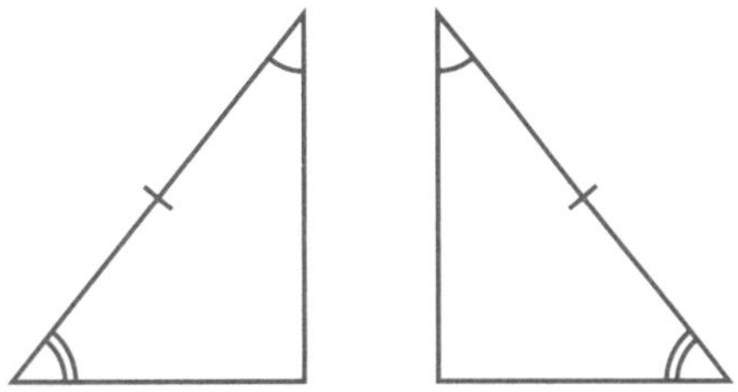

ASA

8.

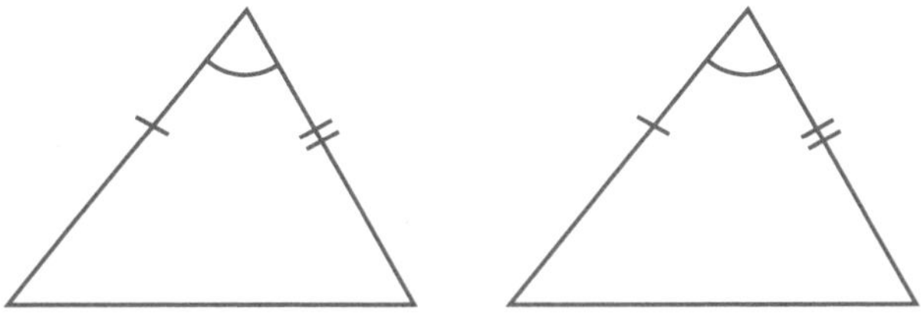

SAS

9.

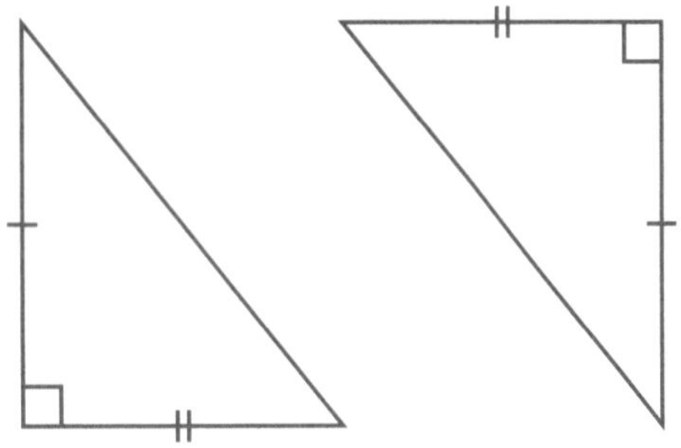

SAS

10.

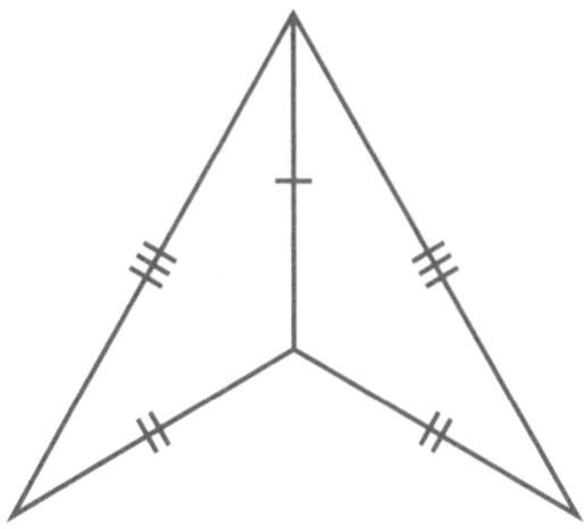

SSS

*Use with Lesson 10-6, text pages 282–283.

Copyright © Sadlier-Oxford

Customary Units*

Name ____________________

Date ____________________

Length	Weight	Capacity
1 ft = 12 in.	1 lb = 16 oz	1 c = 8 fl oz
1 yd = 3 ft = 36 in.	1 T = 2000 lb	1 pt = 16 fl oz
1 mi = 1760 yd = 5280 ft		1 qt = 2 pt = 32 fl oz
		1 gal = 4 qt = 8 pt

Complete.

1. 12 qt = 3 gal
2. 3 yd 3 ft = 144 in.
3. 24 oz = $1\frac{1}{2}$ lb
4. $4\frac{1}{4}$ ft = 51 in.
5. $3\frac{1}{2}$ gal = 14 qt
6. 7′ 2″ = 86 in.
7. 3 T = 6000 lb
8. 114 oz = $7\frac{1}{8}$ lb
9. 4 mi = 7040 yd
10. 2 qt 2 pt = 96 fl oz

Compute.

11. 3 lb 9 oz + 6 lb 7 oz = 10 lb
12. 1 mi 200 ft − 780 ft = 4700 ft
13. 6 gal 1 qt − 3 gal 3 qt = 2 gal 2 qt
14. 3 c 8 fl oz − 10 fl oz = 2 c 6 fl oz
15. 4 gal 2 qt 1 pt + 3 gal 3 qt 1 pt = 8 gal 2 qt
16. 6 yd 2 ft 5 in. + 1 yd 3 ft 4 in. = 8 yd 2 ft 9 in.
17. 2(4 qt 1 pt) = 9qt
18. (75 yd 16 in.) ÷ 4 = 18 yd 2 ft 7 in.

Solve.

19. Super-Glo floor wax is sold for $2.89 per quart. How much will 6 gal cost? $69.36

C = 6 × 4 × $2.89

20. A mechanic has two 1-gal containers for oil. One container is full and the other is $\frac{1}{4}$ full. How many quarts of oil is this? 5 qt

$(1 \times 4) + (\frac{1}{4} \times 4)$

*Use with Lesson 10-7, text pages 284–285.

Copyright © Sadlier-Oxford

Metric Units of Length*

Name ______________________

Date ______________________

Complete with km, m, cm, or mm to make reasonable statements.

1. A pencil is approximately 16 cm long.
2. A book may be 21 mm thick.
3. An adult's height may be 1.87 m.
4. The distance Mary walks in 1 hour is 3.5 km.
5. A jaguar is approximately 75 cm high at the shoulders.
6. Earth is approximately 152 000 000 km from the sun.

Complete.

7. 84 cm = 8.4 dm
8. 31.6 dam = 0.316 km
9. 807 dm = 0.0807 km
10. 8 km = 80 hm
11. 3.6 cm = 36 mm
12. 31.6 m = 316 dm
13. 240 mm = 0.24 m
14. 0.826 m = 0.00826 hm
15. 240 dam = 24 hm
16. 27 m = 27 000 mm
17. 0.24 dam = 24 dm
18. 20 dam = 200 000 mm
19. 4000 hm = 400 km
20. 2300 mm = 2.3 m
21. 0.5 m = 0.0005 km
22. 8000 mm = 0.008 km
23. 98.1 km = 98 100 m
24. 1900 mm = 0.19 dam
25. 2.6 cm = 0.026 m
26. 27.5 hm = 2.75 km
27. 300 cm = 0.03 hm
28. 4.2 cm = 42 mm
29. 0.91 m = 0.091 dam
30. 0.4 hm = 400 dm
31. 7.2 dm = 0.072 dam
32. 6200 mm = 6.2 m
33. 6 km = 600 000 cm
34. 31 m = 3100 cm
35. 810 cm = 8100 mm
36. 900 m = 9 hm

Express each measure as a single unit.

37. 8 m 26 cm = 826 cm
38. 9 m 18 mm = 9.018 m
39. 16 m 47 mm = 16.047 m
40. 4 cm 3 mm = 43 mm
41. 3 km 2 m = 3.002 km
42. 8 km 6 hm = 8600 m
43. 80 km 5 m = 80 005 m
44. 6 cm 9 mm = 6.9 cm
45. 6 km 19 m = 6019 m
46. 3 km 6 hm = 36 hm
47. 3 m 46 cm = 3.46 m
48. 18 hm 7 dm = 1.8007 km

*Use with Lesson 10-8, text pages 286–287.

Copyright © Sadlier-Oxford

Changing Metric Units*

Name ______________________

Date ______________________

Complete this chart so that each row shows equivalent measurements.

	kilometer	hectometer	dekameter	meter	decimeter	centimeter	millimeter
1.	0.005	0.05	0.5	5	50	500	5000
2.	0.072	0.72	7.2	72	720	7200	72000
3.	0.0406	0.406	4.06	40.6	406	4060	40 600
4.	0.00066	0.0066	0.066	0.66	6.6	66	660
5.	6.8	68	680	6800	68000	680 000	6 800 000
6.	0.003	0.03	0.3	3	30	300	3000

Complete. Use the shortcut.

7. 15 m = 1500 cm

8. 9 km = 9000 m

9. 25 m = 25 000 mm

10. 4.5 km = 45 000 dm

11. 6.2 km = 620 dam

12. 525 m = 52 500 cm

13. 0.46 dam = 0.0046 km

14. 0.82 hm = 820 dm

15. 0.003 dm = 0.3 mm

Compare. Write <, =, or >.

16. 525 cm > 5 m

17. 0.62 hm = 62 m

18. 7.4 m > 70 dm

19. 52.1 km = 521 hm

20. 221 cm < 20 hm

21. 0.7 dam > 28 mm

Solve.

22. A rug measures 12 m 20 cm. What will it cost to place a border around the rug at $11.50 per meter?

C = 12.2 × $11.50

$140.30

23. The distance from the principal's office to the library is 24 m 7 dm, and the distance from the library to the math workshop room is 24 m 56 cm. Which is the greater distance? How much greater?

24.7 m − 24.56 m = 0.14 m

*Use with Lesson 10-9, text pages 288–289.

Copyright © Sadlier-Oxford

Precision in Measurement*

Name ______________________

Date ______________________

Circle the more precise measurement.

1. (2.5 cm) or 0.3 m
2. 19 cm or (18.6 mm)
3. (48 mm) or 4.81 cm
4. (713 m) or 0.71 km
5. 0.6 m or (6.1 dm)
6. (85 dm) or 9 m
7. 7.3 km or (7314 m)
8. 6 hm or (62 m)
9. (142 cm) or 1.4 m
10. (8.2 mm) or 0.8 cm

Complete the chart.

	Measure	Unit	GPE	Range of Measure
11.	16.1 cm	0.1 cm	0.05 cm	16.1 ± 0.05 cm
12.	83 mm	1 mm	0.5 mm	83 ± 0.5 mm
13.	7 dm	1 dm	0.5 dm	7 ± 0.5 dm
14.	81 m	1 m	0.5 m	81 ± 0.5 m
15.	2.7 m	0.1 m	0.05 m	2.7 ± 0.05 m
16.	3 km	1 km	0.5 km	3 ± 0.5 km
17.	9.6 dam	0.1 dam	0.05 dam	9.6 ± 0.05 dam
18.	0.04 mm	0.01 mm	0.005 mm	0.04 ± 0.005 mm
19.	18 cm	1 cm	0.5 cm	18 ± 0.5 cm

Measure items around your classroom or your house. Vary the units of measurement you choose. Complete the following chart. Answers will vary.

	Item	Measure	Unit	GPE	Range of Measure
20.	Your height				
21.	A glass				
22.	Refrigerator				
23.					
24.					

*Use with Lesson 10-10, text pages 290–291.

Copyright © Sadlier-Oxford

Nonroutine Problems*

Name ______________________

Date ______________________

Solve. Strategies may vary.

1. Ms. Alvarez travels 5 mi east, 6 mi south, 4 mi west, and 6 mi north. How far from the starting point is she?

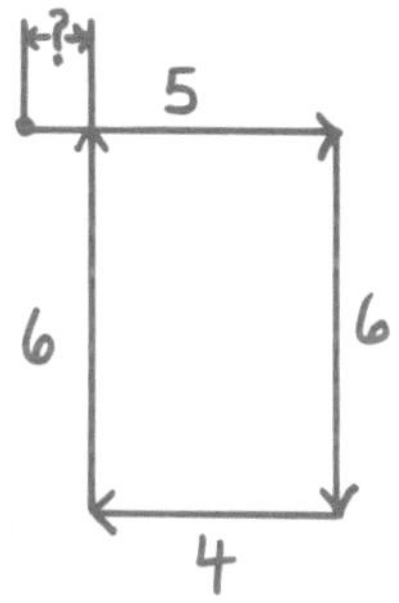

Drawing a picture: 1 mi

2. The National Monuments and the White House are part of the National Park System. The White House grounds contain about 18 acres. The acreage of the National Monuments is about 2.69×10^5 times as great. About how many acres are occupied by the National Monuments?

Using simpler numbers: $(2.69 \times 10^5) \times 18 = 4{,}842{,}000$ acres; about 4.8×10^6 acres or about 5,000,000 acres

3. Two towns are considering building a walkway over the river that separates them. They poll their citizens to find out how they feel about the project. In town A 360 of the 580 people polled like the idea. In Town B 270 of the 690 people polled like the idea. What percent in each town like the plan? What percent of both towns together like the plan?

Using percentage formulas: $R = \frac{P}{B}$; town A: $R = \frac{360}{580} \approx 62\%$; town B: $R = \frac{270}{690} \approx 39\%$; both towns: $R = \frac{630}{1270} \approx 50\%$

4. It costs $13,640 daily to produce 150,000 copies of a daily newspaper. If the circulation remains the same but the prices increase 7% this year, what will be the daily production cost of the newspaper? What is the daily production cost of one newspaper?

Solving multi-step problems:
Daily production costs: \$13,640 + 7% (\$13,640) = \$14,594.80;
daily cost per paper: \$14,594.80 ÷ 150,000 ≈ \$.10

5. Students at Progressive University can study mathematics with three different professors. In a sample group of 30 students, 12 study with professor A and 9 with professor B. Of professor A's students, $\frac{1}{3}$ also study with professor B and another $\frac{1}{3}$ study with professor C. Of professor B's students, $\frac{2}{3}$ also study with professor C. Three students study with all of them and four students study with none of them. How many students study with professor C?

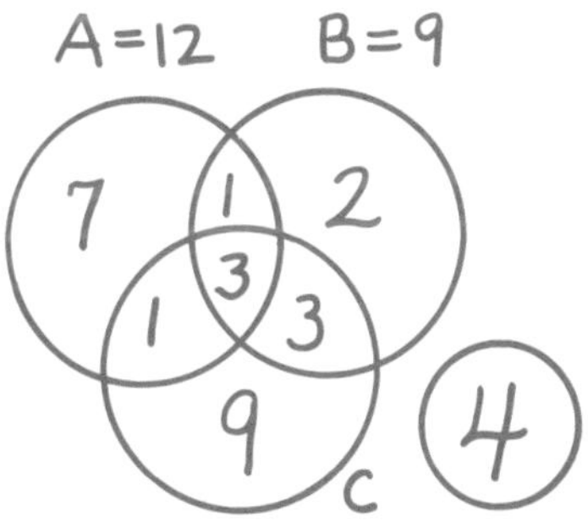

Using Venn diagrams:
$\frac{1}{3} \times 12 = 4$; $\frac{1}{3} \times 9 = 3$; $\frac{2}{3} \times 9 = 6$
$C = 30 - (7 + 1 + 2 + 4)$; 16 students

Copyright © Sadlier-Oxford

Name ____________________

Date ____________________

6. Adult meals at a club benefit luncheon sell for $4 each. Is $135 enough to pay for the meals for 34 company executives? Explain.

Interpreting the remainder: $\$135 \div \$4 = 33\frac{3}{4}$ meals
No, because $135 will pay for only 33 complete meals.

7. Two students are playing a game of Hopping Squares. There are 29 numbered squares in a straight line separating them. Each player makes a prescribed number of moves. Player A starts at square 1 and moves forward 3 squares and back 1. Player B starts at square 29 and moves forward 5 squares and back 2. If they continue moving toward one another in this way, in which square will they meet?

Drawing a picture: A: $^{+}3 - 1 = 2$ moves; B: $^{+}5 - 2 = 3$ moves;

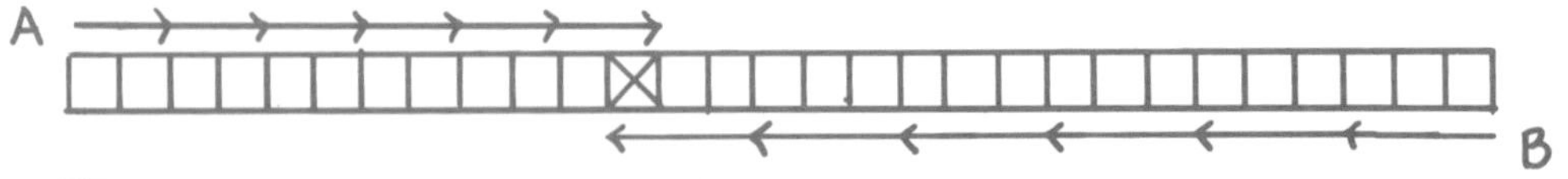

They meet in a square 12.

8. When a large collection of pictures of world leaders is counted by 2's, 3's, 4's, 5's, or 6's, one picture always remains. When counted by 7's, there is no remainder. What is the fewest number of pictures that can be in the collection?

Logical reasoning; guess and test: The number is divisible by 7; it ends in 6 or 1 because when divided by 5 the remainder is 1; it is odd because when divided by 2 the remainder is 1. Therefore the number is a multiple of 7 ending in 1. So the possible factors are 7 and numbers ending in 3. By guess-and-test the number is $301 - 7 \times 43$

9. One of the angles of a right triangle is 2 more than 3 times the other. What is the measure of each angle?

Writing equations; drawing a picture;
$x + 3x + 2 + 90 = 180$; $x = 22$
22°, 68°, 90°

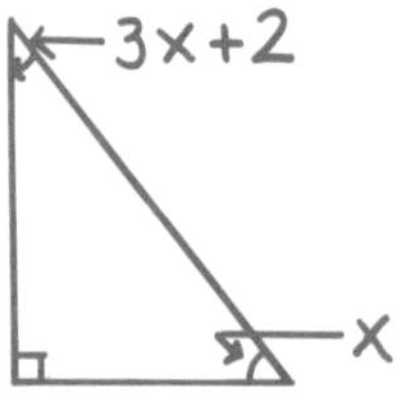

10. The ratio of the length to width of a rectangle is 3:2. The perimeter is 70 cm. What are the dimensions of the rectangle?

Writing equations: $P = 2(\ell \times w)$
$70 = 2(3x + 2x)$; $x = 7$
length: 21 cm; width: 14 cm

*Use for Chapters 5-10.

Copyright © Sadlier-Oxford

Perimeter*

Name ______________________

Date ______________________

Find the perimeter.

1.

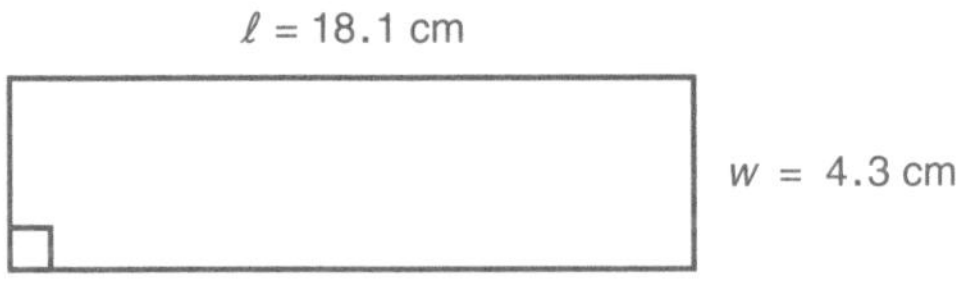

P = 44.8 cm

2.

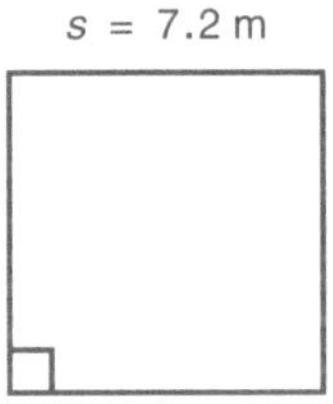

P = 28.8 m

3.

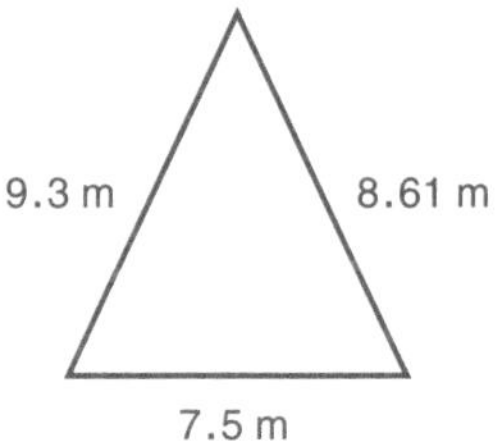

P = 25.41 m

4.

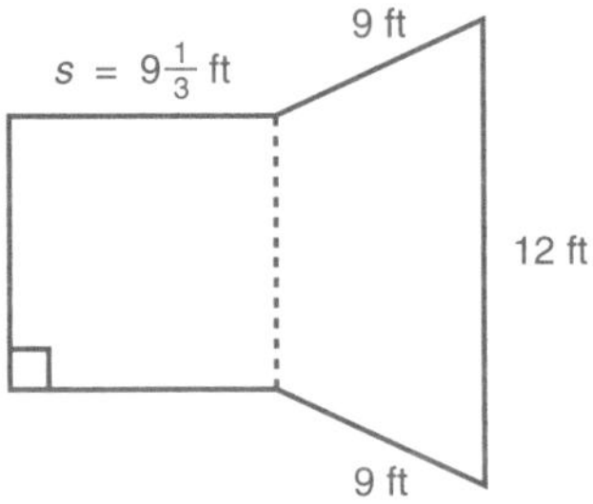

P = 58 ft

5.

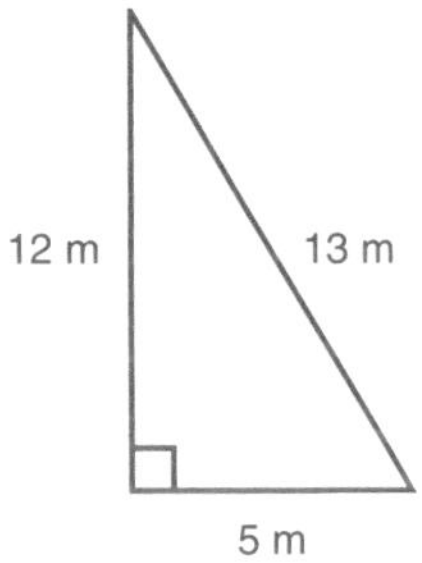

P = 30 m

6.

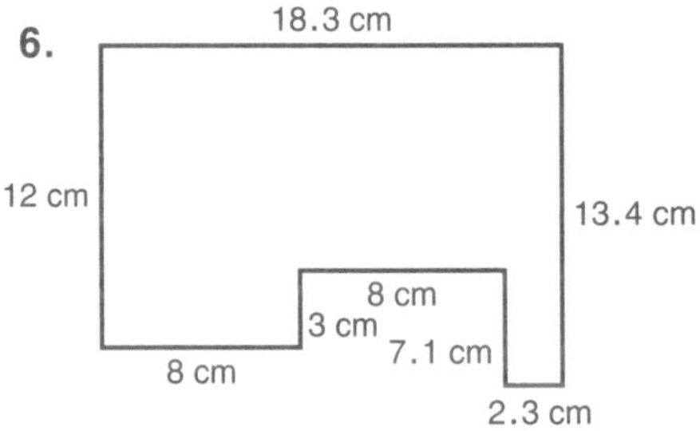

P = 72.1 cm

Draw each figure and solve.

7. Find the perimeter in centimeters of an equilateral triangle measuring 84 mm on a side.
$P = 3 \times 8.4$

25.2 cm

8. Determine the perimeter of a regular pentagon 3 m 49 cm on a side.
$P = 5 \times 349$

1745 cm or 17.45 m

9. Part of the edging around a regular decagon having a perimeter of 213 cm was used to edge a regular octagon. If the sides of the octagon are the same length as those of the decagon, how much edging was used for the octagon?
$P = 8(213 \div 10)$

170.4 cm

10. A garden 40 meters wide and 72 meters long is to be enclosed by a fence. At $8.90 per meter, what will the fencing cost?
$P = 2(40+72)$; $\$8.90 \times 224$

$1993.60

11. In a class of 32 students, each student needs yarn to edge an art project. About how many yards of yarn are needed for the class if the projects are squares, 8 inches on a side.
$P = 4 \times \frac{8}{36}$; $\frac{8}{9} \times 32$

about 29 yd

12. David walked around a rectangular field 3 times. How far did he walk if the field's dimensions are 65 meters by 55 meters?
$P = 2(65+55)$; 3×240

720 m

Copyright © Sadlier-Oxford

Area: Rectangles, Squares, Parallelograms*

Name ______________________

Date ______________________

Find the area of each.

1. Rectangle
   length: 16 cm
   width: 15 cm
   A = $240\ cm^2$

2. Rectangle
   length: 8 cm
   width: 13.4 cm
   A = $107.2\ cm^2$

3. Square
   side: $8\frac{1}{3}$ in.
   A = $69\frac{4}{9}\ in.^2$

Complete each chart.

Rectangle $A = l \times w$

	length	width	Area
4.	14 cm	8.1 cm	$113.4\ cm^2$
5.	6.3 m	4.2 m	$26.46\ m^2$
6.	90 cm	52 cm	$4680\ cm^2$
7.	7 ft	$6\frac{1}{3}$ ft	$44\frac{1}{3}\ ft^2$
8.	4 yd	2 ft	$2\frac{2}{3}\ yd^2$ or $24\ ft^2$

Parallelogram $A = b \times h$

	base	height	Area
9.	21.3 m	10 m	$213\ m^2$
10.	2 m	90 cm	$1.8\ m^2$ or $18000\ cm^2$
11.	6 dm	1.2 m	$0.72\ m^2$ or $72\ dm^2$
12.	9 in.	3.5 in.	$31.5\ in.^2$
13.	5 yd	12 ft	$20\ yd^2$ or $180\ ft^2$

Solve:

14. How many square yards of floor space are there in a cafeteria 23 yd by 18 yd?
    $A = 23 \times 18$
    $414\ yd^2$

15. The janitor is painting the floor of a room 25 m by 40 m. How many containers of paint will he need if one container covers 50 m^2?
    $A = 25 \times 40;\ 1000 \div 50$
    20 containers

16. The neighborhood playground is shaped like a parallelogram with a base of 130 ft and a height of 95 ft. What is the area of the playground?
    $A = 130 \times 95$
    $12{,}350\ ft^2$

17. How many square meters of plastic will be needed to make 8 place mats each of which is 40 cm long and 30 cm wide?
    $A = 40 \times 30 \times 8;\ 9600 \div 10\,000$
    $0.96\ m^2$

18. A square parking lot measures approximately 0.8 km on a side. Estimate the area of the lot.
    $A = (0.8)^2$
    $0.64\ km^2$

19. Which has a larger area, a square 12 ft on a side or a rectangle 10 ft long and 14 ft wide?
    $A = 12^2;\ A = 10 \times 14$
    square: $144\ ft^2$
    rectangle: $140\ ft^2$

20. How many tiles 3 in. on a side are needed to cover a space $5\frac{1}{4}$ ft by $3\frac{1}{2}$ ft?
    $A = 5\frac{1}{4} \times 3\frac{1}{2} \times 144;\ 2646 \div (3)^2$
    294 tiles

*Use with Lesson 11-2, text pages 306–307.

Copyright © Sadlier-Oxford

Area: Triangles*

Name ______________________

Date ______________________

Find the area of each triangle.

1. 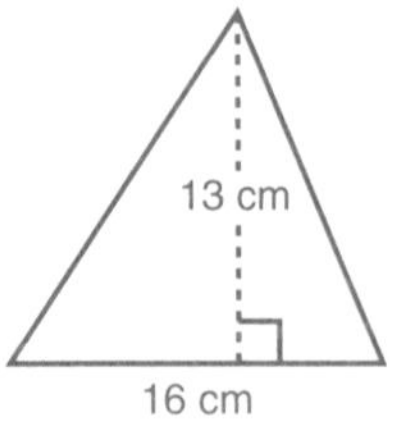

$A = $ 104 cm^2

2. 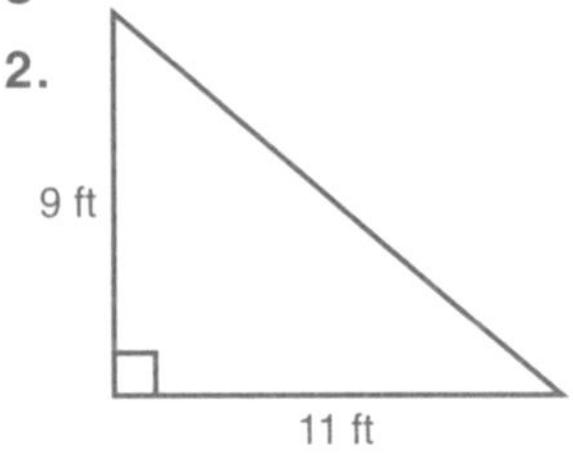

$A = $ 49.5 ft^2

3. 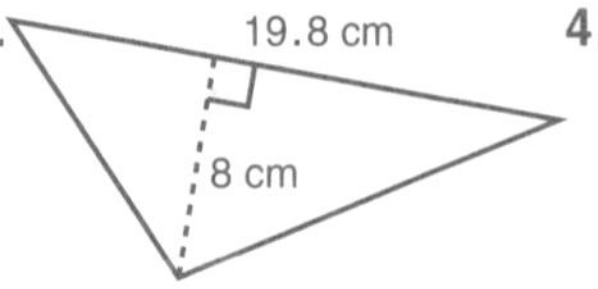

$A = $ 79.2 cm^2

4. 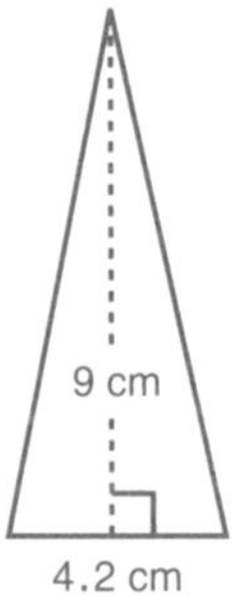

$A = $ 18.9 cm^2

Complete the chart for each triangle. $A = \frac{1}{2}bh$

	base	height	Area
5.	4 m	3 m	6 m^2
6.	18 cm	31 cm	279 cm^2
7.	3 dm	5.6 dm	8.4 dm^2
8.	40 m	28 m	560 m^2
9.	52 cm	90 cm	2340 cm^2
10.	3 km	1.6 km	2.4 km^2
11.	$6\frac{1}{3}$ yd	15 yd	$47\frac{1}{2}$ yd^2
12.	15 ft	18 ft	135 ft^2

Solve.

13. Find the area of a triangular sail if the base is 3 m and the height is 5 m.
$A = \frac{1}{2}(3)(5)$
7.5 m^2

14. How many square meters of decorative paper would be used for a design made of 6 triangles, each of which has a base of 60 cm and a height of 42 cm?
$A = \frac{1}{2}(0.6)(0.42) \times 6$
0.756 m^2

15. A gardener planted flowers in a triangular corner of his garden. What is the area of the flower bed if its base is 20 ft and its height is 16.5 ft?
$A = \frac{1}{2}(20)(16.5)$
165 ft^2

16. The perimeter of an equilateral triangle is 18 cm and the height is 5.2 cm. What is the area of the triangle? $s = 18 \div 3$; $A = \frac{1}{2}(6)(5.2)$
15.6 cm^2

*Use with Lesson 11-3, text pages 308–309.

Copyright © Sadlier-Oxford

Area: Trapezoids, Mixed Polygons*

Name ______________________

Date ______________________

Find the area of each. $A = \frac{1}{2}(b_1 + b_2)h$

1.

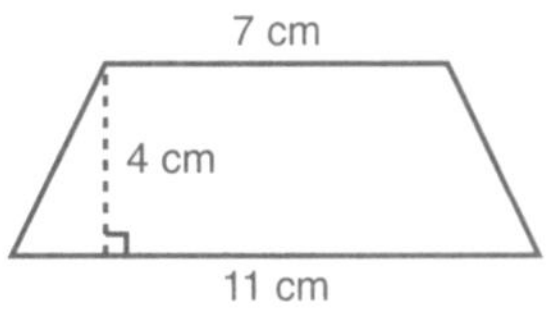

$A =$ 36 cm^2

2.

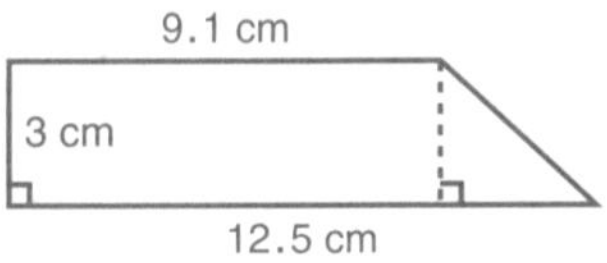

$A =$ 32.4 cm^2

3.

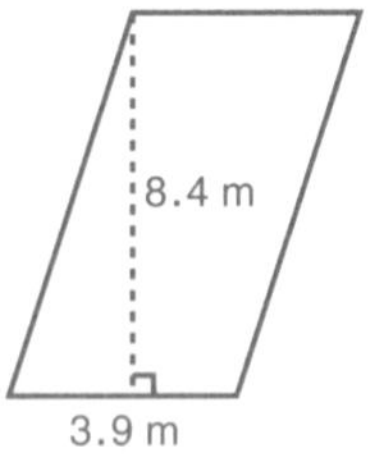

$A =$ 32.76 m^2

Find the area of each trapezoid. Write the area in the unit of measure indicated. Change units where necessary.

4. bases: 9 cm, 23 mm
height: 8 cm

Area: 45.2 cm^2

5. bases: 4 ft, 2 yd
height: 2 ft

Area: $1\frac{1}{9}$ yd^2

6. bases: 4 m, 600 cm
height: 30 m

Area: 150 m^2

Solve:

7. A tabletop shaped like a trapezoid has parallel bases of 40 cm and 62 cm and a height of 34 cm. Find the area.

$A = \frac{1}{2}(40+62)(34)$; 1734 cm^2

8. Lauren placed a square lamp, measuring 25 cm on each edge, on a table shaped like a trapezoid. The table had parallel bases of 32 cm and 48 cm and a height of 34 cm. Find the number of square centimeters not covered by the lamp.

$A = (25)^2$; 625 cm^2

$A = \frac{1}{2}(32+48)(34)$; 1360 cm^2

$1360 - 625 = 735$ cm^2

9. A bulletin board is shaped like a trapezoid. If the bases are 45 cm and 65 cm and the height is 40 cm, what is the area?

$A = \frac{1}{2}(45+65)40$; 2200 cm^2

10. Find the area of a trapezoid having a height of 32 in. and parallel bases measuring 49 in. and 61 in.

$A = \frac{1}{2}(49+61)32$; 1760 $in.^2$

11. A trapezoid has a height of 3 yd and parallel bases of 7 ft and 10 ft. What is its area?

$A = \frac{1}{2}(7+10)9$; $76\frac{1}{2}$ ft^2

12. A line segment drawn parallel to the 12-cm height of a right triangle divides the base into segments of 3 cm and 6 cm and the hypotenuse into segments of 5 cm and 10 cm. This produces a new right triangle and a trapezoid. Find the area of each. (Hint: Use proportion to find the length of the missing side/base. Two sets of answers to the area problem are possible.)

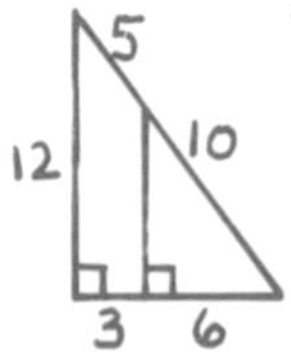

$\frac{6}{?} = \frac{9}{12}$

$? = 8$

$A = \frac{1}{2}(6)(8)$; 24 cm^2

$A = \frac{1}{2}(8+12)3$; 30 cm^2

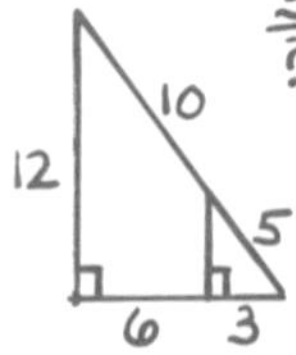

$\frac{3}{?} = \frac{9}{12}$

$? = 4$

$A = \frac{1}{2}(3)(4)$; 6 cm^2

$A = \frac{1}{2}(4+12)6$; 48 cm^2

*Use with Lesson 11-4, text pages 310–311.

Copyright © Sadlier-Oxford

Circumference*

Name ______________________

Date ______________________

Complete each table. C = πd or C = 2πr

Use 3.14 for π.

	Diameter	Circumference
1.	3 m	9.42 m
2.	22 cm	69.08 cm
3.	30 mm	94.2 mm
4.	8.1 m	25.434 m
5.	1.6 km	5.024 km
6.	9.3 dm	29.202 dm

Use $\frac{22}{7}$ for π.

	Diameter	Circumference
7.	7 cm	22 cm
8.	21.7 cm	68.2 cm
9.	42 dm	132 dm
10.	3.5 km	11 km
11.	5.6 m	17.6 m
12.	$3\frac{1}{2}$ ft	11 ft

Find the distance around each figure.

13.

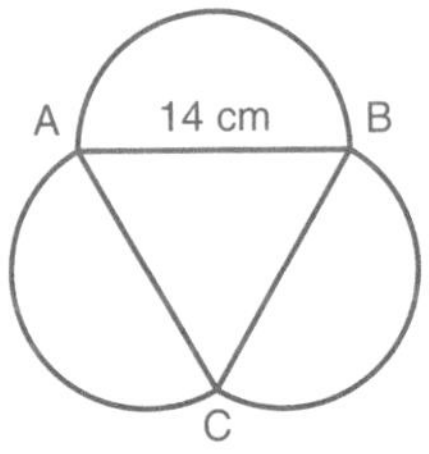

$P = 1\frac{1}{2}\pi(14)$

Inside the figure, ABC is an equilateral triangle. Semicircles are positioned on each side.

66 cm

14.

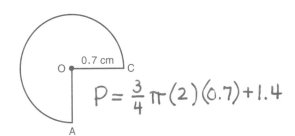

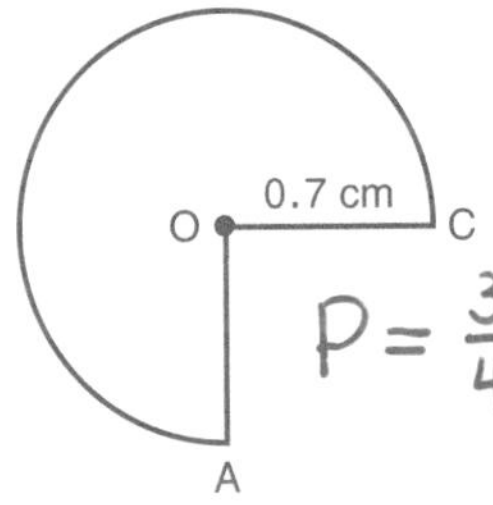

$P = \frac{3}{4}\pi(2)(0.7) + 1.4$

m∠ AOC = 90°
$\overline{OC}$ = 0.7 cm

4.7 cm

Solve:

15. How much fencing is needed to enclose a circular garden whose radius is 4.5 yards?

C = 2π(4.5); 28.26 yd

16. Find the circumference of a bicycle wheel if one spoke from the center measures 24 cm.

C = 2π(24); 150.72 cm

17. A gardener measured 4.2 m as the diameter of a circular flower bed. What was the circumference of the flower bed?

C = π(4.2); 13.2 m

Copyright © Sadlier-Oxford

Area: Circles*

Name ______________________

Date ______________________

Remember the formula: $A = \pi r^2$

Give the area in the specified square units. Change units where necessary.

1. $r = 7$ cm
   $A \approx$ 154 cm²
2. $r = 4$ cm
   $A \approx$ 50.24 cm²
3. $r = 12$ m
   $A \approx$ 452.16 m²
4. $r = 41$ m
   $A \approx$ 5278.34 m²
5. $d = 50$ ft
   $A \approx$ $218\frac{16}{63}$ yd²
   or 218.06
6. $d = 11$ m
   $A \approx$ 94.985 m²
7. $d = 40$ mm
   $A \approx$ 12.56 cm²
8. $d = 2.5$ mm
   $A \approx$ 4.90625 mm²

Find the area.

9.

615.44 mm²

10.
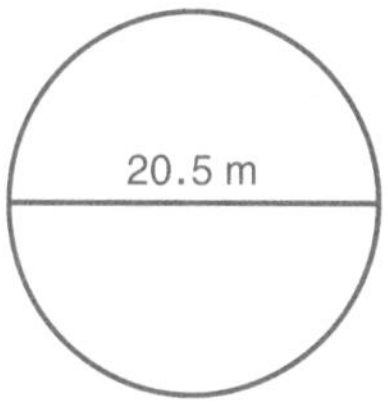

329.8963 m²

11.

113.04 in.²

12.
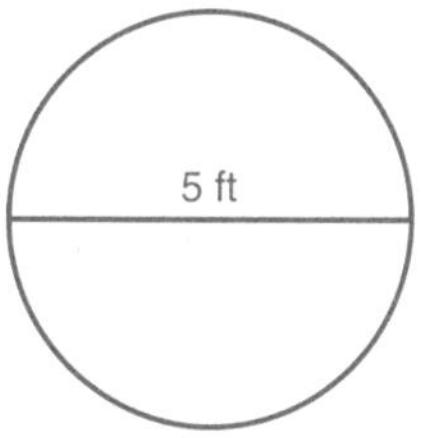

19.625 ft²

13.
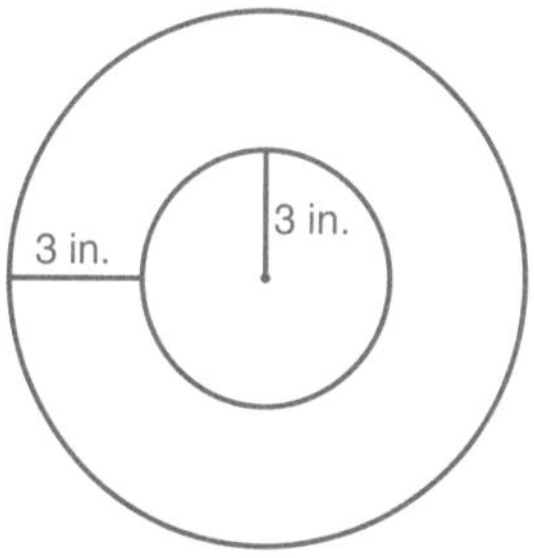

113.04 in.²

14.
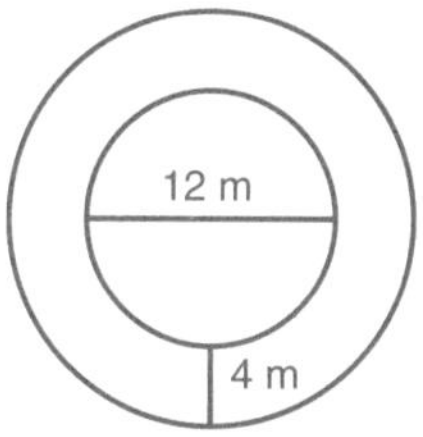

314 m²

Use a calculator to find these areas.

15. $d = 7.02$ m
    38.6851 m²
16. $r = 0.015$ m
    0.0007065 m²
17. $d = 0.529$ cm
    0.2197 cm²
18. $d = 4.12$ m
    13.32 m²
19. $d = 426$ km
    142458.66 km²
20. $r = 42.8$ m
    5751.9776 m²
21. $d = 96$ m
    7234.56 m²
22. $d = 6.054$ m
    28.77097 m²

23. How many times larger is the area of a circle with a diameter of 20 cm than one with a diameter of 5 cm?
    $A=\pi(10)^2$; $A=\pi(2.5)^2$; $(10)^2 \div (2.5)^2$
    16 times
24. The radius of an ice-skating rink is 75 meters. How many square meters of ice surface will it take to cover it?
    $A=\pi(75)^2$
    17662.5 m²
25. A semicircle has a diameter of 8.7 m. What is its area?
    $A=\frac{1}{2}\pi(4.35)^2$
    29.7083 m²

*Use with Lesson 11-6, text pages 314–315.

Copyright © Sadlier-Oxford

Area: Irregular Figures*

Name ______________________

Date ______________________

Find the area of each figure.

1. $A = \ell \times w$; $A = \pi r^2$

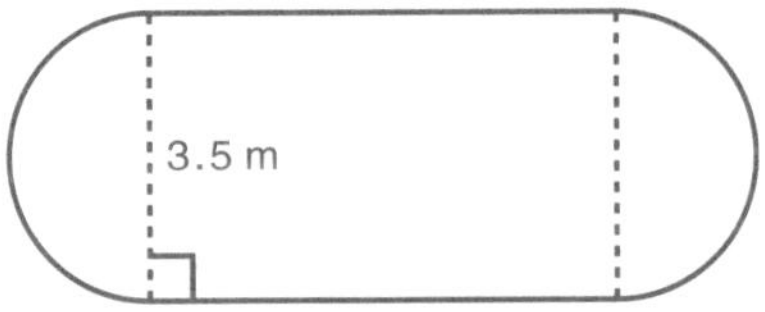

$A \approx$ 27.125 m^2

2. $A = \pi r^2$

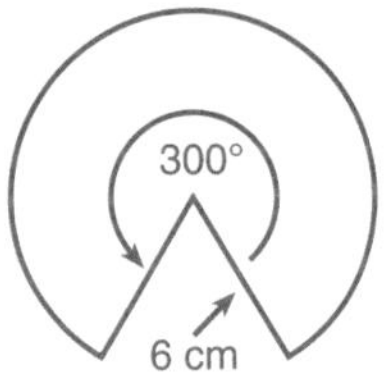

$A \approx$ 94.2 cm^2

3. $A = \pi r^2$

$A = \frac{1}{2}(b_1 + b_2)h$

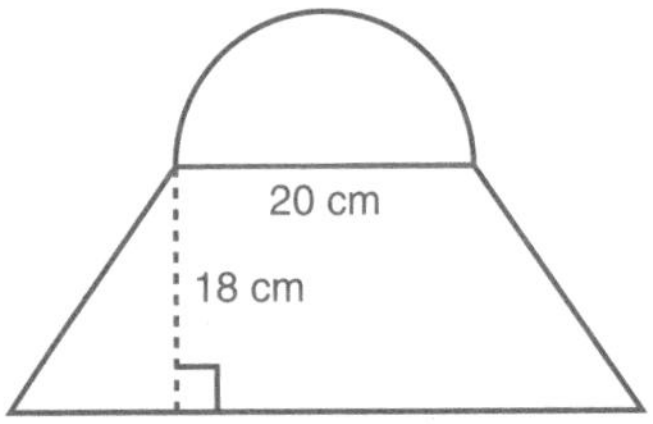

$A \approx$ 625 cm^2

Find the area of the *shaded region* of each figure.

4. $A = \frac{1}{2}(b_1 + b_2)h$

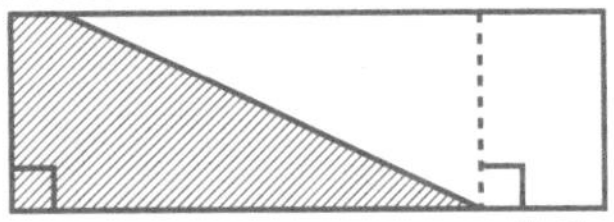

$A =$ 22.55 cm^2

5. $A = \pi r^2$

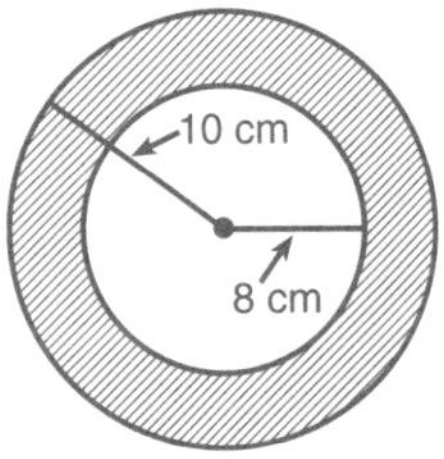

$A \approx$ 113.04 cm^2

6. $A = \ell \times w$; $A = \frac{1}{2}bh$

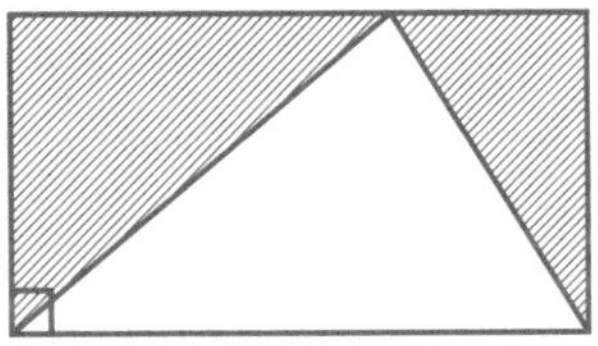

$A =$ 216 cm^2

7. $A = \pi r^2$; $A = s^2$

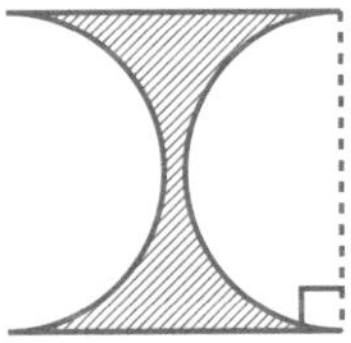

$A \approx$ 17.415 cm^2

8. $A = \frac{1}{2}(b_1 + b_2)h$; $A = \frac{1}{2}bh$

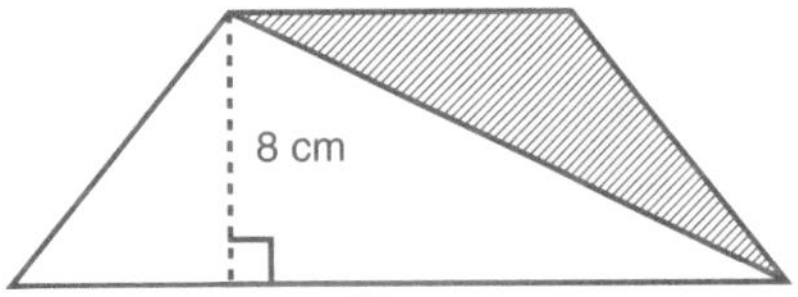

$A =$ 48 cm^2

9. $A = \pi r^2$

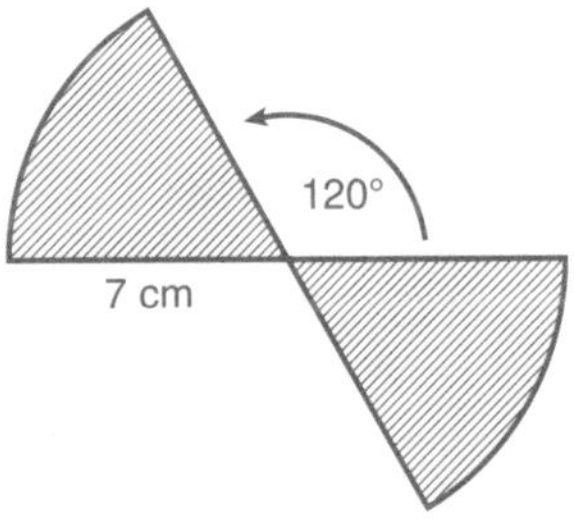

$A \approx$ $51.\overline{3}$ cm^2

*Use with Lesson 11-7, text pages 316–317.

Copyright © Sadlier-Oxford

Missing Dimensions*

Name ______________________

Date ______________________

Find the missing dimension.

1. Rectangle: $A = 229.2\ m^2$
   length: 19.1 m
   width: 12 m

2. Triangle: $A = 1024\ yd^2$
   height: 20 yd
   base: 102.4 yd

3. Square: $A = 2.25\ ft^2$
   side: 1.5 ft

Complete each of the following charts.

Rectangle

	length	width	Area
4.	78 cm	53 cm	$4134\ cm^2$
5.	0.9 m	0.72 m	$0.648\ m^2$
6.	$4\frac{1}{2}$ ft	$\frac{2}{3}$ ft	$3\ ft^2$
7.	$6\frac{3}{4}$ ft	$1\frac{1}{3}$ ft	$1\ yd^2$
8.	500 m	20 m	1 ha

Parallelogram

	length	width	Area
9.	9.1 cm	8 cm	$72.8\ cm^2$
10.	78 cm	63 cm	$4914\ cm^2$
11.	$4\frac{1}{2}$ yd	$6\frac{1}{3}$ yd	$28\frac{1}{2}\ yd^2$
12.	8.5 ft	12 ft	$102\ ft^2$
13.	500 m	300 m	15 ha

Square

	side	Area
14.	1.3 m	$1.69\ m^2$
15.	18 ft	$324\ ft^2$
16.	1.7 ft	$2.89\ ft^2$
17.	14 yd	$196\ yd^2$
18.	50 m	$2500 m^2$

Triangle

	base	height	Area
19.	13 cm	18.6 cm	$120.9\ cm^2$
20.	24 m	5.2 m	$62.4\ m^2$
21.	$8\frac{1}{3}$ ft	2 ft	$8\frac{1}{3}\ ft^2$
22.	12 ft	24 ft	$16\ yd^2$
23.	2.4 yd	3 yd	$3.6\ yd^2$

Solve.

24. One rectangular section of a farm covers an area of 3 hectares. If the length of this section is 250 m, what is its width?
$w = (3 \times 10\,000) \div 250$
120 m

25. The area of a triangular stained glass window is $0.315\ m^2$. The base of the window measures 0.7 m. What is its height?
$h = 2(0.315) \div 0.7$
0.9 m

26. A lamp with a circular base 14 cm in diameter was on a square mat with an area of $196\ cm^2$. How many cm^2 of the mat were uncovered?
$A = \pi(7)^2;\ 196 - 154$
$42\ cm^2$

*Use with Lesson 11-9, text pages 320–321.

Copyright © Sadlier-Oxford

Repeating Decimals As Fractions*

Name ______________________

Date ______________________

Change each to the fractional form.

1. $71 = \frac{71}{1}$
2. $^-0.9 = \frac{-9}{10}$
3. $2\frac{4}{5} = \frac{14}{5}$
4. $^-1.7 = \frac{-17}{10}$
5. $^-314 = \frac{-314}{1}$
6. $0.08 = \frac{8}{100}$ or $\frac{2}{25}$
7. $3.06 = \frac{306}{100}$ or $\frac{153}{50}$
8. $0.003 = \frac{3}{1000}$

Complete.

9.
$x = 0.\overline{63}$
$100x = 0.\overline{63} \times$ 100
$100x = 63.\overline{63}$
$-x = 0.\overline{63}$
$99x = 63.00$
$x = \frac{63}{99} = \frac{7}{11}$

10.
$x = 0.08\overline{3}$
$100x = 8.\overline{3}$
$1000x = 83.\overline{3}$
$-100x = 8.\overline{3}$
$900x = 75.0$
$x = \frac{75}{900} = \frac{1}{12}$

Change each to a fraction.

11. $0.\overline{16} = \frac{16}{99}$
12. $0.\overline{09} = \frac{1}{11}$
13. $0.\overline{1} = \frac{1}{9}$
14. $0.\overline{25} = \frac{25}{99}$
15. $0.8\overline{7} = \frac{79}{90}$
16. $0.1\overline{6} = \frac{1}{6}$
17. $0.8\overline{3} = \frac{5}{6}$
18. $0.\overline{81} = \frac{9}{11}$
19. $0.\overline{7} = \frac{7}{9}$
20. $0.\overline{18} = \frac{2}{11}$
21. $0.41\overline{6} = \frac{5}{12}$
22. $0.\overline{26} = \frac{26}{99}$

*Use with Lesson 12-1, text pages 332–333.

Copyright © Sadlier-Oxford

Squares, Square Roots, Irrational Numbers*

Name ______________________

Date ______________________

Find the square.

1. 0.5 0.25
2. 0.7 0.49
3. 0.06 0.0036
4. $\frac{1}{4}$ $\frac{1}{16}$
5. $\frac{2}{7}$ $\frac{4}{49}$
6. $\frac{4}{5}$ $\frac{16}{25}$
7. 0.9 0.81
8. 0.04 0.0016
9. $\frac{6}{7}$ $\frac{36}{49}$
10. $\frac{3}{4}$ $\frac{9}{16}$
11. 0.8 0.64
12. 0.02 0.0004
13. 0.09 0.0081
14. $\frac{5}{6}$ $\frac{25}{36}$
15. $\frac{2}{9}$ $\frac{4}{81}$
16. $\frac{5}{8}$ $\frac{25}{64}$
17. 0.07 0.0049
18. $\frac{1}{8}$ $\frac{1}{64}$
19. 0.05 0.0025
20. $\frac{3}{5}$ $\frac{9}{25}$

This table shows the squares of whole numbers from 1–20.
Use it to find each square root below.

Number	1	2	3	4	5	6	7	8	9	10	11	12	13	14	15	16	17	18	19	20
Square	1	4	9	16	25	36	49	64	81	100	121	144	169	196	225	256	289	324	361	400

21. $\sqrt{\frac{49}{144}} =$ $\frac{7}{12}$
22. $\sqrt{\frac{16}{225}} =$ $\frac{4}{15}$
23. $\sqrt{\frac{81}{256}} =$ $\frac{9}{16}$
24. $\sqrt{\frac{169}{400}} =$ $\frac{13}{20}$
25. $\sqrt{3.61} =$ 1.9
26. $\sqrt{0.36} =$ 0.6
27. $\sqrt{2.89} =$ 1.7
28. $\sqrt{1.69} =$ 1.3
29. $\sqrt{2.25} =$ 1.5
30. $\sqrt{\frac{49}{324}} =$ $\frac{7}{18}$
31. $\sqrt{\frac{25}{121}} =$ $\frac{5}{11}$
32. $\sqrt{1.96} =$ 1.4

Between which two whole numbers would the square root be?

33. $\sqrt{7}$ 2 and 3
34. $\sqrt{12}$ 3 and 4
35. $\sqrt{23}$ 4 and 5
36. $\sqrt{35}$ 5 and 6
37. $\sqrt{142}$ 11 and 12
38. $\sqrt{66}$ 8 and 9
39. $\sqrt{300}$ 17 and 18
40. $\sqrt{72}$ 8 and 9
41. $\sqrt{120}$ 10 and 11
42. $\sqrt{250}$ 15 and 16
43. $\sqrt{350}$ 18 and 19
44. $\sqrt{5}$ 2 and 3
45. $\sqrt{69}$ 8 and 9
46. $\sqrt{299}$ 17 and 18
47. $\sqrt{170}$ 13 and 14
48. $\sqrt{150}$ 12 and 13
49. $\sqrt{168}$ 12 and 13
50. $\sqrt{380.6}$ 19 and 20

*Use with Lesson 12-2, text pages 334–335.

Copyright © Sadlier-Oxford

Square-Root Algorithm*

Name ______________________

Date ______________________

Complete to find the square root.

1. $\sqrt{6'05'16.}$ = 2 4 6

2	−4
	2 05
44	−1 76
	29 16
486	−29 16

2. $\sqrt{21'90'24.}$ = 4 6 8

4	−16
	5 90
86	−5 16
	74 24
928	−74 24

3. $\sqrt{6'05.16'}$ = 2 4.6

2	−4
	2 05
44	−1 76
	29 16
486	−29 16

Find the square root of each of the following.

4. $\sqrt{3025}$ = 55

5. $\sqrt{2304}$ = 48

6. $\sqrt{8281}$ = 91

7. $\sqrt{6889}$ = 83

8. $\sqrt{11,664}$ = 108

9. $\sqrt{55,225}$ = 235

10. $\sqrt{66,049}$ = 257

11. $\sqrt{90,601}$ = 301

12. $\sqrt{0.0784}$ = 0.28

13. $\sqrt{36.4816}$ = 6.04

14. $\sqrt{800.89}$ = 28.3

15. $\sqrt{0.4761}$ = 0.69

16. $\sqrt{9350.89}$ = 96.7

17. $\sqrt{1989.16}$ = 44.6

18. $\sqrt{942.49}$ = 30.7

19. $\sqrt{1310.44}$ = 36.2

*Use with Lesson 12-3, text pages 336–337.

Copyright © Sadlier-Oxford

Real Number System*

Name ______________________

Date ______________________

Remember: Every point on a number line can be associated with a real number.

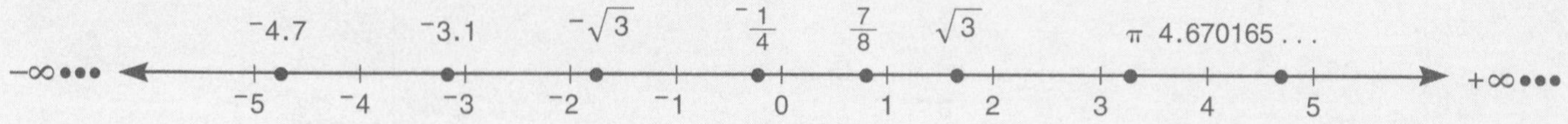

Classify each real number as rational or irrational.

1. 6 rational
2. 0.4321 rational
3. $\sqrt{12}$ irrational
4. $(^+6.3)^2$ rational
5. 0.2 rational
6. $^-0.7\overline{07}$ rational
7. $^-17$ rational
8. $\sqrt{5}$ irrational
9. $2\frac{4}{5}$ rational
10. $(^-0.3)^2$ rational

Solve.

11. If $a^2 = 16$, then $a =$ ± 4
12. If $b^2 = 121$, then $b =$ ± 11
13. If $y^2 = 64$, then $y =$ ± 8
14. If $x^2 = 361$, then $x =$ ± 19
15. If $c^2 = 49$, then $c =$ ± 7
16. If $d^2 = 196$, then $d =$ ± 14

Find the midpoint between each pair of numbers.

17. 0.2 and 0.3 0.25
18. 3.6 and 3.71 3.655
19. $\frac{5}{7}$ and $\frac{6}{7}$ $\frac{11}{14}$
20. $8\frac{1}{2}$ and $8\frac{2}{3}$ $8\frac{7}{12}$
21. 0.008 and 0.009 0.0085
22. $^-0.36$ and $^-0.37$ $^-0.365$

Name two irrational numbers between each pair. Answers may vary.

23. 7 and 8 $\sqrt{50}, \sqrt{63}$
24. 12 and 13 $\sqrt{145}, \sqrt{168}$
25. 5 and 6 $\sqrt{26}, \sqrt{35}$
26. 15 and 16 $\sqrt{226}, \sqrt{255}$
27. 17 and 18 $\sqrt{290}, \sqrt{323}$
28. 19 and 20 $\sqrt{362}, \sqrt{399}$

*Use with Lesson 12-4, text pages 338–339.

Copyright © Sadlier-Oxford

Real Number Solutions for Inequalities*

Name ______________________

Date ______________________

$$r + 7 > 10.5$$
$$r + 7 - 7 > 10.5 - 7$$
$$r > 3.5 \rightarrow \{r{:}r > 3.5\}$$

Write the solution set.

1. $r - {}^{-}11 > 3$
   $\{r{:}r > {}^{-}8\}$

2. $7n + {}^{-}2 > {}^{-}16$
   $\{n{:}n > {}^{-}2\}$

3. $11x - 5 \leq 50$
   $\{x{:}x \leq 5\}$

4. $\frac{a}{8} + 1 \leq 2$
   $\{a{:}a \leq 8\}$

5. $\frac{b}{3} - {}^{-}3 \geq 5$
   $\{b{:}b \geq 6\}$

6. $4a - 7 > 21$
   $\{a{:}a > 7\}$

7. $\frac{x}{4} + {}^{-}5 \leq 7$
   $\{x{:}x \leq 48\}$

8. $6m + 11 \geq 41$
   $\{m{:}m \geq 5\}$

9. $10t + 9 < 69$
   $\{t{:}t < 6\}$

10. $\frac{b}{12} - 3 \leq 2$
    $\{b{:}b \leq 60\}$

11. $\frac{y}{3} \leq {}^{-}19$
    $\{y{:}y \leq {}^{-}57\}$

12. $33x \neq 2508$
    $\{x{:}x \neq 76\}$

13. $12a < 252$
    $\{a{:}a < 21\}$

14. $q + 9 \leq {}^{-}18$
    $\{g{:}g \leq {}^{-}27\}$

15. $k - 4.8 \leq 6.3$
    $\{k{:}k \leq 11.1\}$

16. $1.2b > 4.8$
    $\{b{:}b > 4\}$

17. $a - 7 \neq {}^{-}3$
    $\{a{:}a \neq 4\}$

18. $\frac{y}{3} \leq 2$
    $\{y{:}y \leq 6\}$

19. $\frac{2r}{3} \leq \frac{4}{5}$
    $\{r{:}r \leq 1\frac{1}{5}\}$

20. $\frac{b}{2.7} \geq 0.3$
    $\{b{:}b \geq 0.81\}$

*Use with Lesson 12-5, text pages 340–341.

Copyright © Sadlier-Oxford

The Pythagorean Theorem*

Name ______________________

Date ______________________

Find the missing dimension for each right triangle.

1.

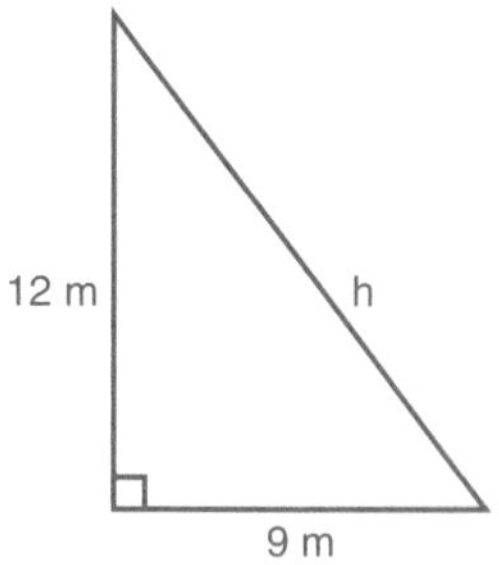

h = 15 m

2.

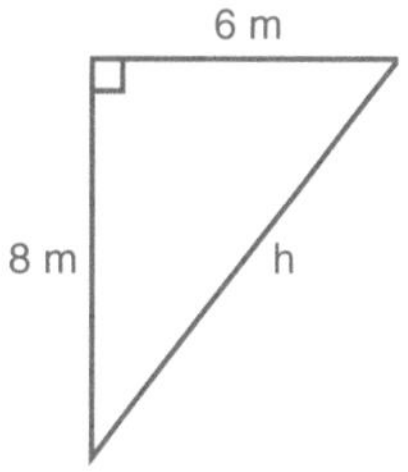

h = 10 m

3.

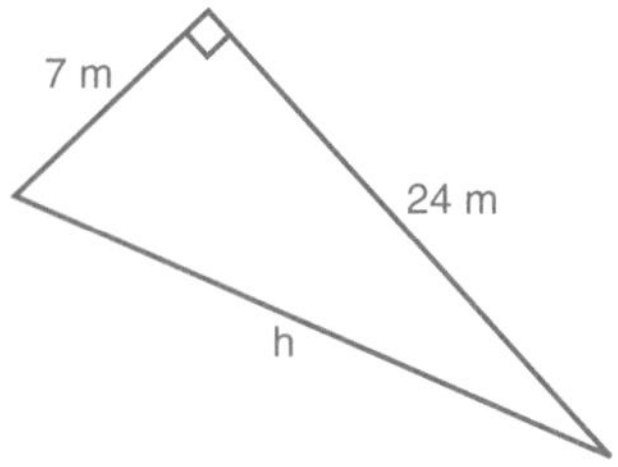

h = 25 m

4.

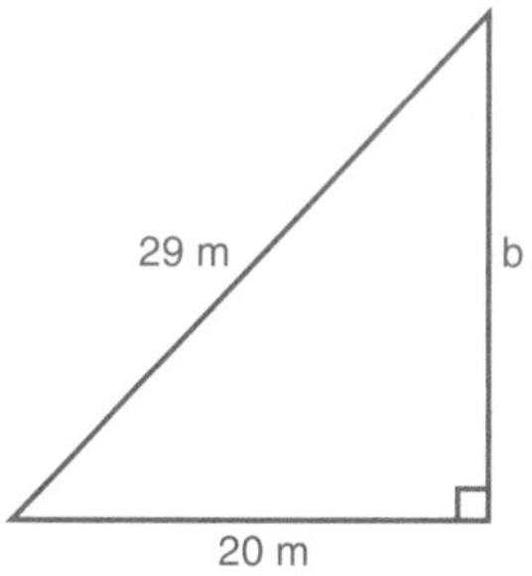

b = 21 m

5.

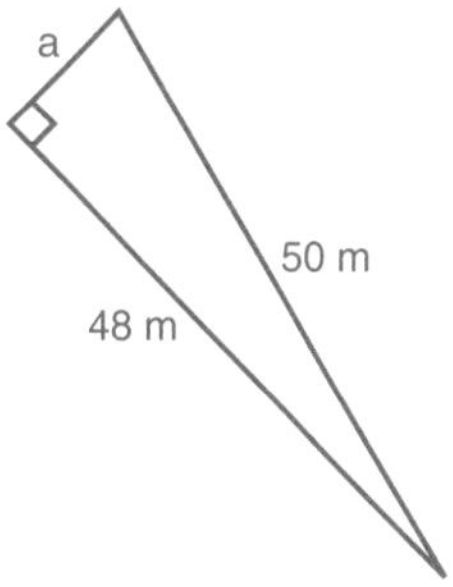

a = 14 m

6.

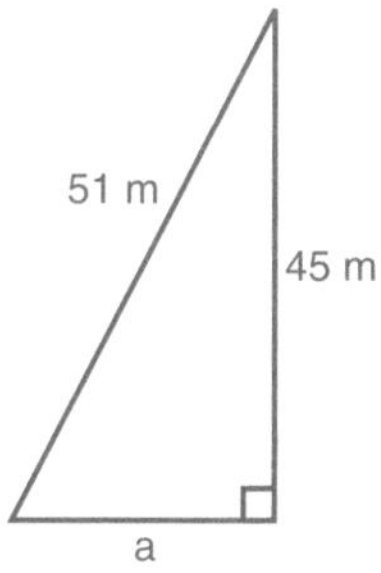

a = 24 m

Complete. Find the missing dimension for each right triangle.

	7.	8.	9.	10.
hypotenuse	105 m	200 cm	250 m	130 m
side a	63 m	120 cm	150 m	78 m
side b	84 m	160 cm	200 m	104 m

Draw a picture and solve. Check students' drawings.

11. A rectangular lot measures 12 m by 16 m. How long is the walk that runs diagonally across it?

$d^2 = 12^2 + 16^2$; 20 m

12. A 17-ft ladder is leaning against a house. The top of the ladder touches the house at a point 15 ft above the ground. How far out from the house is the foot of the ladder.

$17^2 = 15^2 + a^2$; 8 ft

*Use with Lesson 12-6, text pages 342–343.

Copyright © Sadlier-Oxford

Surface Area: Rectangular Prisms and Cubes*

Name ______________________

Date ______________________

Find the surface area of each rectangular prism. $S = 2[(\ell w + (\ell h) + (wh)]$

	length	width	height	Surface Area
1.	10 in.	8 in.	4 in.	304 in.^{2}
2.	14 ft	9 ft	4 ft	436 ft^2
3.	4 m	4 m	5.2 m	115.2 m^2
4.	8 ft	1.6 ft	6 ft	140.8 ft^2
5.	2.4 cm	4 cm	1.2 cm	34.56 cm^2
6.	24 ft	14 ft	8 ft	1280 ft^2
7.	12 cm	20 cm	6 cm	864 cm^2
8.	2.4 m	1.6 m	4 m	39.68 m^2

Find the surface area of a cube with an edge of: $S = 6e^2$

9. 18 in. $S =$ 1944 in.^{2}

10. 9 ft $S =$ 486 ft^2

11. 16 ft $S =$ 1536 ft^2

12. 2.4 cm $S =$ 34.56 m^2

Solve.

13. Find the surface area of an aluminum baking pan 25 cm wide, 32 cm long, and 10 cm deep. $S = 32(25) + 2[(32)(10) + (25)(10)]$; 1940 cm^2

14. Estimate to the nearest tenth the number of square yards of fabric needed to line a suitcase 2 ft long, 1 ft 6 in. wide, and 6 in. deep. $S = 2[2(1\frac{1}{2}) + 2(\frac{1}{2}) + 1\frac{1}{2}(\frac{1}{2})]$; 9.5 ft^2 $\approx$ 1.1 yd^2

15. Find the surface area of a cubical planter measuring 30 in. on a side. (The planter has no lid.) $S = 5(30)^2$; 4500 in.^{2}

16. How many square yards of cedar wood will be needed to line the walls and ceiling of a closet 2 yd long, $1\frac{2}{3}$ yd wide, and $2\frac{1}{2}$ yd high? $S = 2(1\frac{2}{3}) + 2[2(2\frac{1}{2}) + 1\frac{2}{3}(2\frac{1}{2})]$; $21\frac{2}{3}$ yd^2

17. What is the surface area of a utility cabinet 60 cm long, 46 cm wide, and 32 cm high? $S = 2[60(46) + 60(32) + 46(32)]$; 12 304 cm^2

18. A cubical ice-cream freezer is 20 cm on a side. What is its surface area? $S = 6(20)^2$; 2400 cm^2

*Use with Lesson 13-1, text pages 354–355.

Copyright © Sadlier-Oxford

Surface Area: Triangular Prisms*

Name ______________________

Date ______________________

Find the surface area of each triangular prism.

$S = 2\left(\frac{1}{2}bh\right) + (\ell_1 w) + (\ell_2 w) + (\ell_3 w)$

1.

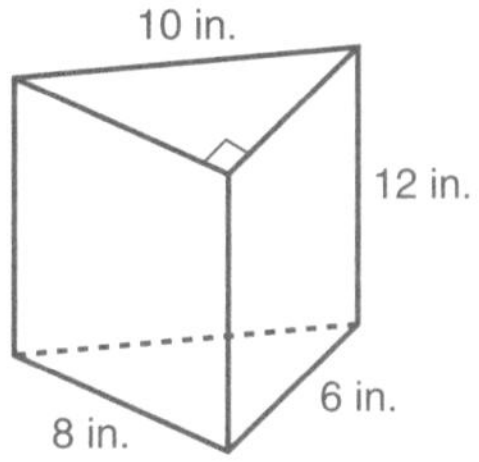

$S =$ 336 in.^{2}

2.

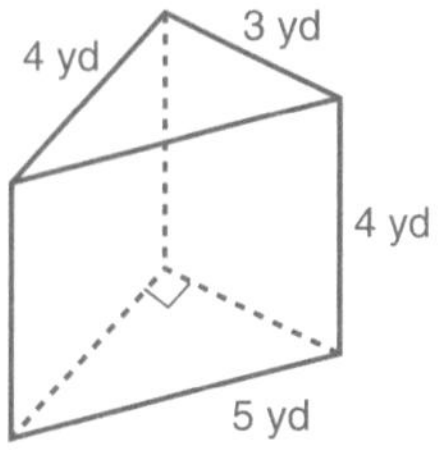

$S =$ 60 yd^2

3.

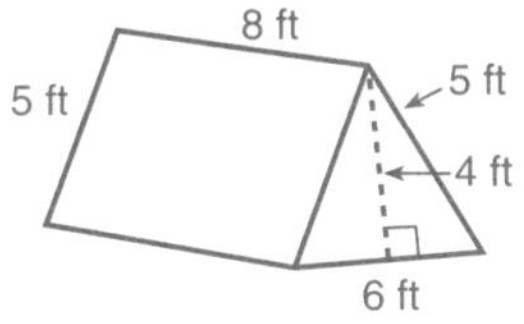

$S =$ 152 ft^2

4.

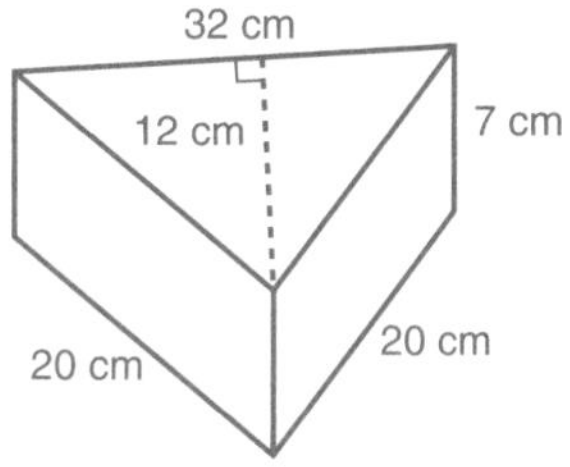

$S =$ 888 cm^2

5.

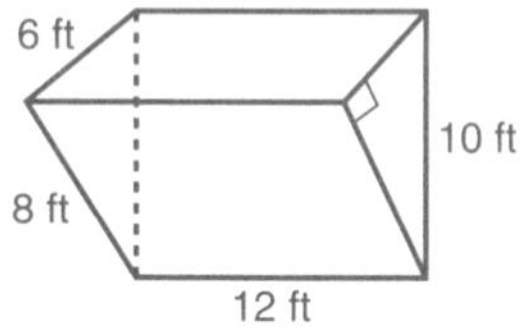

$S =$ 336 ft^2

6.

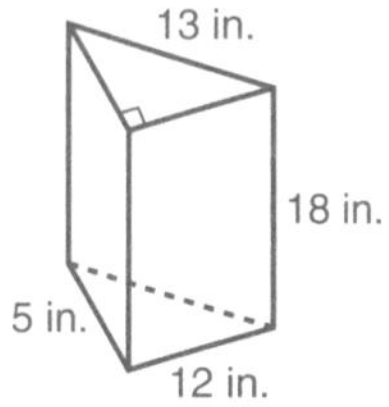

$S =$ 600 in.^{2}

7.

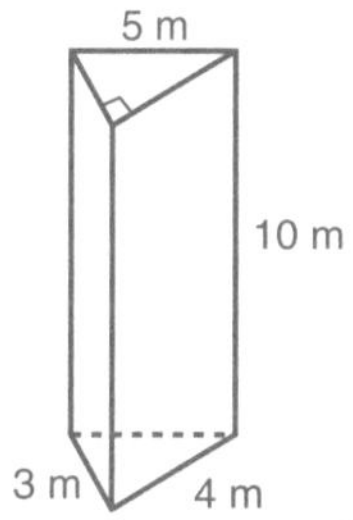

$S =$ 132 m^2

8.

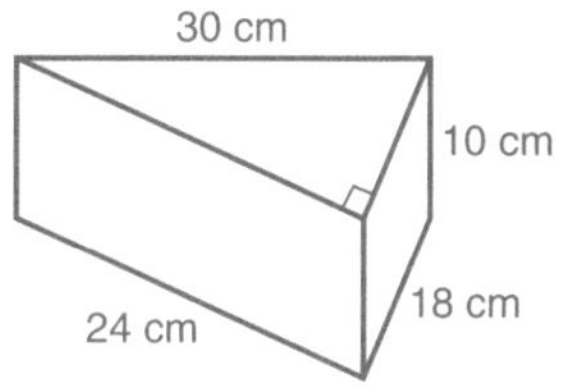

$S =$ 1152 cm^2

Solve.

9. Mr. Grant made a triangular playhouse for his children in one corner of the family room. The triangular base has a height of 1.6 m and a base of 2.1 m. How many square meters of plywood did Mr. Grant use if the playhouse is 1.8 m tall and 2.6 m wide?

$S = 2(\frac{1}{2} \times 2.1 \times 1.6) + (1.6 \times 1.8) + (2.1 \times 1.8) + (2.6 \times 1.8)$

14.7 m^2

10. For a geometry project, the math class made space figures. Three students made right triangular prisms, with the dimensions given here. Who used the most paper?

	Stephanie	Yolanda	Joanna
base	16 cm	20 cm	7 cm
height	12 cm	15 cm	24 cm
length	10 cm	22 cm	28 cm
width	20 cm	25 cm	25 cm

St: $S = 2(\frac{1}{2} \times 16 \times 12) + (16 \times 10) + (12 \times 10) + (20 \times 10)$; 672 cm^2

Y: $S = 2(\frac{1}{2} \times 20 \times 15) + (20 \times 22) + (15 \times 22) + (25 \times 22)$; 1620 cm^2

J: $S = 2(\frac{1}{2} \times 7 \times 24) + (7 \times 28) + (24 \times 28) + (25 \times 28)$; 1736 cm^2

*Use with Lesson 13-1, text pages 354–355.

Copyright © Sadlier-Oxford

Surface Area: Pyramids*

Name ____________________

Date ____________________

Find the surface area of each pyramid.

S = The sum of the areas of all the surfaces

1.

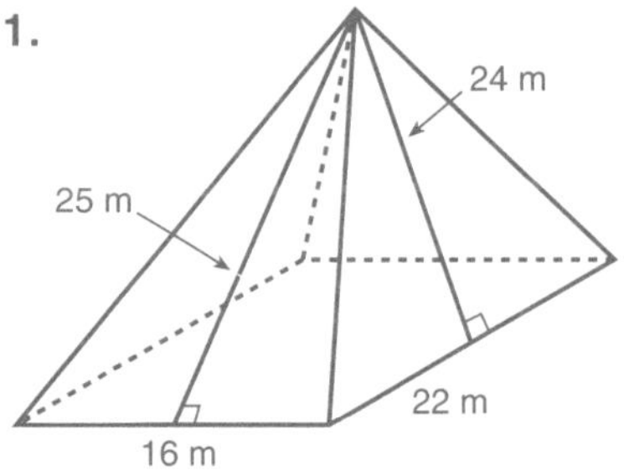

S = 1280 m^2

2.

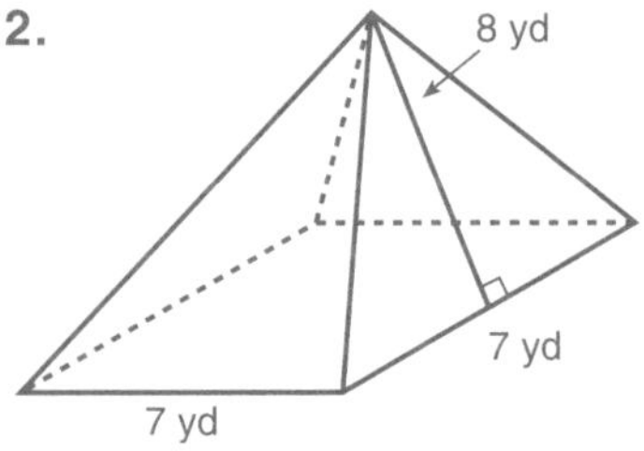

S = 161 yd^2

3. The faces are congruent equilateral triangles.

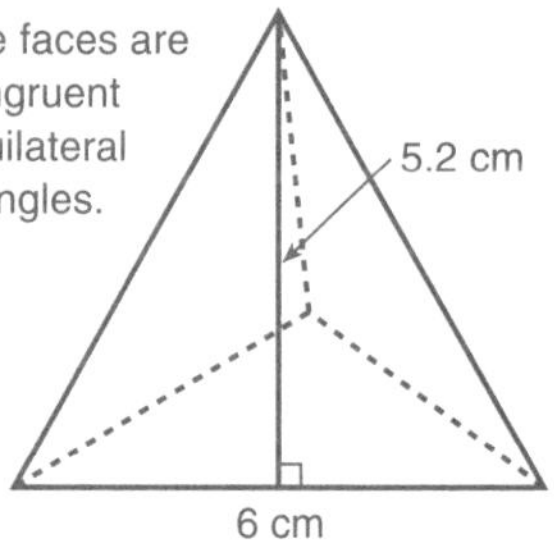

S = 62.4 cm^2

4. The base is a regular hexagon with an area of 10.4 cm^2.

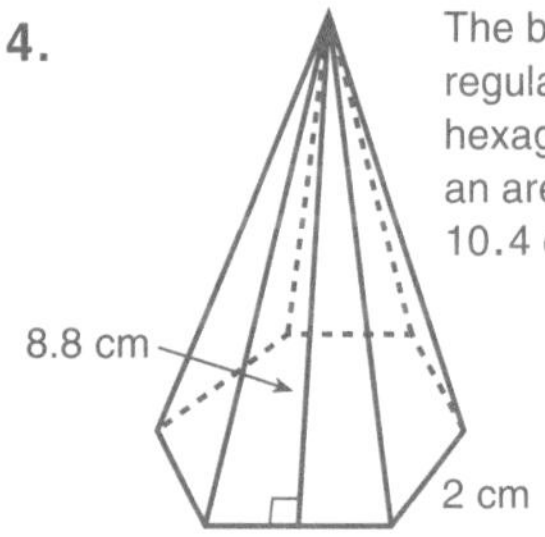

S = 63.2 cm^2

5.

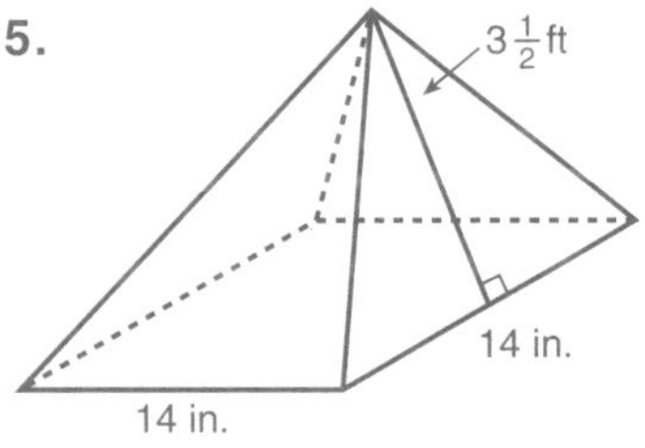

S = 1372 $in.^2$

6. The base is an equilateral triangle.

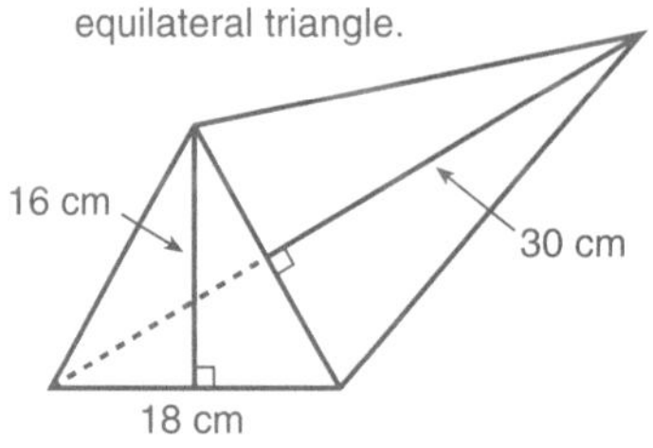

S = 954 cm^2

Solve.

7. How many square centimeters of colored paper did Jane use in constructing a rectangular pyramid with base measurements of 20 cm by 16 cm and triangle heights of 22 cm?

$S = (20 \times 16) + 2\left(\frac{1}{2} \times 16 \times 22\right) + 2\left(\frac{1}{2} \times 20 \times 22\right)$

1112 cm^2

8. Ryan made a clear plastic case shaped like a square pyramid to enclose a prized athletic trophy. Find the surface area of the case if the edge of the base measures 30 cm and the height of each triangle is 25 cm.

$S = (30)^2 + 4\left(\frac{1}{2} \times 30 \times 25\right)$

2400 cm^2

9. Dolores mistakenly ordered sturdy plastic material to make 3 cubes 20 cm on a side. She should have ordered material for 3 square pyramids formed by a square base 20 cm on a side and triangles having heights of 20 cm. How much plastic did Dolores overorder?

cubes: $S = 3[6 \times (20)^2]$; 7200 cm^2

pyramids: $S = 3[(20)^2 + 4(\frac{1}{2} \times 20 \times 20)]$; 3600 cm^2

$7200 - 3600 = 3600$ cm^2

10. Find the surface area of a triangular pyramid if the area of the base is 6.9 m^2, the height of each triangle is 5 m, and each base is 4 m.

$S = 6.9 + 3\left(\frac{1}{2} \times 4 \times 5\right)$

36.9 m^2

Copyright © Sadlier-Oxford

Surface Area: Cylinders*

Name ______________________

Date ______________________

Find the surface area. Use 3.14 or $\frac{22}{7}$ for π.

$S = (2 \times \pi r^2) + (2\pi r \times h)$

1.

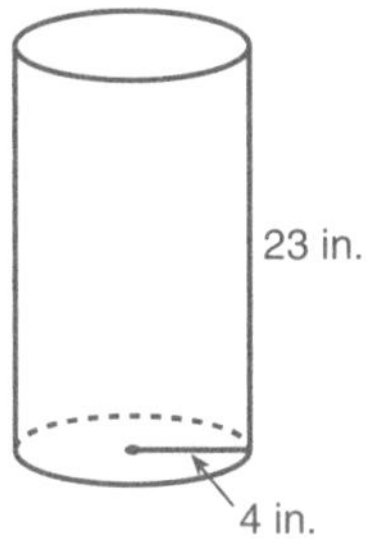

$S \approx$ 678.24 in.^{2}

2.

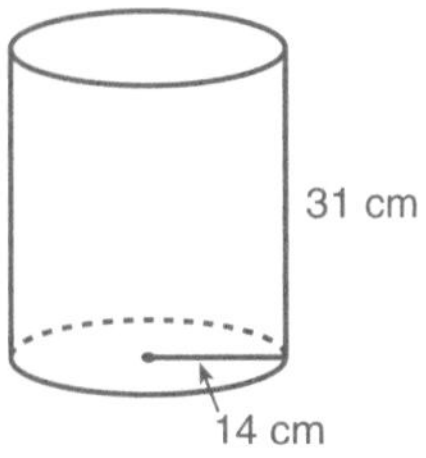

$S \approx$ 3960 cm^2

3.

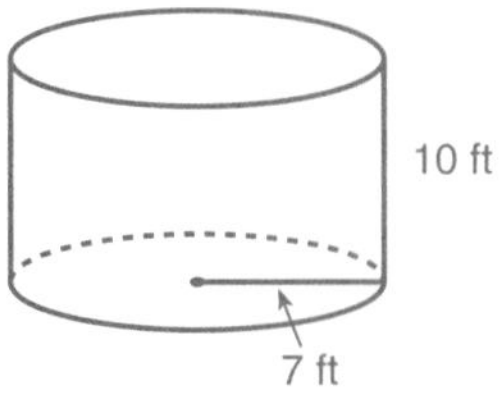

$S \approx$ 748 ft^2

4.

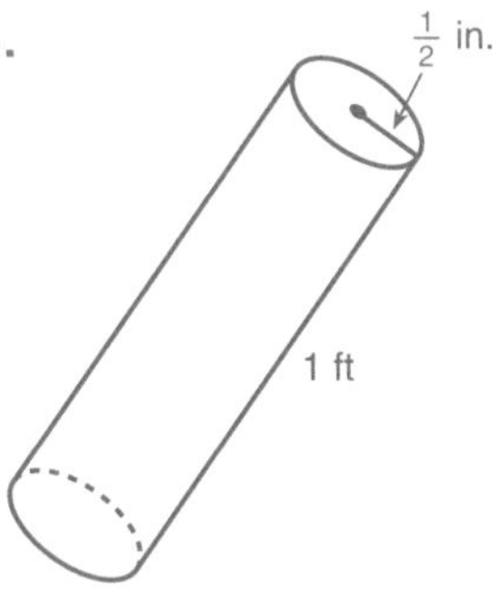

$S \approx$ 39.25 in.^{2}

Complete the table. Use 3.14 or $\frac{22}{7}$ for π as indicated.

	radius	height	π	Surface Area
5.	3 yd	10 yd	3.14	244.92 yd^2
6.	4 ft	9 ft	3.14	326.56 ft^2
7.	7 ft	20 ft	$\frac{22}{7}$	1188 ft^2
8.	6 m	6 m	3.14	452.16 m^2
9.	28 cm	50 cm	$\frac{22}{7}$	13 728 cm^2
10.	40 cm	10.3 cm	3.14	12 635.36 cm^2
11.	5 ft	20 ft	3.14	785 ft^2
12.	$3\frac{1}{2}$ ft	4 ft	$\frac{22}{7}$	165 ft^2
13.	4.2 m	2.6 m	3.14	179.3568 m^2
14.	9 in.	7 ft	3.14	5 256.36 in.^{2}

Solve.

15. Cans made by a local canning company are 6.4 cm in diameter and 12.5 cm high. How much aluminum is needed to make 100 cans?

$S \approx 100[(2\times3.14\times3.2^2)+(2\times3.14\times3.2\times12$

31 550.72 cm^2

16. A basket is shaped like a cylinder. The diameter is 28 cm and the height is 40 cm. Find the surface area to the nearest tenth square meter.

$S \approx (\frac{22}{7}\times14^2)+(2\times\frac{22}{7}\times14\times40)$;

4136 cm^2 $\approx$ 0.4 m^2

*Use with Lesson 13-3, text pages 358–359.

Copyright © Sadlier-Oxford

Surface Area: Cones and Spheres*

Name ______________________

Date ______________________

Find the surface area of each cone. $S = \pi r^2 + \pi r\ell$

1.

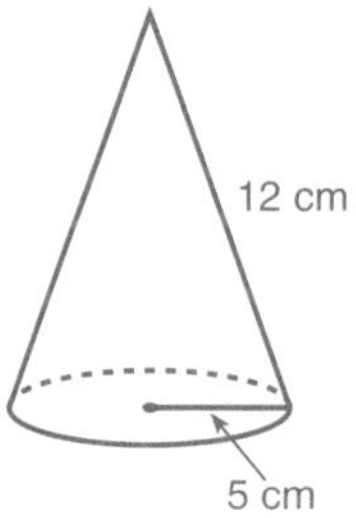

$S \approx$ 266.9 cm^2

2.

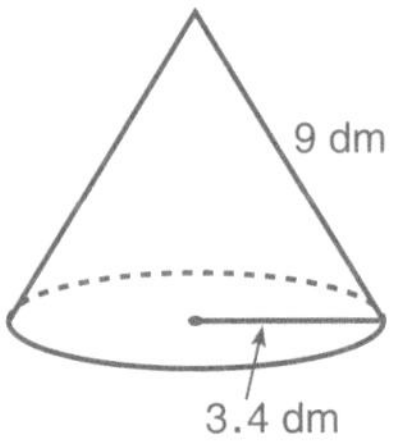

$S \approx$ 132.3824 dm^2

3.

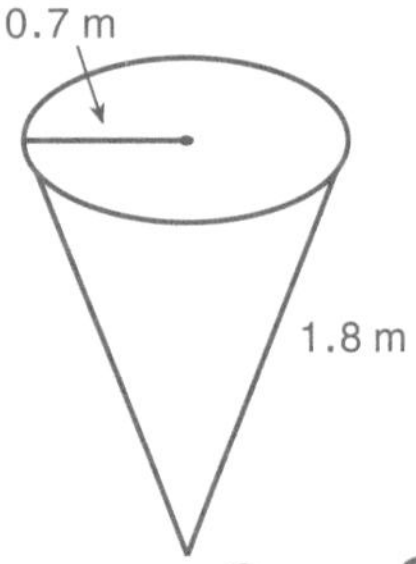

$S \approx$ 5.495 m^2

4.

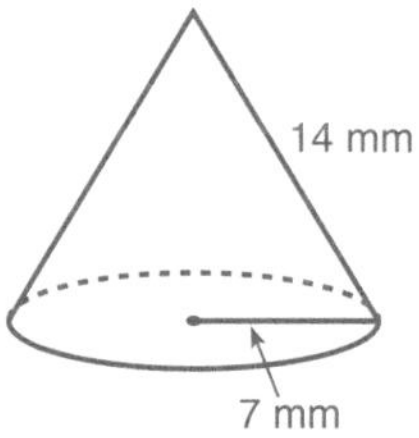

$S \approx$ 462 mm^2

Find the surface area of each sphere. $S = 4\pi r^2$

5.

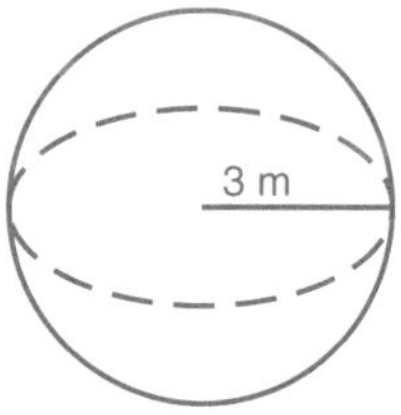

$S \approx$ 113.04 m^2

6.

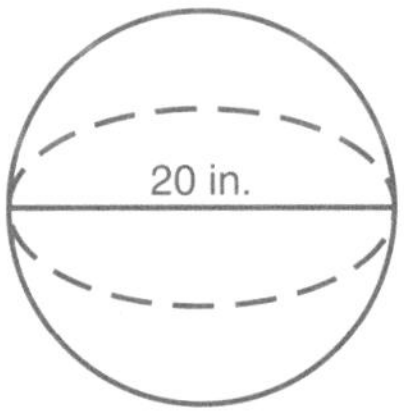

$S \approx$ 1256 $in.^2$

7.

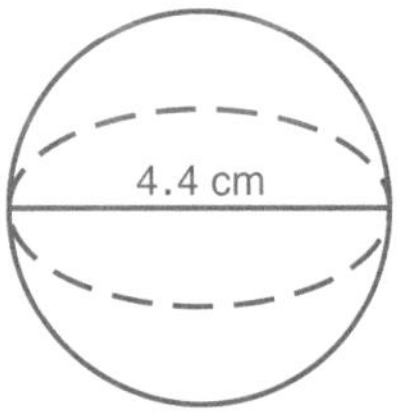

$S \approx$ 60.7904 cm^2

8.

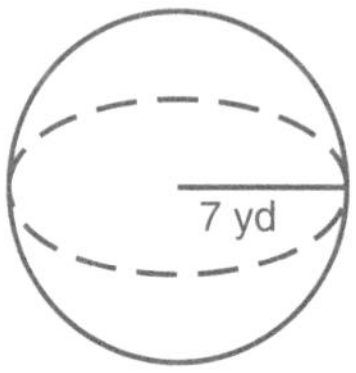

$S \approx$ 616 yd^2

Solve.

9. How much cardboard is needed to make 6 megaphones each of which has a radius of 32 cm and a slant height of 36 cm? (Find the area of the curved surfaces only.)

$S \approx 6(3.14)(32)(36)$; 21 703.68 cm^2

10. Find the surface area of a kickball having an 8-in. diameter.

$S \approx 4(3.14)(4)^2$; 200.96 $in.^2$

11. The entertainment committee made 20 party hats in the shape of cones. Each had a radius of 7 cm and a slant height of 15 cm. Find the total area of the curved surfaces.

$S \approx 20(\frac{22}{7})(7)(15)$; 6600 cm^2

12. Find the surface area of a balloon which, when blown up, has a diameter of 30 cm.

$S \approx 4(3.14)(15)^2$; 2826 cm^2

13. The globe used in social studies class has a diameter of 42 cm. What is its surface area?

$S \approx 4(\frac{22}{7})(21)^2$; 5544 cm^2

14. How much felt was used to make 10 cone-shaped hats each of which has a diameter of 22 cm and slant height of 30 cm?

$S \approx 10(3.14)(11)(30)$; 10 362 cm^2

*Use with Lesson 13-3, text pages 358–359.

Copyright © Sadlier-Oxford

Volume: Cubes*

Name ______________________

Date ______________________

Find the volume of each cube. $V = e^3$

1. 6 ft

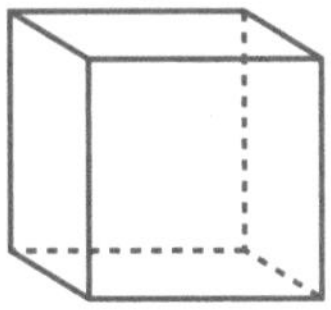

$V =$ 216 ft^3

2. 4 in.

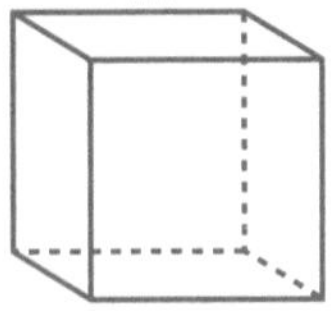

$V =$ 64 $in.^3$

3. 1.2 m

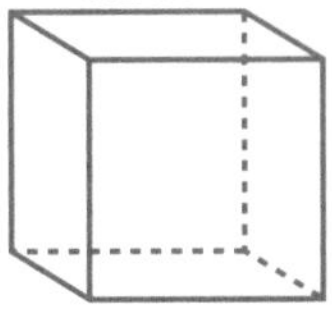

$V =$ 1.728 m^3

4. $1\frac{1}{2}$ ft

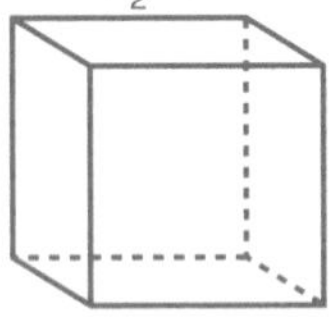

$V =$ $3\frac{3}{8}$ ft^3

Examine the cube below and then answer questions 5–9.

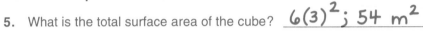

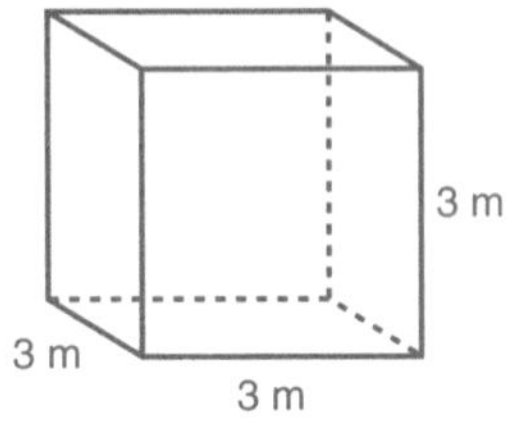

5. What is the total surface area of the cube? $6(3)^2$; 54 m^2

6. What is the volume of the cube? $(3)^3$; 27 m^3

7. If the length of each edge is doubled, what happens to the volume?

$V=(2e)^3$; $8e^3$; volume is 8 times greater

8. How many cubes 1.5 m on an edge would fit inside this cube, which is 3 m on each edge?

$(3)^3 \div (1.5)^3$; 8 cubes

9. Could the contents of this cube fit perfectly into a rectangular box? Would the dimensions of the box be unique?

Yes; no, for example: 9m × 3m × 1m, 6m × 3m × 1.5, etc.

Solve.

10. How many cubic feet are there in a block of marble $2\frac{1}{2}$ feet on each edge?

$V = (2\frac{1}{2})^3$; $15\frac{5}{8}$ ft^3

11. How many cubes 4 cm on an edge can fit into a cubical box 72 cm on an edge?

$V=(72)^3$; $V=(4)^3$; 373 248 ÷ 64; 5832 cubes

12. What is the volume of a swimming pool 11 feet wide, 11 feet long, and 11 feet deep?

$V=(11)^3$; 1331 ft^3

13. A statue is resting on a marble cube 60 cm on an edge. What is the volume of the cube to the nearest cubic meter?

$V=(0.6)^3$; 0.216 m^3; 0 m^3

14. Find the surface area and the volume of a cubical container 6 ft on an edge.

$S=6(6)^2$; 216 ft^2

$V=(6)^3$; 216 ft^3

*Use with Lesson 13-4, text pages 360–361.

Copyright © Sadlier-Oxford

Volume: Rectangular Prisms*

Name ______________________

Date ______________________

Find the volume of each rectangular prism. $V = Bh$

1.

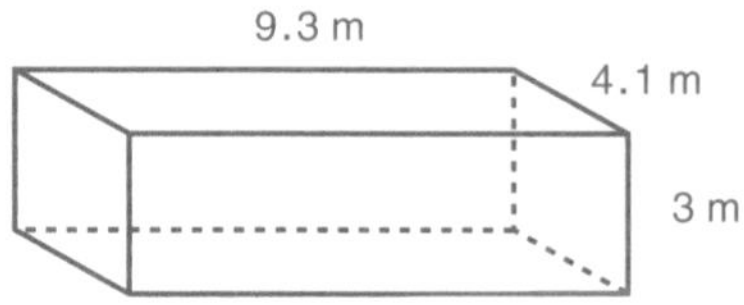

$V = 114.39 \text{ m}^3$

2.

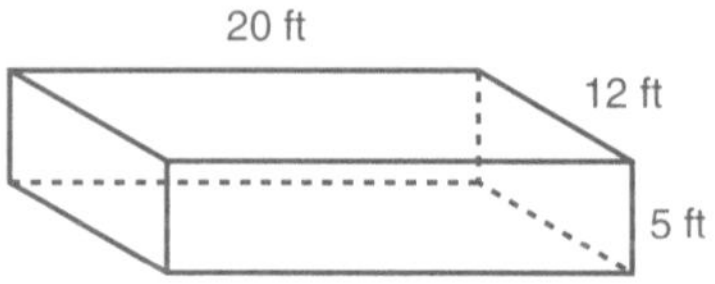

$V = 1200 \text{ ft}^3$

3.

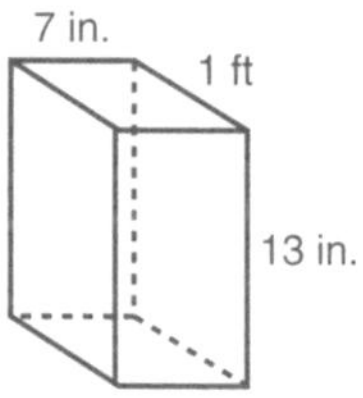

$V = 1092 \text{ in.}^3$

4.

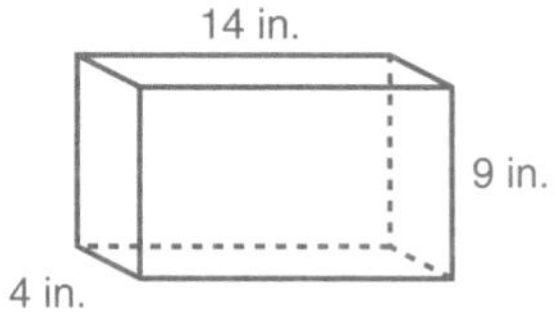

$V = 504 \text{ in}^3$

5.

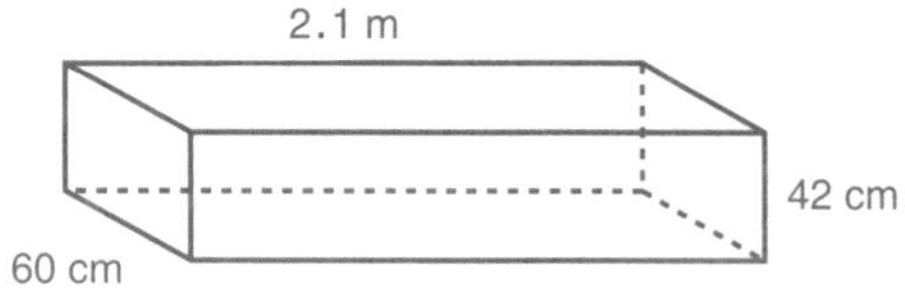

$V = 529\,200 \text{ cm}^3$

Solve.

6. A box is $6\frac{1}{2}$ ft long, $4\frac{1}{4}$ ft wide, and 3 ft high. Find the volume of 7 such boxes.

   $V = 7(6\frac{1}{2})(4\frac{1}{4})(3)$; $580\frac{1}{8} \text{ ft}^3$

7. Find the volume of a rectangular basket 20 cm long, 15.6 cm wide, and 30.4 cm high.

   $V = 20(15.6)(30.4)$; 9484.8 cm^3

8. Find, to the nearest tenth, the number of cubic yards of wood there are in a solid mahogany table top $3\frac{1}{2}$ ft long, 2 ft wide, and 3 in. thick. (Hint: 1 cubic yard occupies 27 cubic feet of space.)

   $V = 3\frac{1}{2}(2)(\frac{1}{4})$; $1\frac{3}{4} \div 27$
   $\frac{7}{108} \text{ yd}^3 \approx 0.1 \text{ yd}^3$

9. What is the volume of a rectangular window box measuring 60 cm long, 24 cm wide, and 20 cm high?

   $V = 60(24)(20)$; $28\,800 \text{ cm}^3$

10. How many cubic yards of air are there in a room 30 yd long, 28 yd wide, and 9 yd high?

    $V = 30(28)(9)$; 7560 yd^3

11. At the produce market a vegetable bin 1.6 m long and 90 cm wide is filled to a depth of 76 cm. Find, to the nearest whole number, how many cubic meters of space are used.

    $V = 1.6(0.9)(0.76)$; $1.0944 \text{ m}^3 \approx 1 \text{ m}^3$

12. A walk-in refrigerator is $6\frac{1}{2}$ ft long, 4 ft wide, and $6\frac{1}{4}$ ft high. About how many cubic yards of space does it occupy?

    $V = 6\frac{1}{2}(4)(6\frac{1}{4})$; $162\frac{1}{2} \div 27$
    $6\frac{1}{54} \text{ yd}^3 \approx 6 \text{ yd}^3$

*Use with Lesson 13-5, text pages 362–363.

Copyright © Sadlier-Oxford

Volume: Triangular Prisms*

Name ____________________

Date ____________________

Find the volume of each triangular prism. $V = Bh; B = \frac{1}{2}bh$

1.

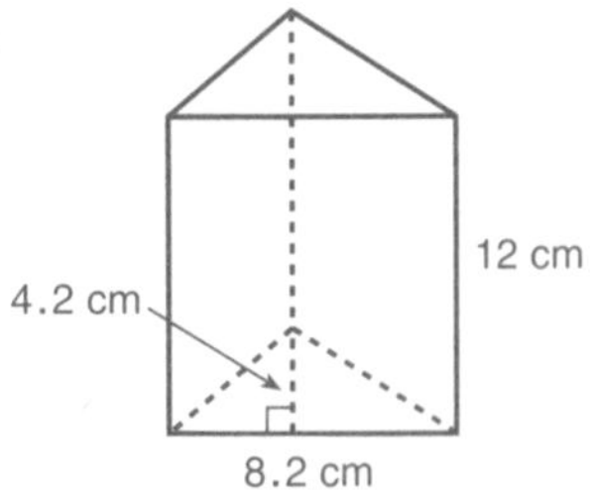

$V =$ 206.64 cm^3

2.

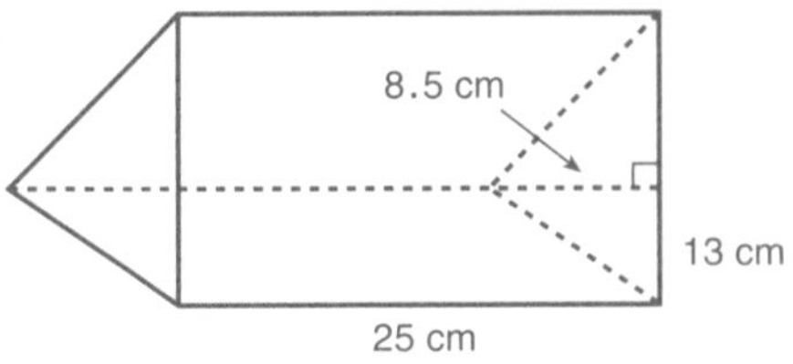

$V =$ 1381.25 cm^3

3.

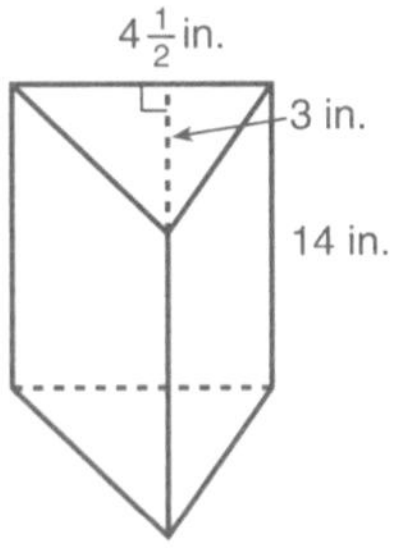

$V =$ 94.5 in.^{3}

4.

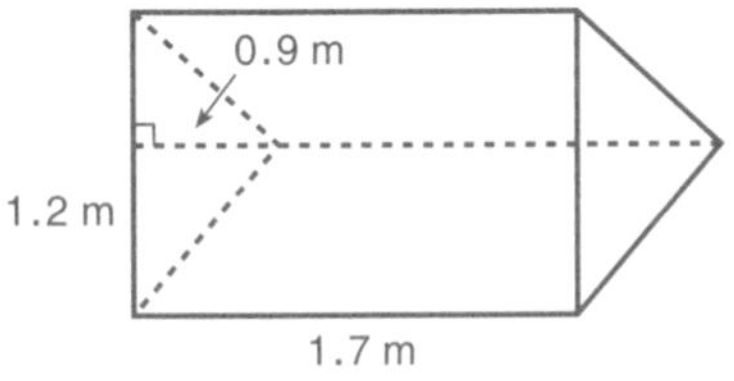

$V =$ 0.918 m^3

5.

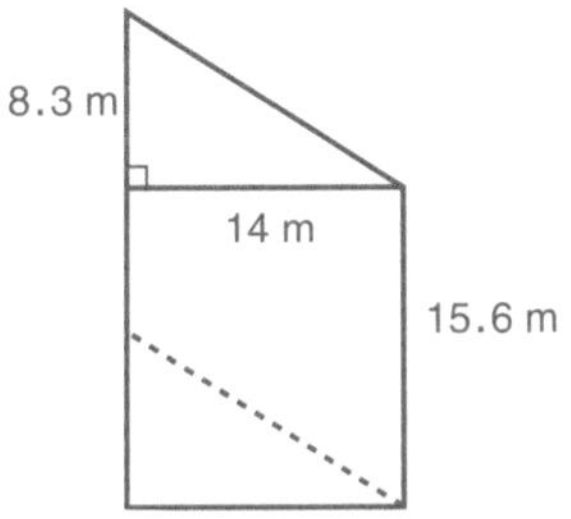

$V =$ 906.36 m^3

6.

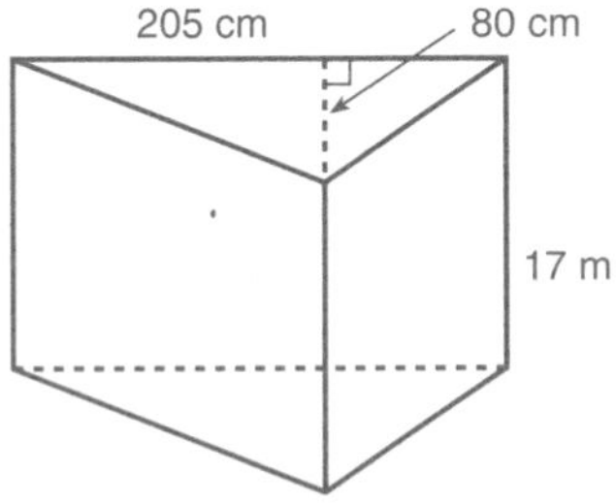

$V =$ 13.94 m^3 or 13 940 000 cm^3

Solve.

7. A porch is supported by 6 columns shaped like triangular prisms. Find the amount of concrete used in making these columns if each is 4 yd high, and the area of its base is 15 square yards.

$V = 6(4)(15)$; 360 yd^3

8. Mr. Ford built a triangular closet in the corner of a room. The floor of the closet is a triangle whose base is 4 ft and whose height is 2 ft. The height of the closet is $6\frac{1}{2}$ ft. How many cubic feet of air will the closet hold?

$B = \frac{1}{2}(4)(2)$; $V = 4(6\frac{1}{2})$; 26 ft^3

9. What is the difference in volume between a rectangular prism whose base measures 3 ft by 4 ft and whose height is 2 ft, and a 3-foot high triangular prism whose base is 6 ft long and 3 ft high?

rect: $V = (3 \times 4)(2)$; 24 ft^3
tri: $V = (\frac{1}{2} \times 6 \times 3)(3)$; 27 ft^3; 3 ft^3

10. Find the volume of the laundry container at the right.

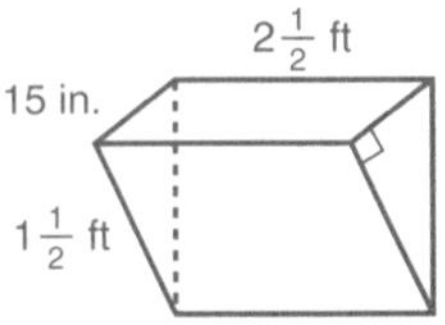

$V = (\frac{1}{2} \times 1\frac{1}{2} \times 1\frac{1}{4})(2\frac{1}{2})$; $2\frac{11}{32}$ ft^3

*Use with Lesson 13-5, text pages 362–363.

Copyright © Sadlier-Oxford

Volume: Pyramids*

Name ______________________

Date ______________________

Find the volume of each pyramid. $V = \frac{1}{3}Bh$

1.

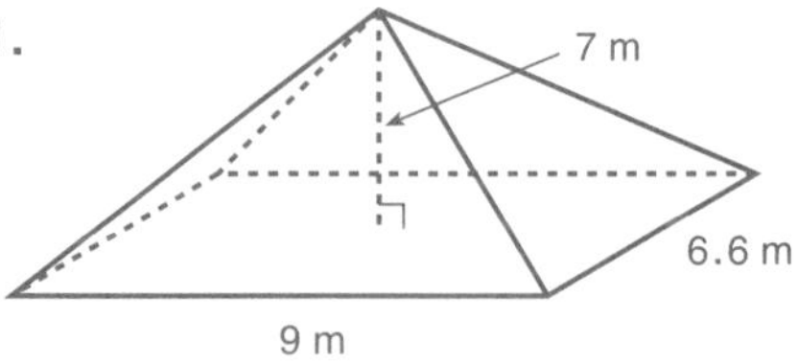

$V =$ 138.6 m^3

2.

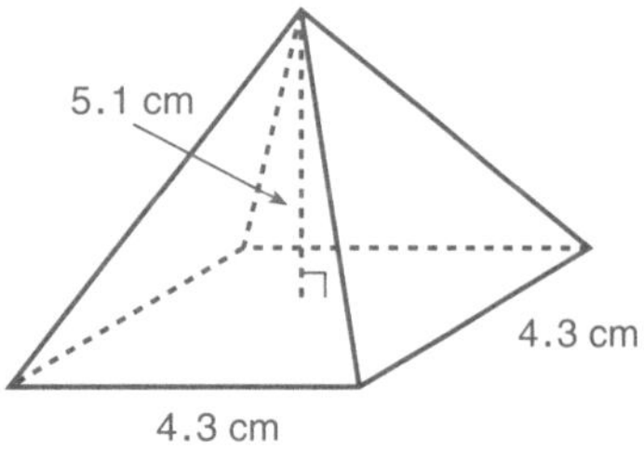

$V =$ 31.433 cm^3

3.

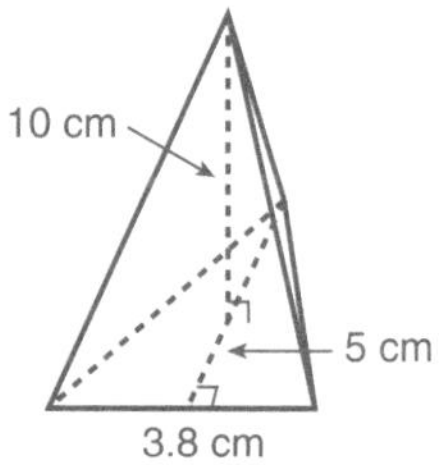

$V = 31\frac{2}{3}$ cm^3

4.

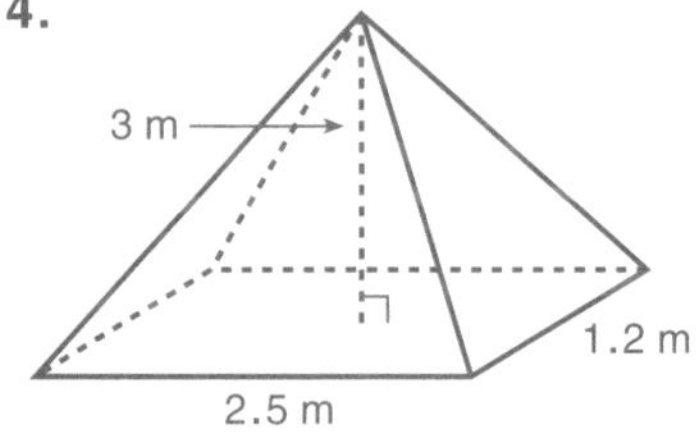

$V =$ 3 m^3

5.

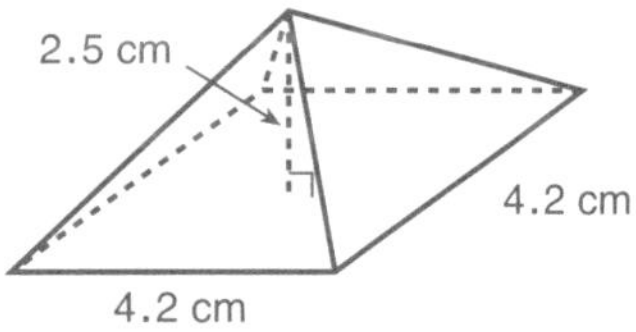

$V =$ 14.7 cm^3

6.

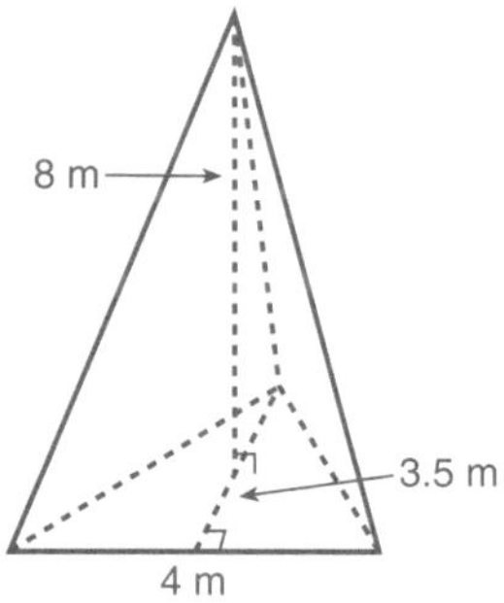

$V = 18\frac{2}{3}$ m^3

Solve.

7. A pyramid has an 8-in. square base. The height of the pyramid is 1 ft. Find the volume.

$V = \frac{1}{3}(8 \times 8)(12)$; 256 $in.^3$

8. How many cubic feet of space are occupied by a pyramid-shaped tent with a 9-ft square base and a height of 8 ft?

$V = \frac{1}{3}(9 \times 9)(8)$; 216 ft^3

9. What is the difference in volume between a square prism with a base measuring 6 cm on an edge and a height of 8.5 cm and a square pyramid with a base measuring 9 cm on an edge and a height of 1 dm?

prism: $V = (6 \times 6)(8.5)$; 306 cm^3
pyramid: $V = \frac{1}{3}(9 \times 9)(10)$; 270 cm^3; 36 cm^3

10. Find the volume of a square pyramid if the edge of the base measures 10 m and the height is 15 m.

$V = \frac{1}{3}(10 \times 10)(15)$; 500 m^3

*Use with Lesson 13-5, text pages 362–363.

Copyright © Sadlier-Oxford

Volume: Cylinders and Cones*

Name ____________________

Date ____________________

Find the volume. Use 3.14 or $\frac{22}{7}$ for π.

Cylinder: $V = \pi r^2 h$

Cone: $V = \frac{1}{3}\pi r^2 h$

1.

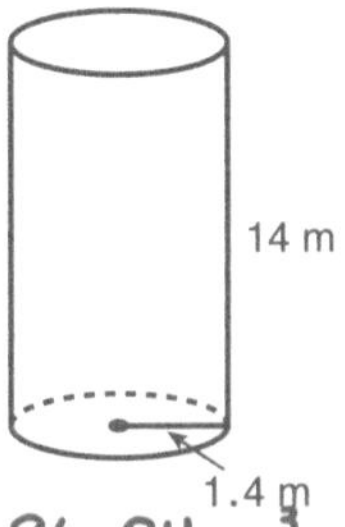

$V \approx$ 86.24 m³

2.

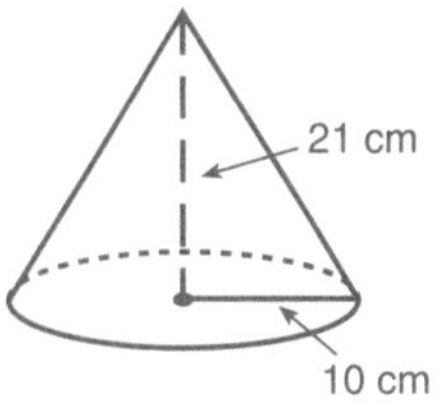

$V \approx$ 2200 cm³

3.

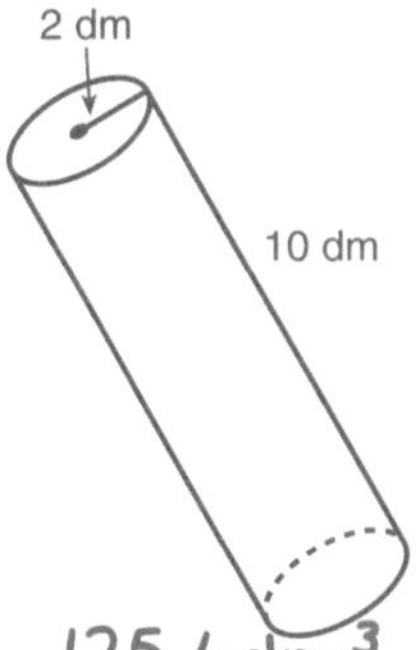

$V \approx$ 125.6 dm³

4.

$V \approx$ 1.59 m³

5.

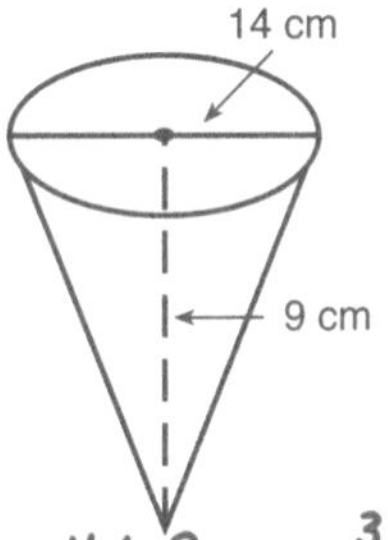

$V \approx$ 462 cm³

6.

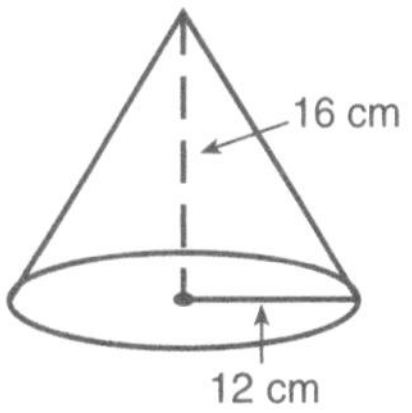

$V \approx$ 2411.52 cm³

7.

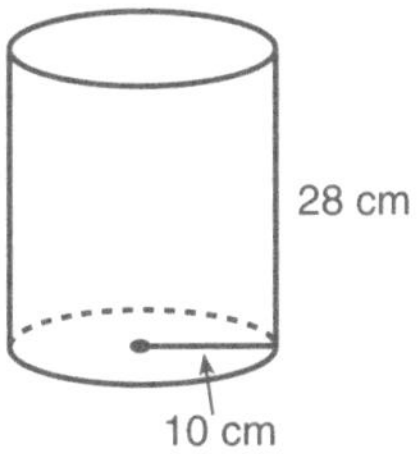

$V \approx$ 8800 cm³

8.

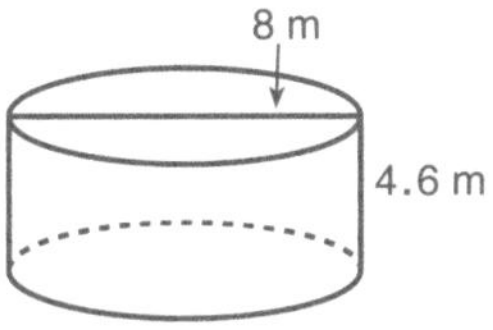

$V \approx$ 231.104 m³

Solve.

9. What is the volume of a can with a diameter of 6 in. and a height of 10 in.?

   $V \approx 3.14(3)^2(10)$; 282.6 in.³

10. How many cubic meters of water will it take to fill a swimming pool that has a radius of 3.5 m and an average depth of 1.5 m?

    $V \approx \frac{22}{7}(3.5)^2(1.5)$; 57.75 m³

11. Estimate the volume of a box of salt that has a radius of 2 in. and a height of $5\frac{1}{2}$ in.

    $V \approx 3.14(2)^2(5\frac{1}{2})$; 69.08 in.³

12. A flower pot has a radius of 8 cm and a depth of 12 cm. How many cubic centimeters of soil will it hold?

    $V \approx 3.14(8)^2(12)$; 2411.52 cm³

13. Round to the nearest cubic centimeter the total volume of 12 cans of tomatoes. Each can has a base whose diameter is 14 cm and a height of 18 cm.

    $V \approx 12\left(\frac{22}{7}\right)(7)^2(18)$; 33 264 cm³

14. How much sand will a conical container hold if its base has a diameter of 5 in. and a height of 1 ft 3 in.?

    $V \approx \frac{1}{3}(3.14)(2.5)^2(15)$; 98.125 in.³

15. Which holds more, a cylindrical container 6 yd in diameter and 10 yd long or a cubical container 6 yd on an edge?

    cylinder: $V \approx 3.14(3^2)(10)$; 282.6 yd³
    cube: $V = (6)^3$; 216 yd³; 66.6 yd³ more

*Use with Lesson 13-6, text pages 364–365.

Copyright © Sadlier-Oxford

Metric Units: Liquid Volume*

Name ______________________

Date ______________________

Check the best unit of measure for each.

	Item	milliliter	liter	kiloliter
1.	glass of ice tea	✓		
2.	bathtub of water		✓	
3.	water in swimming pool			✓
4.	tear drop	✓		
5.	oil in tank of a car		✓	
6.	medicine in eye dropper	✓		

Change each to the unit indicated.

7. 8 dm^3 = 8 L
8. 28 m^3 = 28 kL
9. 70 dm^3 = 70 L
10. 25 cm^3 = 25 mL
11. 6 cm^3 = 6 mL
12. 80 m^3 = 80 kL
13. 45 dm^3 = 45 L
14. 18 dm^3 = 18 L
15. 30 cm^3 = 30 mL
16. 3.4 cm^3 = 0.0034 L
17. 18 dm^3 = 18 000 mL
18. 6280 cm^3 = 6.28 L
19. 3.4 cm^3 = 3.4 mL
20. 376 m^3 = 376 000 L
21. 8756 cm^3 = 8.756 L

Find the volume.

22.

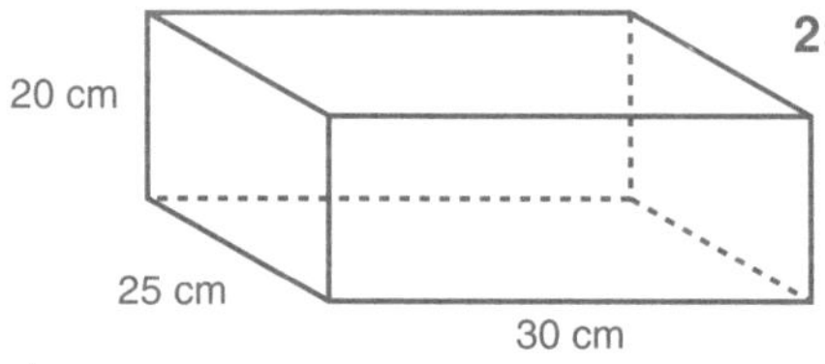

V = 15 000 mL

23.

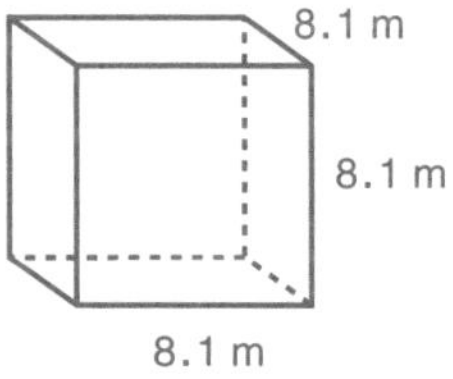

V = 531.441 kL

24.

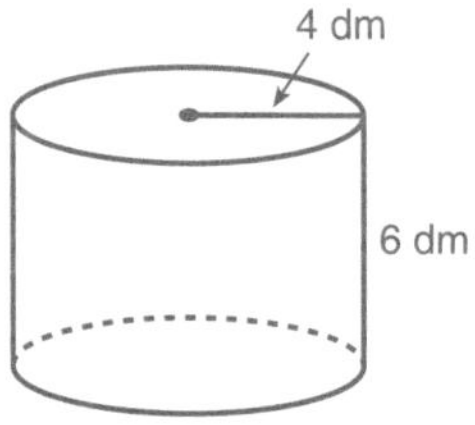

V = 301.44 L

Solve.

25. How many liters of water will a bucket hold if it is 2.8 dm in diameter and 3 dm in height? (Use $\pi = \frac{22}{7}$.)

$V \approx \frac{22}{7}(1.4)^2(3)$; 18.48 dm^3; 18.48 L

26. How many milliliters of water will fill a cone-shaped paper cup that is 9 cm in diameter and 8 cm high?

$V \approx \frac{1}{3}(3.14)(4.5)^2(8)$; 169.56 cm^3; 169.56 mL

27. A water tank is 8 m in diameter and 15 m deep. How many kiloliters will it hold when it is three fourths filled?

$V \approx \frac{3}{4}(3.14)(4)^2(15)$; 565.2 m^3; 565.2 kL

*Use with Lesson 13-7, text pages 366–367.

Copyright © Sadlier-Oxford

Metric Units: Mass*

Name ______________________

Date ______________________

Check the best unit of measure for each.

	Item	grams	milligrams	kilograms	metric tons
1.	box of cereal	✓			
2.	load of coal				✓
3.	your weight			✓	
4.	raisin		✓		
5.	2 cookies	✓			
6.	dime		✓		
7.	candy bar	✓			
8.	basket of apples			✓	

Complete.

9. 6 dm^3 weighs 6 kg

10. 5 cm^3 weighs 5 g

11. 0.006 cm^3 weighs 6 mg

12. 147 dm^3 weighs 147 kg

13. 25 cm^3 weighs 25 g

14. 14 dm^3 weighs 14 kg

15. 135 dm^3 weighs 135 kg

16. 6000 cm^3 weighs 6 kg

17. 2500 kg weighs 2.5 t

18. 1000 cm^3 weighs 1000 g

19. 0.007 cm^3 weighs 7 mg

20. 5000 kg weighs 5 t

Solve.

21. A rectangular tank is 15 cm long, 10 cm wide, and 12 cm deep. How many kg of water will it hold when filled?

$V=(15)(10)(12)$; 1800 cm^3; 1800 g; 1.8 kg

22. What is the weight of a small block of ice 7 cm long, 5.5 cm wide, and 4 cm high?

$V=(7)(5.5)(4)$; 154 cm^3; 154 g

*Use with Lesson 13-8, text pages 368–369.

Copyright © Sadlier-Oxford

Metric Units: Mass* (cont'd)

Name ____________________

Date ____________________

Complete each matching exercise with the most reasonable measure.

23. e mass of a tennis racquet — **a.** 145 g

24. c mass of a golf ball — **b.** 5 kg

25. a mass of a baseball — **c.** 40 g

26. b mass of a bowling ball — **d.** 20 g

27. d mass of a Ping-Pong ball — **e.** 350 g

Complete.

28. 9 g = 9000 mg

29. 5 kg = 5000 g

30. 46 cg = 0.00046 kg

31. 6.8 t = 6800 kg

32. 0.025 cg = 0.00025 g

33. 490 cg = 4.9 g

34. 7.63 g = 7630 mg

35. 2.9 kg = 2900 g

36. 0.48 mg = 0.00048 g

37. 38 g = 3800 cg

38. 470 cg = 4.7 g

39. 890 000 mg = 890 g

40. 11.5 t = 11 500 kg

41. 11 300 kg = 11.3 t

Complete the charts.

	Capacity	Cubic Volume	Mass
42.	2 L	2 dm^3	2 kg
43.	2 mL	2 cm^3	2 g
44.	5 mL	5 cm^3	5 g
45.	1 kL	1 m^3	1000 kg
46.	10 mL	10 cm^3	1 dg

	Capacity	Cubic Volume	Mass
47.	10.5 L	10.5 dm^3	10.5 kg
48.	100 mL	100 cm^3	100 g
49.	35 kL	35 m^3	35 000 kg
50.	8.9 L	8.9 dm^3	8.9 kg
51.	10 L	10 dm^3	10 kg

***Use with Lesson 13-8, text pages 368–369.**

Copyright © Sadlier-Oxford

Graphing on the Real Number Line*

Name ______________________

Date ______________________

Find the solution. Graph it on a real number line.

1. $x + 8 = 5$ $x = {}^-3$

2. $x - 7 = {}^-6$ $x = 1$

3. $x + 6 = 10$ $x = 4$

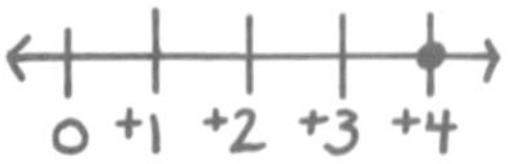

4. $x - 12 = 8$ $x = 20$

5. $6x = {}^-18$ $x = {}^-3$

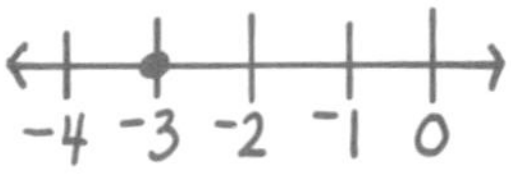

6. $5x = 0$ $x = 0$

Graph the solution on a real number line.

7. $x + 6 \geq 4$ $\{x : x \geq {}^-2\}$

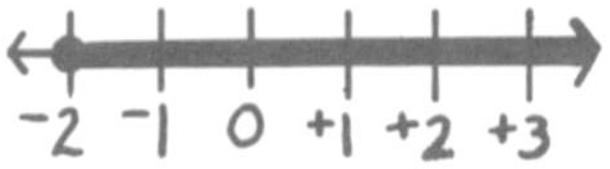

8. $x - 3 \geq 2$ $\{x : x \geq {}^+5\}$

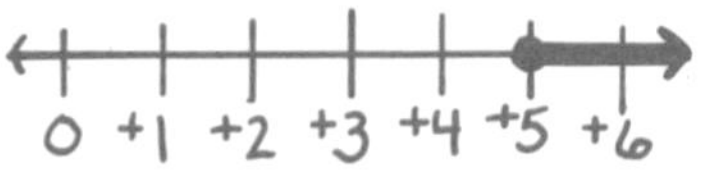

9. $x + 5 \leq 7$ $\{x : x \leq {}^+2\}$

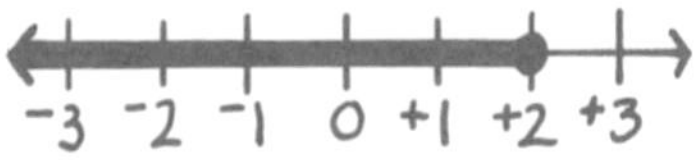

10. $2x - 6 \leq {}^-2$ $\{x : \leq {}^+2\}$

11. $4x > 8$ $\{x : x > {}^+2\}$

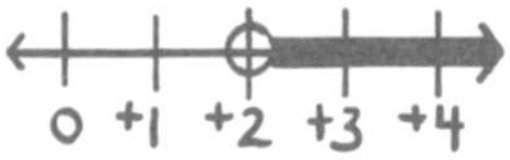

12. ${}^-5x \leq 20$ $\{x : x \geq {}^-4\}$

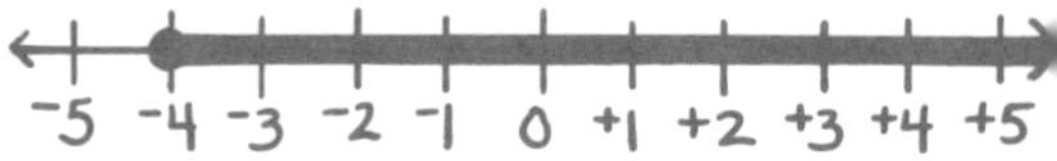

Write an equation or inequality for each graph.

13.

$x \leq {}^+\frac{1}{2}$

14.

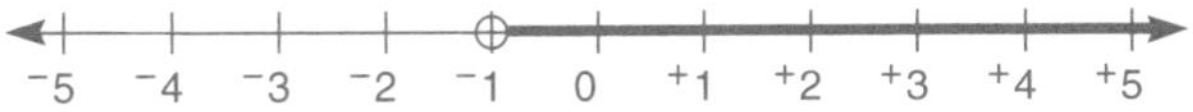

$x > {}^-1$

15.

$x = {}^+2$

16.

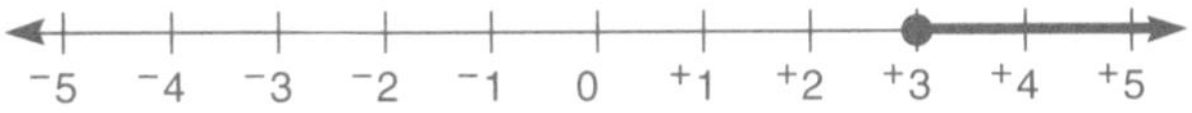

$x \geq {}^+3$

17.

$x > 0$

18.

$x < {}^+2$

19.

${}^-3 \leq x \leq {}^+2$

20.

${}^-4 \leq x < {}^+2$

*Use with Lesson 14-1, text pages 380–381.

Copyright © Sadlier-Oxford

Graphing on the Coordinate Plane* (Four Quadrants)

Name ______________________

Date ______________________

Graph the point for each ordered pair.

1. A (2, 6)
2. B (⁻4, 3)
3. C (⁻5, ⁻2)
4. D (7, ⁻5)
5. E (6, 6)
6. F (0, 0)
7. G (⁻4, ⁻8)
8. H (⁻8, 2)
9. I (6, ⁻1)
10. J (⁻1, 0)
11. K (0, ⁻4)
12. L (2, 0)
13. M (8, ⁻8)
14. N (0, 7)
15. O (2, 4)
16. P (⁻1, ⁻6)
17. Q (3, ⁻2)
18. R (⁻5, 6)
19. S (5, 5)
20. T (⁻5, ⁻5)

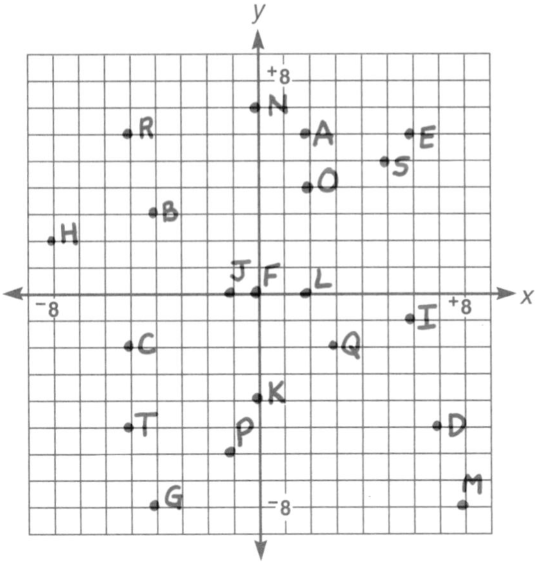

21. Which points are in Quadrant I? A, O, E, S
22. Which points are in Quadrant II? H, B, R
23. Which points are in Quadrant III? C, T, P, G
24. Which points are in Quadrant IV? Q, I, D, M

Draw a pair of coordinate axes. Graph these points.

25. A (⁻6, 2)
26. B ($4\frac{1}{2}$, ⁻2)
27. C (⁻2, ⁻5)
28. D (3, 3)
29. E (1, ⁻4)
30. F (0, 3)

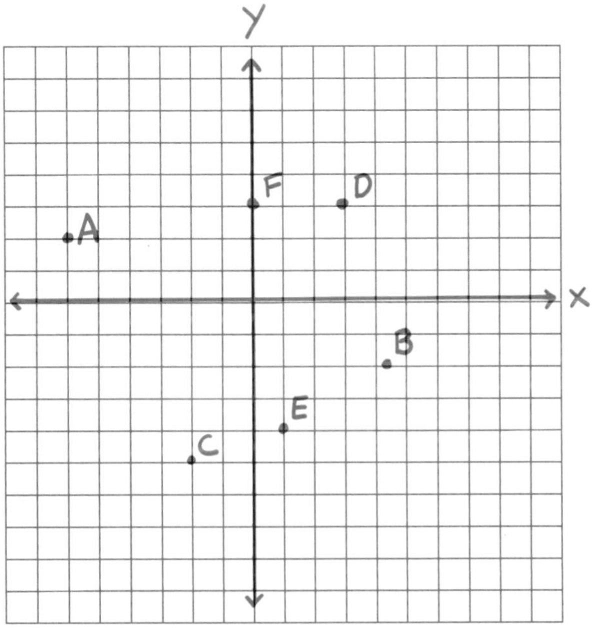

*Use with Lessons 14-2, 14-3, text pages 382–385.

Copyright © Sadlier-Oxford

Equations with Two Variables*

Name ____________________

Date ____________________

Complete each table of values.

1. $y = x + 6$

x	⁻3	⁻2	⁻1	0	1	2	3
y	3	4	5	6	7	8	9

2. $y = x - 3$

x	⁻3	⁻2	⁻1	0	1	2	3
y	⁻6	⁻5	⁻4	⁻3	⁻2	⁻1	0

3. $y - x = 8$

x	⁻3	⁻2	⁻1	0	1	2	3
y	5	6	7	8	9	10	11

4. $y = 2x + 2$

x	⁻3	⁻2	⁻1	0	1	2	3
y	⁻4	⁻2	0	2	4	6	8

5. $y = 3x - 1$

x	⁻3	⁻2	⁻1	0	1	2	3
y	⁻10	⁻7	⁻4	⁻1	2	5	8

6 $y = 4x - 3$

x	⁻3	⁻2	⁻1	0	1	2	3
y	⁻15	⁻11	⁻7	⁻3	1	5	9

Complete each table of values.

	x	$x + 3$	y	ordered pair
7.	⁻2	⁻2 + 3	1	(⁻2, 1)
8.	⁻1	⁻1 + 3	2	(⁻1, 2)
9	0	0 + 3	3	(0, 3)
10.	1	1 + 3	4	(1, 4)
11.	2	2 + 3	5	(2, 5)

	x	$3x$	y	ordered pair
12.	⁻2	3(⁻2)	⁻6	(⁻2, ⁻6)
13.	⁻1	3(⁻1)	⁻3	(⁻1, ⁻3)
14	0	3(0)	0	(0, 0)
15.	1	3(1)	3	(1, 3)
16.	2	3(2)	6	(2, 6)

For each equation, find the *y*-value that completes the ordered pair.

17. $y + x = 10$

(⁻2, 12); (⁻1, 11); (2, 8); (3, 7);

18. $y - 2x = 5$

(⁻2, 1); (⁻1, 3); (0, 5); (1, 7)

19. $x + y = {}^-6$

(⁻1, ⁻5); (0, ⁻6); (1, ⁻7); (2, ⁻8);

20. $x + 5y = 8$

(⁻7, 3); (⁻2, 2); (3, 1); (8, 0)

*Use with Lesson 14-4, text pages 386–387.

Copyright © Sadlier-Oxford

Graphing Equations*

Name ______________________

Date ______________________

Complete each table and graph the equation on the given coordinate grid.

1. $y = x + 3$

x	$^-2$	$^-1$	0	1	2
y	1	2	3	4	5

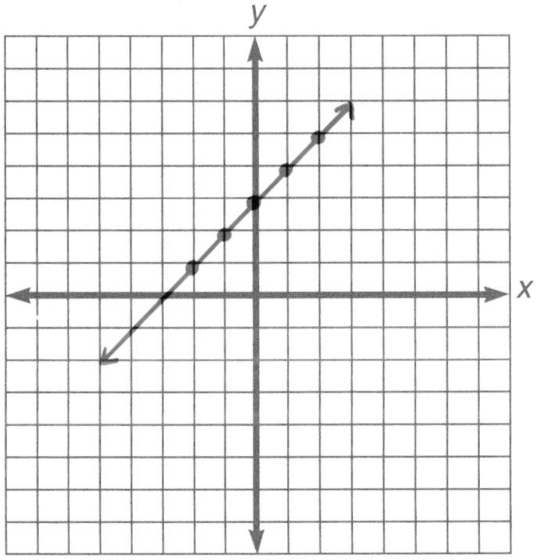

2. $y = 2x - 1$

x	$^-2$	$^-1$	0	1	2
y	$^-5$	$^-3$	$^-1$	1	3

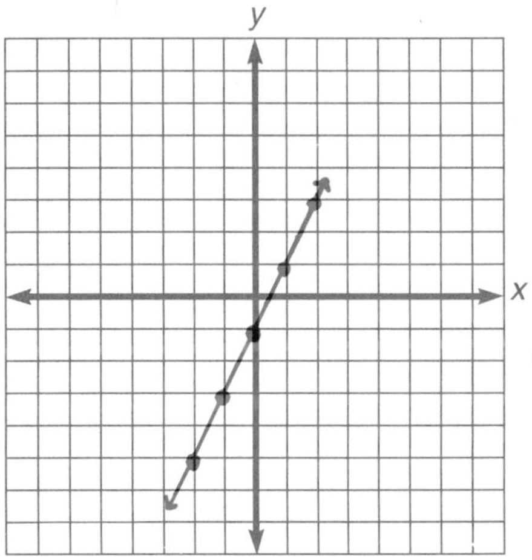

3. $y = 3 - 2x$

x	$^-2$	$^-1$	0	1	2
y	7	5	3	1	$^-1$

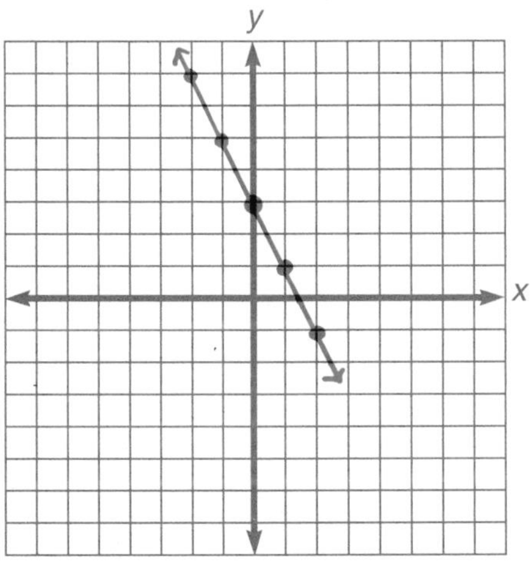

4. $y = \frac{x}{2} + 5$

x	$^-4$	$^-2$	0	2	4
y	3	4	5	6	7

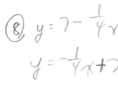

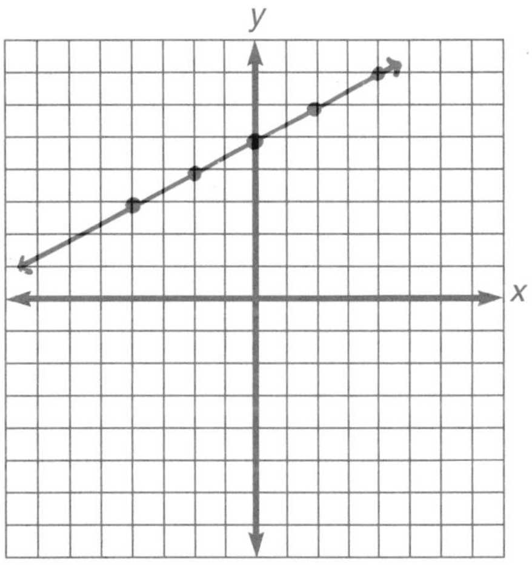

(6) $y = 3 - 2x$

$y = -2x + 3$

x	y
-3	9
-2	7
-1	5
0	3
1	1
2	-1
3	-3

(8) $y = 7 - \frac{1}{4}x$

$y = -\frac{1}{4}x + 7$

x	y
-3	$7\frac{3}{4}$
-2	$7\frac{2}{4}$
-1	$7\frac{1}{4}$
0	7
1	$6\frac{3}{4}$
2	$6\frac{1}{2}$
3	$6\frac{1}{4}$

Draw a pair of coordinate axes and graph each equation using 5 points. Check students' graphs.

5. $y = x - 4$

6. $y = 3 - 2x$

7. $y = \frac{1}{3}x + 2$

8. $y = 7 - \frac{1}{4}x$

---

*Use with Lesson 14-5, text pages 388–389.

Copyright © Sadlier-Oxford

Solving Systems of Equations*

Name ______________________

Date ______________________

Complete each function table. Graph each pair of equations on the same coordinate grid. What is their common solution?

1. $y = x + 2$; $y = 3x$

x	y
$^-3$	$^-1$
$^-2$	0
$^-1$	1
0	2
1	3
2	4
3	5

x	y
$^-3$	$^-9$
$^-2$	$^-6$
$^-1$	$^-3$
0	0
1	3
2	6
3	9

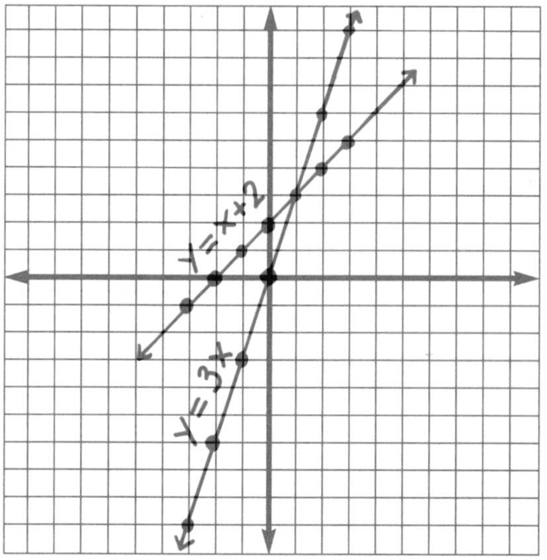

Common Solution: (1, 3)

2. $y = 3x + 1$; $y = 2x - 1$

x	y
$^-3$	$^-8$
$^-1$	$^-2$
$-\frac{1}{3}$	0
0	1
1	4
2	7

x	y
$^-4$	$^-9$
$^-2$	$^-5$
$-\frac{1}{2}$	$^-2$
0	$^-1$
1	1
2	3

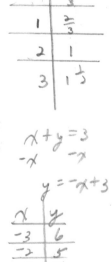

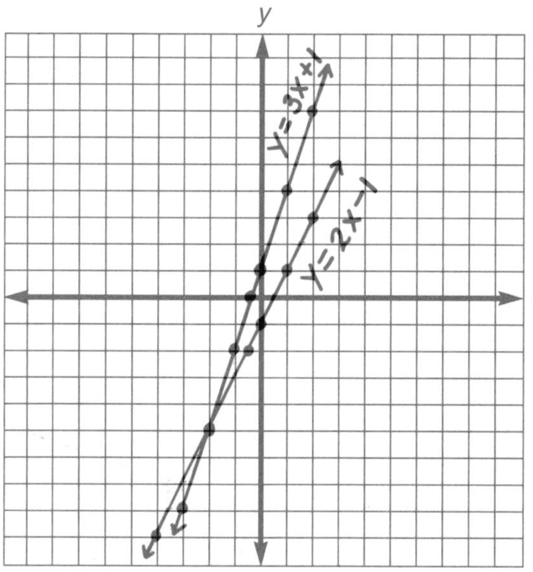

Common Solution: ($^-2$, $^-5$)

Draw a pair of coordinate axes and graph each pair of equations. Where do they intersect? (Use separate paper.) Check students' graphs. Common solutions are given.

3. $y = 2 - x$
$y = x + 8$
($^-3$, 5)

4. $x + y = 0$
$x - y = 2$
(1, $^-1$)

5. $y = \frac{x}{2}$
$y = x + 1$
($^-2$, $^-1$)

6. $3y + x = 1$
$x + y = 3$
(4, $^-1$)

*Use with Lesson 14-6, text pages 390–391.

Copyright © Sadlier-Oxford

Simultaneous Equations*

Name ______________________

Date ______________________

$y = 2x + 2$ and $y - x = 3$ (Remember: $y - x = 3$ is the same as $y = x + 3$)

$x + 3 = 2x + 2$

$\cancel{x} + 3 - \cancel{x} - 2 = 2x + \cancel{2} - x - \cancel{2}$

$3 - 2 = 2x - x$ $y - 1 = 3$ Solution: (1, 4)

$1 = x$ $y = 4$

Solve the equations by substitution and find the common solution.

1. $y = 6x$
   $y = x - 10$
   $6x = x - 10$
   $5x = {}^-10;\ x = {}^-2$
   $({}^-2, {}^-12)$

2. $y = {}^-7x$
   $y = x + 8$
   ${}^-7x = x + 8$
   ${}^-8x = 8;\ x = {}^-1$
   $({}^-1, 7)$

3. $y = \frac{x}{4}$
   $y = x + 3$
   $\frac{x}{4} = x + 3$
   $x = 4x + 12$
   $({}^-4, {}^-1)$

4. $y = \frac{-x}{5}$
   $y = x - 6$
   $\frac{-x}{5} = x - 6$
   $-x = 5x - 30;\ 6x = 30$
   $(5, -1)$

5. $y = x + 5$
   $y = 4x - 1$
   $x + 5 = 4x - 1$
   $6 = 3x;\ x = 2$
   $(2, 7)$

6. $y = {}^-x + 4$
   $y = 2x - 5$
   $-x + 4 = 2x - 5$
   $9 = 3x$
   $3 = x$
   $(3, 1)$

7. $y = {}^-5x + 2$
   $y = 3x - 14$
   ${}^-5x + 2 = 3x - 14$
   $16 = 8x;\ 2 = x$
   $(2, {}^-8)$

8. $x + y = 5$
   $2x - 3y = 5$
   $2(5 - y) - 3y = 5$
   $10 - 5y = 5;\ y = 1$
   $(4, 1)$

9. $x + y = 0$
   $5x + y = 4$
   $5x - x = 4$
   $4x = 4;\ x = 1$
   $(1, -1)$

Solve the equations by addition or subtraction. Then find the common solution.

10. $x + y = 12$
    $\underline{x - y = 8}$
    $2x = 20$
    $x = 10$
    $(10, 2)$

11. $3x + y = 7$
    $\underline{{}^-3x + y = 13}$
    $2y = 20$
    $y = 10$
    $({}^-1, 10)$

12. $4x - y = 3$
    $\underline{2x - y = 7}$
    $2x = {}^-4$
    $x = {}^-2$
    $({}^-2, {}^-11)$

13. $2x + 3y = 2$
    $\underline{2x - y = {}^-6}$
    $4y = 8$
    $y = 2$
    $({}^-2, 2)$

14. $x - y = 6$
    $\underline{2x - y = 4}$
    ${}^-x = 2$
    $x = {}^-2$
    $({}^-2, {}^-8)$

15. $6x - 2y = 36$
    $\underline{5x - 2y = 25}$
    $x = 11$
    $(11, 15)$

*Use with Lesson 14-7, text pages 392–393.

Copyright © Sadlier-Oxford

Graphing Inequalities*

Name ______________________

Date ______________________

Write *y* in terms of *x*. Describe each boundary line.

1. $3x - y < 5$ $y > 3x - 5$; dotted
2. $x - y < 4$ $y > x - 4$; dotted
3. $2x + y < 3$ $y < 3 - 2x$; dotted
4. $6x - 4y > 8$ $y < \frac{3}{2}x - 2$; dotted
5. $4x - 6y \geq 2$ $y \leq \frac{2}{3}x - \frac{1}{3}$; solid
6. $4x + 4y \leq 12$ $y \leq 3 - x$; solid
7. $x + 2y \geq 6$ $y \geq \frac{-x}{2} + 3$; solid
8. $5x - y > {}^-3$ $y < 5x + 3$; dotted

Choose test points to solve each graph. Shade the correct half-plane. Test points may vary.

9. $x + y \geq 2$

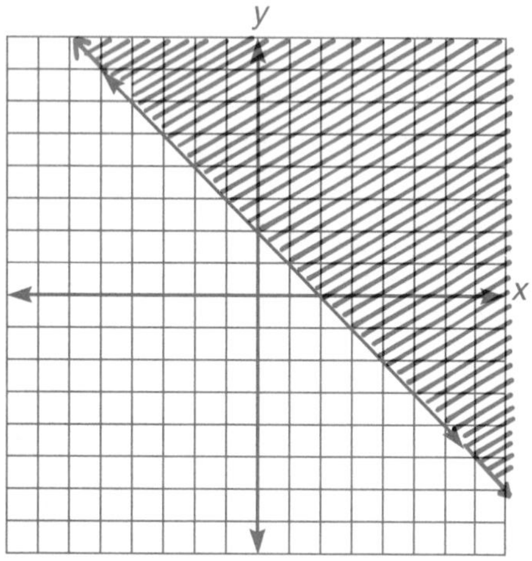

10. $y < \frac{1}{2}x + 3$

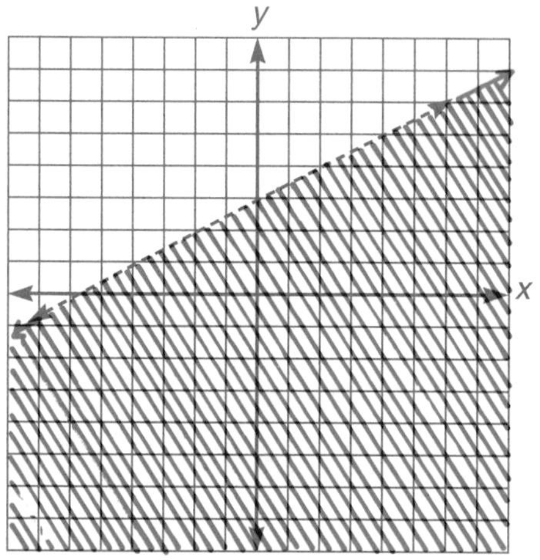

Describe each boundary line. Graph the solution set.

11. $3x + y \geq 4$ solid

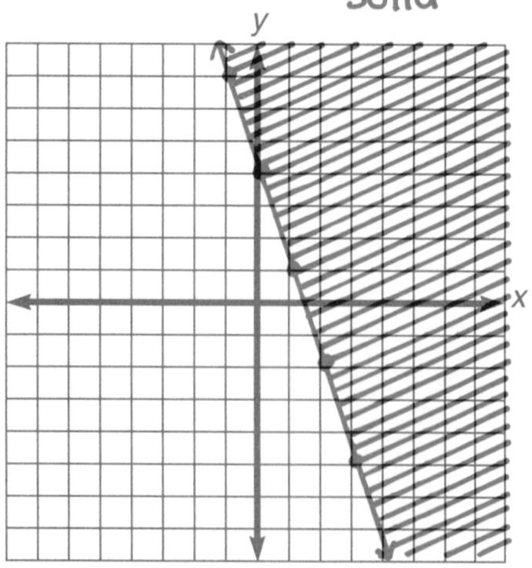

x	-1	0	1	2	3
y	7	4	1	-2	-5

12. $2x - 5y > 5$ dotted

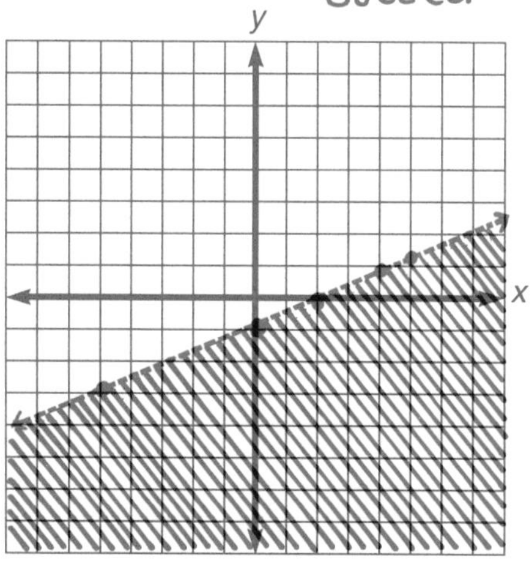

x	-5	0	2	4	5
y	-3	-1	$-\frac{1}{5}$	$\frac{3}{5}$	1

*Use with Lesson 14-8, text pages 394–395.

Copyright © Sadlier-Oxford

Graphing Systems of Inequalities*

Name ______________________

Date ______________________

Which point is part of the solution set of the given system of inequalities? Circle the correct answer.

1. $x + y \leq 4$
$x + y \geq {}^-2$

(**a.**) (0, 0) **b.** (3, 3) **c.** $({}^-2, {}^-2)$ **d.** $({}^-2, {}^-3)$

2. $y - 2x \geq 0$
$y - x > 2$

a. (0, 0) **b.** (1, 1) (**c.**) $({}^-4, {}^-1)$ **d.** $(4, {}^-1)$

3. $x - y \leq 1$
$2x - y \geq 2$

a. (0, 0) (**b.**) (2, 2) **c.** $({}^-3, {}^-2)$ **d.** $({}^-2, 3)$

Graph the solution set of each system of inequalities. Use the coordinate grid.

4. $x < 0$
$x + 2y < 2$

x	y
−2	2
0	1
1	½
2	0
4	−1

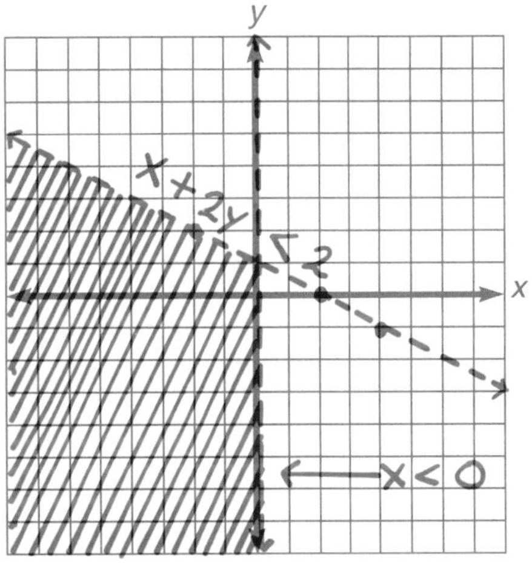

5. $y > {}^-2x$
$y - 2x > 3$

y > −2x

x	y
−1	2
0	0
1	−2
2	−4
3	−6

y − 2x > 3

x	y
1	5
0	3
−1	1
−2	−1
−3	−3

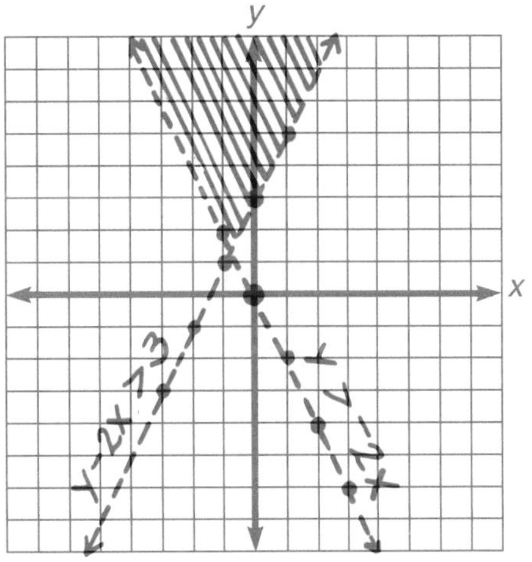

*Use with Lesson 14-9, text pages 396–397.

Copyright © Sadlier-Oxford

Graphing a Curve*

Name ______________________

Date ______________________

Complete each function table and graph the ordered pairs. Connect the points with a smooth curve.

1. $y = x^2 + 1$

x	y
$^-3$	10
$^-2$	5
$^-1$	2
0	1
1	2
2	5
3	10

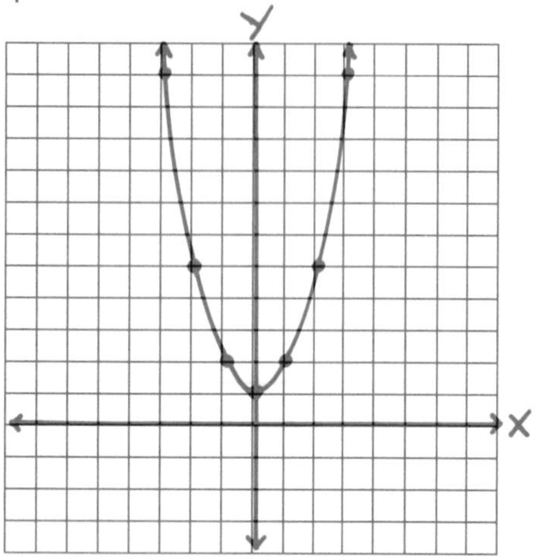

2. $y = x^2 + 2$

x	y
$^-3$	11
$^-2$	6
$^-1$	3
0	2
1	3
2	6
3	11

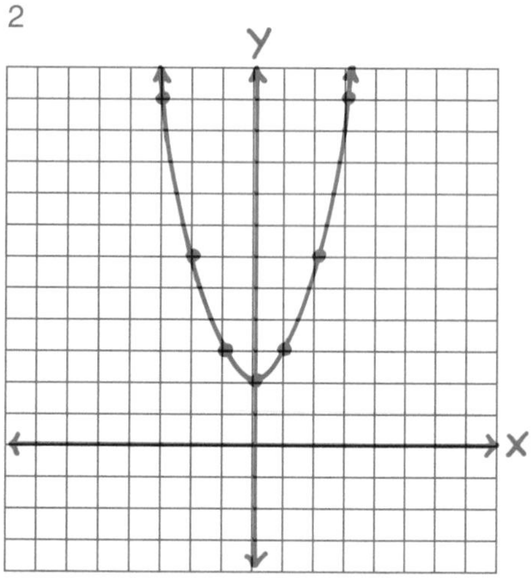

3. $y = x^2 - 2$

x	y
$^-3$	7
$^-2$	2
$^-1$	$^-1$
0	$^-2$
1	$^-1$
2	2
3	7

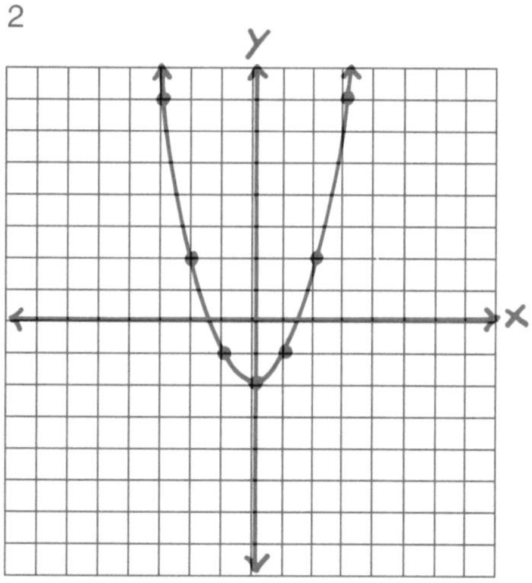

4. $y = 2x^2 - 1$

x	y
$^-3$	17
$^-2$	7
$^-1$	1
0	$^-1$
1	1
2	7
3	17

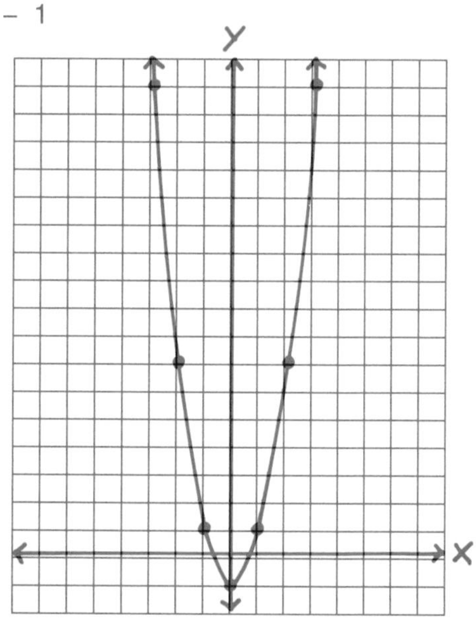

5. $y = {}^-(x^2)$

x	y
$^-3$	$^-9$
$^-2$	$^-4$
$^-1$	$^-1$
0	0
1	$^-1$
2	$^-4$
3	$^-9$

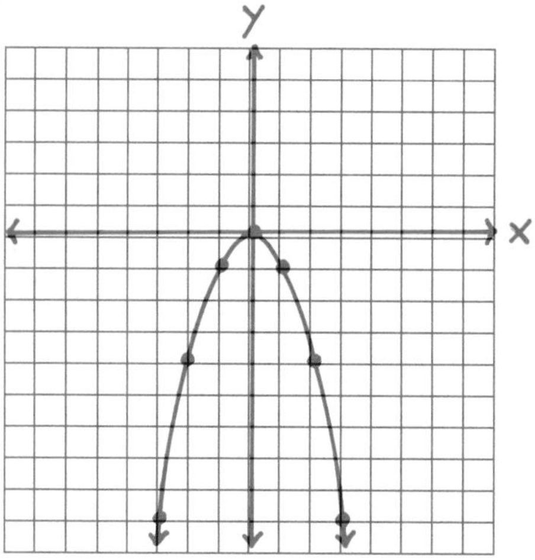

*Use with Lesson 14-10, text pages 398–399.

Copyright © Sadlier-Oxford

Progress Test: Chapters 8–14*

Name ______________________

Date ______________________

Write each answer on the numbered line. Do all computations on a separate sheet of paper.

Choose the correct answer. Write the letter.

1. A profit of 9.2% on \$350 is:
   a. \$.32 b. \$3.22 c. \$32.20 d. \$322

2. A new clock has a list price of \$38 and a discount of 15%. How much will it cost?
   a. \$5.70 b. \$32.30 c. \$33.30 d. \$42.70

3. A sofa bed is marked \$650 plus tax. If the sales tax is $7\frac{1}{2}$%, what is the total cost?
   a. \$698.75 b. \$698.25 c. \$697.75 d. \$697.25

4. Find the rate of commission on a total sales of \$3600 and a commission of \$9.
   a. 40% b. 0.25% c. 25% d. 2.5%

5. The number of degrees in 75% of a circle is:
   a. 360° b. 270° c. 180° d. 90°

6. The mean for the test scores 76, 89, 83, 90, 92, 80 is:
   a. 82 b. 84 c. 85 d. 90

7. The probability of getting a number that is a multiple of 6 when tossing a number cube whose faces are marked 3, 6, 9, 12, 15, 18 is:
   a. $\frac{1}{2}$ b. $\frac{1}{3}$ c. $\frac{1}{4}$ d. $\frac{1}{6}$

8. $\frac{6!}{(6-2)!} = \underline{\ ?\ }$ a. 6 b. 12 c. 24 d. 30

9. Which of the following is *true*?
   a. A line contains only 2 points.
   b. Parallel lines intersect.
   c. Ray ST is the same as ray TS.
   d. ∠PRT can also be called ∠TRP.

10. Which of the following is *false*?
    a. Two right angles are supplementary.
    b. Two acute angles may be complementary.
    c. Angles that have a common vertex are vertical.
    d. Adjacent angles have a common side and common vertex.

11. What is the length of a rectangle whose perimeter is 64 cm if the length is 3 times the width?
    a. 24 cm b. 18 cm c. 16 cm d. 8 cm

12. Find the side of a square whose area is the same as that of a rectangle 7 inches wide and 28 inches long.
    a. 7 in. b. 14 in. c. 16 in. d. 18 in.

13. The radius of a circle whose area is equal to its circumference is:
    a. 1 b. 6 c. 2 d. 4

Answers

1. c (8–1)
2. b (8–2)
3. a (8–4)
4. b (8–5)
5. b (9–10)
6. c (9–11)
7. a (9–1)
8. d (9–3)
9. d (10–1)
10. c (10–4)
11. a (11–1)
12. b (11–5)
13. c (11–5)

*Next to each item is given the lesson number in the text where the item was taught.

Copyright © Sadlier-Oxford

Progress Test: Chapters 8–14*

Name ______________________

Date ______________________

14. The area of a trapezoid whose altitude is 5 ft and bases are 8 ft and 6 ft is:
a. 70 sq ft **b.** 50 sq ft **c.** 45 sq ft **d.** 35 sq ft

14. d (11–4)

15. $0.\overline{7}$ = ?
a. $\frac{7}{11}$ **b.** $\frac{7}{8}$ **c.** $\frac{7}{9}$ **d.** $\frac{7}{10}$

15. c (12–1)

16. $\sqrt{200}$ would be between which two whole numbers?
a. 14 and 15 **b.** 13 and 14 **c.** 12 and 13 **d.** 10 and 11

16. a (12–2)

17. The square of a number is 0.64. Find the number.
a. 0.08 **b.** 0.8 **c.** 8 **d.** 16

17. b (12–3)

18. The surface area of a cube with an edge of 8 cm is:
a. 256 cm^2 **b.** 384 cm^2 **c.** 192 cm^2 **d.** 64 cm^2

18. b (13–1)

19. The volume of a cube with an edge of 6 in. is:
a. 196 $in.^3$ **b.** 392 $in.^3$ **c.** 108 $in.^3$ **d.** 216 $in.^3$

19. d (13–4)

20. The volume of a cylinder that has an altitude of 5 ft and the radius of its base equal to 7 ft is approximately:
a. 850 ft^3 **b.** 840 ft^3 **c.** 770 ft^3 **d.** 720 ft^3

20. c (13–6)

21. Which point satisfies the equation $y = x - 2$?
a. (2, 1) **b.** (2, $^-4$) **c.** (3, $^-5$) **d.** (4, 2)

21. d (14–4)

22. Which point lies in Quadrant II?
a. ($^-3$, 0) **b.** (6, $^-2$) **c.** ($^-6$, 2) **d.** (3, 0)

22. c (14–3)

23. The given graph

is the solution of which inquality?
a. $x < {}^-2$ **b.** $x \geq {}^-2$ **c.** $x > {}^-2$ **d.** $x \leq {}^-2$

23. c (14–1)

24. Write y in terms of x for the equation $4x + 3y = 7$.
a. $y = \frac{-4}{3}x + \frac{7}{3}$ **b.** $y = \frac{-4}{3}x + 7$
c. $y = {}^-4x + \frac{7}{3}$ **d.** $y = {}^-4x + 7$

24. a (14–7)

Solve.

25. Find the interest on \$750 for 5 years at $5\frac{1}{2}$%. I = \$750 × 5 × 0.055

25. \$206.25 (8–7)

26. By selling a painting valued at \$150 for \$195, an art museum realized what rate of gain? R = (\$195 − \$150) ÷ \$150

26. 30% (8–6)

27. One of the angles of a right triangle measures 53°. What are the measures of the other two angles? $x + 53 + 90 = 180$

27. 90°; 37° (10–5)

28. Find the height of a triangle if its area is 68.8 cm^2 and its base is 16 cm. $68.8 = \frac{1}{2}(16) \times h$

28. 8.6 cm (11–3)

29. What is the surface area of 6 spherical candles each having a diameter of 7 inches? $S = 6 \times 4\pi\left(\frac{7}{2}\right)^2$

29. 924 $in.^2$ (13–3)

30. The sum of two numbers is 66. The larger number is 4 more than the smaller number. Find the numbers.
$x + y = 66$
$x = y + 4$

30. 31; 35 (14–13)

*Next to each item is given the lesson number in the text where the item was taught.

Copyright © Sadlier-Oxford

Classifying and Evaluating Polynomials*

Name ______________________

Date ______________________

Classify each polynomial as a *monomial (M)*, *binomial (B)* or *trinomial (T)*. Give its degree.

1. $-3x^3y + 5x$ B; 4
2. $5a + 1$ B; 1
3. $9x^2y + 4x^3 + 3xy^2$ T; 3
4. 21 M; 0
5. $-7m^3n^2$ M; 5
6. $2b^2 - 3b + 1$ T; 2
7. -10 M; 0
8. $\frac{1}{2}a^2b + \frac{3}{4}ab^2$ B; 3
9. $-7x + 9xy + 10xyz$ T; 3
10. $\sqrt{2}x^4y^2 - \sqrt{3}x^3y^3 + \sqrt{5}x^5y^2$ T; 7
11. $1.32mn^2 - 0.35m^3 + 2.43m^4n^2$ T; 6

Evaluate each expression for $x = -3$ and $y = 4$.

12. $-x^3$ 27
13. $(-x)^3$ -27
14. $x^2 + 6xy - 7y^2$ -175

Evaluate each expression for $a = \frac{1}{3}$, $b = \frac{2}{9}$, and $c = -\frac{1}{6}$.

15. abc $-\frac{1}{81}$
16. $a^2c - 6b$ $-1\frac{19}{54}$
17. $a^3 + bc$ 0

For the following geometric figures find the measures represented by the algebraic expressions, given $a = 3$ and $b = 7$. Use these results to find the area of each figure.

18. a square: length of a side $= a + b$. $A = s^2$ $s = 10$; $A = 100$
19. a rectangle: length $= 3a + 2b$; width $= 5a - b$. $A = lw$ $l = 23$; $w = 8$; $A = 184$
20. a triangle: base $= 5a + 2$; height $= 3b - a$. $A = \frac{bh}{2}$ $b = 17$; $h = 18$; $A = 153$
21. a trapezoid: height $= \frac{3a^2 - 7}{5}$; bases $= b + 2$; $2a - 1$. $A = \left(\frac{b_1 + b_2}{2}\right)h$ $h = 4$; $b_1 = 9$; $b_2 = 5$; $A = 28$
22. a circle: radius $= \frac{1}{3}a + 7$. $A = \pi r^2$ $r = 8$; $A = 64\pi$ or $A \approx 200.96$

*Use with Lesson 15-1, text pages 416–417.

Copyright © Sadlier-Oxford

Classifying and Evaluating Polynomials* (con't)

Name ______________________

Date ______________________

Find the volume of each geometric figure, given that the measures of its parts are the algebraic expressions and that $a = 2$, $b = 5$.

23. cube: length of an edge $= 2(5a - b)$ $V = e^3$ $e = 10$; $V = 1000$

24. cube: length of an edge $= 3a^2 - b$ $V = e^3$ $e = 7$; $V = 343$

25. rectangular prism: length $= a + b$, width $= b - 2$, height $= 2a$ $V = lwh$ $l = 7$; $w = 3$; $h = 4$; $V = 84$

26. rectangular pyramid: length of base $= \frac{1}{2}(7a + 2b)$;
width of base $= \frac{1}{3}(4b - a)$
height $= \frac{1}{5}(10a + b)$ $V = \frac{1}{3}lwh$ $l = 12$; $w = 6$; $h = 5$; $V = 120$

27. cylinder: radius of base $= 3b - 4a$; height $= 6a + b$ $V = \pi r^2 h$ $r = 7$; $h = 17$; $V = 833\pi$ or $V \approx 2618$

Choose the values of *m* and *n* that will make each equation true.

28. $m^2 + n^2 = 5$

a. $m = 4$, $n = ^-1$ **b.** $m = ^-2$, $n = 1$ **c.** $m = 3$, $n = 2$ **d.** $m = ^-3$, $n = ^-2$ b

29. $mn + m^2n^2 = 6$

a. $m = 0$, $n = ^-6$ **b.** $m = 6$, $n = 1$ **c.** $m = 1$, $n = ^-3$ **d.** $m = ^-1$, $n = ^-3$ c

30. $m + 3n + 2 = 0$

a. $m = 1$, $n = ^-1$ **b.** $m = 0$, $n = 0$ **c.** $m = ^-1$, $n = 1$ **d.** $m = 2$, $n = ^-2$ a

31. $m^2 - 6mn + 9 = -23$

a. $m = 3$, $n = 2$ **b.** $m = ^-3$, $n = ^-2$ **c.** $m = ^-2$, $n = 3$ **d.** $m = 2$, $n = 3$ d

*Use with Lesson 15-1, text pages 416–417.

Copyright © Sadlier-Oxford

Addition and Subtraction of Polynomials*

Name ______________________

Date ______________________

$9a - 3b + 5a = \underline{?}$	$(4x^2 + 3xy - 9y^2) - (5xy - 4y^2) = \underline{?}$
$9a - 3b$	$4x^2 + 3xy - 9y^2$
$+5a$	$\overset{-}{\cancel{+}}\ 5xy\ \overset{+}{\cancel{-}}\ 4y^2$
$14a - 3b$	$4x^2 - 2xy - 5y^2$

Add or subtract.

1. $16x^2y^3 + 19x^2y^3$

   $35x^2y^3$

2. $(16ab + c) + (12ab - 4c)$

   $28ab - 3c$

3. $(17c - 4d) - (11c + 4d)$

   $6c - 8d$

4. $(x^2 - 23x + 14) + (6x^2 - 8)$

   $7x^2 - 23x + 6$

5. $(\frac{1}{4}pq - \frac{2}{3}cd) + (\frac{3}{8}pq - \frac{4}{9}cd)$

   $\frac{5}{8}pq - 1\frac{1}{9}cd$

6. $(^-\frac{5}{6}rs + \frac{7}{11}m^2n^2) - (^-\frac{2}{3}rs + \frac{3}{22}m^2n^2)$

   $-\frac{1}{6}rs + \frac{1}{2}m^2n^2$

7. $(2b^2 - 1.3n^2) - (3.5n^2 + b^2)$

   $b^2 - 4.8n^2$

8. $(3rs + 1.5s^2) - (2.3s - 5rs)$

   $1.5s^2 + 8rs - 2.3s$

Add.

9. $-23a^2 + 17a + 6$
   $18a^2 + 11a - 7$
   $-5a^2 + 28a - 1$

10. $8xy \quad + 1$
    $-xy - 10y^2$
    $7xy - 10y^2 + 1$

11. $47m^2 - 36mn + 11n^2$
    $16m^2 \quad - 9n^2$
    $63m^2 - 36mn + 2n^2$

12. $11.3x^2 - 13.9x + 15.8$
    $-9.6x^2 + 12.7x - 6.5$
    $1.7x^2 - 1.2x + 9.3$

13. $10d^2 - 3d$
    $7d^2 + 3d - 9$
    $17d^2 - 9$

14. $57.6c^2d^2 + 19.7cd - 64.5$
    $16.1cd - 11.3$
    $57.6c^2d^2 + 35.8cd - 75.8$

Subtract.

15. $98a^2 - 121b^2$
    $24a^2 - 35b^2$
    $74a^2 - 86b^2$

16. $11c^3 - 13$
    $7c^3 - 15$
    $4c^3 + 2$

17. $125x^2y + 57xy^2 - 13xy$
    $90x^2y - 13xy^2$
    $35x^2y + 70xy^2 - 13xy$

18. $16r - 12p$
    $27p + 19$
    $16r - 39p - 19$

19. $-9xy$
    $-9xy - y^2$
    y^2

20. $96.7m^2n^2 + 13.7mn - 105.1n^2$
    $14.3m^2n^2 - 11.3mn - 13.9n^2$
    $82.4m^2n^2 + 25mn - 91.2n^2$

*Use with Lesson 15-2, text pages 418–419.

Copyright © Sadlier-Oxford

Addition and Subtraction of Polynomials* (con't)

Name ______________________

Date ______________________

Write an algebraic expression to represent the perimeter of each geometric figure.

21. square: length of a side $= 5x - 2$ $P = 4s$ — $20x - 8$

22. square: length of a side $= x^2 - 2x + 3$ $P = 4s$ — $4x^2 - 8x + 12$

23. rectangle: length $= 9x + 1$; width $= 3x - 2$ $P = 2(\ell + w)$ — $24x - 2$

24. rectangle: length $= 3x^2 - 4x + 1$; width $= 8x + 3$ $P = 2(\ell + w)$ — $6x^2 + 8x + 8$

Arrange in ascending powers of *a*.

25. $a + 10 - 3a^2$

$10 + a - 3a^2$

26. $5a^3 + a - 6a^2 + 11$

$11 + a - 6a^2 + 5a^3$

27. $4ab + 10 - 7a^2b^2 + 9a^4b^3$

$10 + 4ab - 7a^2b^2 + 9a^4b^3$

Arrange in descending powers of *x*.

28. $10x^5 + 9x^3 + 3 - x^4 + x^2$

$10x^5 - x^4 + 9x^3 + x^2 + 3$

29. $x^3y^2 - 15x^5 + 3 - x^4y + x^2y$

$-15x^5 - x^4y + x^3y^2 + x^2y + 3$

30. $-x^4y + 10y + x^8 + 4x^3y^2 - x^6y^5$

$x^8 - x^6y^5 - x^4y + 4x^3y^2 + 10y$

Solve. Show your work.

31. The sum of two polynomials is $8a^2 - 7$. If one of the polynomials is $3a^2 - 2b - 1$, what is the other polynomial?

$8a^2 \quad -7$

$-3a^2 + 2b + 1$

$5a^2 + 2b - 6$

32. From the sum of $3a^2 - 3b$ and $7 - 11b$ subtract $3a^2 - 17$.

$3a^2 - 3b$

$-11b + 7$

$3a^2 - 14b + 7$

$3a^2 - 14b + 7$

$-3a^2 \quad +17$

$-14b + 24$

33. The lengths of the sides of a triangle are represented by $x^2 + 8x - 17$, $3x + 11$, and $3x^2 - 25$. Find the perimeter.

$x^2 + 8x - 17$

$3x + 11$

$3x^2 \quad -25$

$4x^2 + 11x - 31$

34. The length of each side of a square is $\frac{2a}{3} + 1$. Find the perimeter of the square.

$P = 4\left(\frac{2a}{3} + 1\right)$

$\frac{8a}{3} + 4$ or $\frac{8a+12}{3}$

*Use with Lesson 15-2, text pages 418–419.

Copyright © Sadlier-Oxford

Exponents*

Name ______________________

Date ______________________

Simplify using the law(s) of exponents.

1. $a^4 \cdot a^7$ a^{11}
2. $y^3 \cdot y^{10}$ y^{13}
3. $n^2 \cdot n^4 \cdot n$ n^7
4. $b^4 \cdot b^2 \cdot b^3$ b^9
5. $\frac{x^{12}}{x^7}$ x^5
6. $\frac{y^{17}}{y^{25}}$ $\frac{1}{y^8}$
7. $\frac{m^{14}}{m^{14}}$ $m^0 = 1$
8. $\frac{c^{11}}{c^{12}}$ $\frac{1}{c}$
9. $(m^3)^5$ m^{15}
10. $(n^7)^4$ n^{28}
11. $(d^6)^6$ d^{36}
12. $(e^8)^9$ e^{72}
13. $(xy)^7$ x^7y^7
14. $(2abc)^3$ $8a^3b^3c^3$
15. $(3x^2y^3)^4$ $81x^8y^{12}$
16. $(5mn^5)^2$ $25m^2n^{10}$
17. $(10a^3b^2)^3 \cdot (ab^3)^2$ $1000a^{11}b^{12}$
18. $(-xyz^3)^2 \cdot (-xy)^6$ $x^8y^8z^6$
19. $(a^4b^5c^6)^2$ $a^8b^{10}c^{12}$
20. $(m^3n^5y^2)^4$ $m^{12}n^{20}y^8$
21. $\frac{(x^4y^2z^3)^4}{(xyz)^2}$ $x^{14}y^6z^{10}$
22. $\frac{(x^2y^7z^3)^5}{x^{10}y^7}$ $y^{28}z^{15}$
23. $(2x^4yz)^5$ $32x^{20}y^5z^5$
24. $(-2a^5y^4z^8)^3$ $-8a^{15}y^{12}z^{24}$

Find the value of each of the following:

25. $\frac{3^6 \cdot 3^3}{3^5}$ $3^4 = 81$
26. $\frac{8^4 \cdot 8^9}{8^3 \cdot 8^8}$ $8^2 = 64$
27. $\frac{4^3 \cdot 4^0}{4^2 \cdot 4^3}$ $\frac{1}{4^2} = \frac{1}{16}$
28. $\frac{9^{12} \cdot 9^3}{(9^3)^5}$ 1
29. $\frac{7^8}{7^5 \cdot 7}$ $7^2 = 49$
30. $\frac{10^6}{(10^3)^3}$ $\frac{1}{10^3} = \frac{1}{1000}$

*Use with Lesson 15-3, text page 420.

Copyright © Sadlier-Oxford

Multiplication of Monomials*

Name ______________________

Date ______________________

$(-3b^2)(7b^5) = \underline{\ ?\ }$	$2y(3y^2 + 9) = \underline{\ ?\ }$
$(-3)(7)(b^2)(b^5) =$	$(2y \cdot 3y^2) + (2y \cdot 9) = 6y^{1+2} + 18y$
$-21b^{2+5} = -21b^7$	$= 6y^3 + 18y$

Multiply.

1. $15x^4 \cdot 4x^7$ $\underline{60x^{11}}$

2. $-13y^5 \cdot 9y^{10}$ $\underline{-117y^{15}}$

3. $(103a^2)(-2a^4)$ $\underline{-206a^6}$

4. $(-25b^6)(-7b^3)$ $\underline{175b^9}$

5. $(16x^2y^3)(4x^7y^9)$ $\underline{64x^9y^{12}}$

6. $(-17m^4b^7c)(8m^3c^5)$ $\underline{-136m^7b}$

7. $5c^4 \cdot -8c^5 \cdot 2c^3$ $\underline{-80c^{12}}$

8. $-11a^5 \cdot -2a^6 \cdot 4a^3$ $\underline{88a^{14}}$

9. $\left(\frac{2}{3}a^5b^4c^2\right)^3$ $\underline{\frac{8}{27}a^{15}b^{12}c^6}$

10. $\left(-\frac{3}{5}e^6f^7\right)^2$ $\underline{\frac{9}{25}e^{12}f^{14}}$

11. $(-mnp)^5$ $\underline{-m^5n^5p^5}$

12. $(0.2ab^2c)^2$ $\underline{0.04a^2b^4c^2}$

13. $5a^2b(3ab^2 + 4a^3b^3 + 6a^4b)$

    $\underline{15a^3b^3 + 20a^5b^4 + 30a^6b^2}$

14. $\frac{1}{2}ab^2c^3(4a^3b^2c - 18a^5b^3c^4 + 10a^2bc^4)$

    $\underline{2a^4b^4c^4 - 9a^6b^5c^7 + 5a^3b^3c^7}$

15. $-7x^4y^2(9xy^5 - 6x^3y^3 + 7x^5y)$

    $\underline{-63x^5y^7 + 42x^7y^5 - 49x^9y^3}$

16. $-\frac{2}{3}x^2y^2z^2\left(\frac{3}{4}xyz + \frac{9}{14}y^3z^5 - \frac{15}{22}x^4y^7\right)$

    $\underline{-\frac{1}{2}x^3y^3z^3 - \frac{3}{7}x^2y^5z^7 + \frac{5}{11}x^6y^9z^2}$

17. $m^4n^5(-2m^2n^3 + 3m^3n^4 - 7mn^2)$

    $\underline{-2m^6n^8 + 3m^7n^9 - 7m^5n^7}$

18. $1.2ab^3(0.6b - 0.3a^2b^2)$

    $\underline{0.72ab^4 - 0.36a^3b^5}$

19. $-3.4x^2y^3(0.7x^3 + 0.9y^2)$

    $\underline{-2.38x^5y^3 - 3.06x^2y^5}$

20. $-2.1m^3n(0.4n^3 - 0.21m^3)$

    $\underline{-0.84m^3n^4 + 0.441m^6n}$

Fill in the missing factor.

21. $(9a^2b^3c)\ \underline{8a^4b^3c^5} = 72a^6b^6c^6$

22. $\underline{-5a^3b^6c^6}\ (-11a^3bc^2) = 55a^6b^7c^8$

23. $\underline{3a^2k}\ (3k^2 + 7b^2) = 9a^2k^3 + 21a^2kb^2$

24. $18r^3b^2(\underline{4b^2} + 3r^6) = 72r^3b^4 + 54r^9b^2$

Solve.

25. If one pound of beans cost $35y$ cents, what is the cost of $8x$ pounds of beans? $\underline{280xy \text{ cents}}$

26. If a car travels at the rate of $5x^2$ miles per hour, what is the distance traveled by the car in $7x$ hours? $\underline{35x^3 \text{ miles}}$

27. A rectangle has its length equal to $5a^4b$ cm and width equal to $7ab$ cm. Find its area. $\underline{35a^5b^2 \text{ cm}^2}$

*Use with Lesson 15-4, text page 421.

Copyright © Sadlier-Oxford

Multiplication of Polynomials*

Name ______________________

Date ______________________

To multiply polynomials:

- Distribute each term of the first polynomial across each term of the second.
- Simplify the products by combining any similar terms.

$(x - 7)(x + 8) = \underline{?}$

$= (x \cdot x) + (x \cdot 8) + (-7)(x) + (-7)(8)$

$= x^2 + 8x - 7x - 56$

$= x^2 + 1x - 56$

$= x^2 + x - 56$

Multiply.

1. $(x + 3)(x + 4)$ $x^2+7x+12$

2. $(y + 11)(y + 2)$ $y^2+13y+22$

3. $(x - 7)(x - 6)$ $x^2-13x+42$

4. $(y - 10)(y - 8)$ $y^2-18y+80$

5. $(a + 13)(a - 5)$ $a^2+8a-65$

6. $(b - 9)(b + 8)$ b^2-b-72

7. $(c + 12)(c - 7)$ $c^2+5c-84$

8. $(d - 15)(d + 3)$ $d^2-12d-45$

9. $(m + 8)(m + 5)$ $m^2+13m+40$

10. $(n + 14)(n + 7)$ $n^2+21n+98$

11. $(a - 10)(a + 10)$ a^2-100

12. $(b + 16)(b - 16)$ b^2-256

13. $(c + 12)(c + 12)$ $c^2+24c+144$

14. $(a + 13)(a + 13)$ $a^2+26a+169$

15. $(x - 11)^2$ $x^2-22x+121$

16. $(y - 17)^2$ $y^2-34y+289$

17. $(3x + 5)(2x + 3)$ $6x^2+19x+15$

18. $(7x + 2)(6x - 5)$ $42x^2-23x-10$

19. $(2x - 9)(3x - 4)$ $6x^2-35x+36$

20. $(2x + 11)(x - 9)$ $2x^2-7x-99$

21. $(8x - 3)(3x + 7)$ $24x^2+47x-21$

22. $(9x + 2)(8x - 5)$ $72x^2-29x-10$

23. $(4x + 3)(x - 6)$ $4x^2-21x-18$

24. $(5x - 2)(7x - 5)$ $35x^2-39x+10$

25. $(6x + 11)(6x - 11)$ $36x^2-121$

26. $(11x + 3)(11x - 3)$ $121x^2-9$

27. $(7x + 5)(7x + 5)$ $49x^2+70x+25$

28. $(8x + 7)(8x + 7)$ $64x^2+112x+49$

29. $(10x - 1)^2$ $100x^2-20x+1$

30. $(15x - 2)^2$ $225x^2-60x+4$

31. $(7a - 2b)(11a + 3b)$ $77a^2-ab-6b^2$

32. $(4a + 13b)(2a - b)$ $8a^2+22ab-13b^2$

33. $(13a - 5b)(13a + 5b)$ $169a^2-25b^2$

*Use with Lesson 15-5, text pages 422–423.

Copyright © Sadlier-Oxford

Multiplication of Polynomials* (con't)

Name ______________________

Date ______________________

Multiply. Simplify the expressions.

34. $(m + 2n)(11m - 3n)$ $11m^2 + 19mn - 6n^2$

35. $(8a + 15b)(6a - 7b)$ $48a^2 + 34ab - 105b^2$

36. $(5a + 7b)^2$ $25a^2 + 70ab + 49b^2$

37. $(m + 3n)(m - 3n)$ $m^2 - 9n^2$

38. $(6c + d)(6c - d)$ $36c^2 - d^2$

39. $(11a - 6b)^2$ $121a^2 - 132ab + 36b^2$

40. $(x + 2)(x^2 - 2x + 4)$ $x^3 + 8$

41. $(c - 14d)^2$ $c^2 - 28cd + 196d^2$

42. $(y + 4)(y^2 - 4y + 16)$ $y^3 + 64$

43. $(a - 5)(a^2 + 5a + 25)$ $a^3 - 125$

44. $(b - 6)(b^2 + 6b + 36)$ $b^3 - 216$

45. $(x + 2)(x^2 + 4x + 4)$ $x^3 + 6x^2 + 12x + 8$

46. $(y - 4)(y^2 - 8y + 16)$ $y^3 - 12y^2 + 48y - 64$

47. $(a + 6)(a^2 - 3a + 1)$ $a^3 + 3a^2 - 17a + 6$

48. $(a - 7)(a^2 + 2a - 3)$ $a^3 - 5a^2 - 17a + 21$

49. $(a + 1)(6 - 5a - a^2)$ $6 + a - 6a^2 - a^3$

50. $(3 - b)(b^2 - 6b + 5)$ $15 - 23b + 9b^2 - b^3$

51. $(x + 3)(x + 5) - x^2$ $x^2 + 8x + 15 - x^2 = 8x +$

52. $9x^2 - (2x + 5)(3x - 4)$ $9x^2 - 6x^2 - 7x + 20 = 3x^2 - 7x + 20$

53. $x[(x + 4)(x - 4) + 5]$ $x^3 - 16x + 5x = x^3 - 11x$

54. $(a + 5)^2 - (a - 2)^2$ $a^2 + 10a + 25 - a^2 + 4a - 4 = 14a + 21$

Solve.

55. Find the area of a rectangle if its length is $(3x - 7)$ in. and its width is $(x + 9)$ in.
$A = lw$
$(3x - 7)(x + 9) = (3x^2 + 20x - 63)$ in.^{2}

56. A car travels at the rate of $(2x - 5)$ miles per hour. How far can it travel in $(6x - 7)$ hours?
$d = rt$
$(2x - 5)(6x - 7) = (12x^2 - 44x + 35)$ mi

57. Find the area of a square if the length of a side is $(11x - 2)$ cm.
$A = s^2$
$(11x - 2)^2 = (121x^2 - 44x + 4)$ cm^2

58. Find the area of a circle in terms of π if its radius is $(5x - 4)$ cm.
$A = \pi r^2$
$\pi(5x - 4)^2 = (25x^2 - 40x + 16)\pi$ cm^2

*Use with Lesson 15-5, text pages 422–423.

Copyright © Sadlier-Oxford

Monomial Factors of Polynomials*

Name ______________________

Date ______________________

Find the GCF of $6x^2y + 45x^3y^2$.

$6x^2y = 2 \cdot 3 \cdot x \cdot x \cdot y$

$45x^3y^2 = 3 \cdot 3 \cdot 5 \cdot x \cdot x \cdot x \cdot y \cdot y$

So, GCF $= 3 \cdot x \cdot x \cdot y$ or $3x^2y$

$6x^2y + 45x^3y^2 = \underline{?}$

GCF $= 3x^2y$

$\frac{6x^2y}{3x^2y} = 2$ $\qquad \frac{45x^3y^2}{3x^2y} = 15xy$

$6x^2y + 45x^3y^2 = 3x^2y(2 + 15xy)$

Factor.

1. $6x + 9y$ — $3(2x+3y)$
2. $21a - 28b$ — $7(3a-4b)$
3. $a^3b^3c^3 - a^2b^3c^4 + a^3b^2c^4$ — $a^2b^2c^3(ab-bc+ac)$
4. $3m^3 + 4m^2n$ — $m^2(3m+4n)$
5. $5r^6 + 10a^2$ — $5(r^6+2a^2)$
6. $x^5y^3z + x^3y^4z^2 + x^3y^2z$ — $x^3y^2z(x^2y+y^2z+1)$
7. $25a^6 + 10a^2$ — $5a^2(5a^4+2)$
8. $18x^4 - 21x^3$ — $3x^3(6x-7)$
9. $125x^5 + 175x^4 + 200x^2$ — $25x^2(5x^3+7x^2+8)$
10. $a^3b^2 + abc$ — $ab(a^2b+c)$
11. $p^3q^4 - p^2q^3r$ — $p^2q^3(pq-r)$
12. $120a^5 - 140a^4 + 180a^3$ — $20a^3(6a^2-7a+9)$
13. $36x^3y^5z^4 + 48x^5y^2z^2$ — $12x^3y^2z^2(3y^3z^2+4x^2)$
14. $49a^7b^4c^3 - 84a^5b^4c^5$ — $7a^5b^4c^3(7a^2-12c^2)$
15. $p^8 + p^{12} + p^{20}$ — $p^8(1+p^4+p^{12})$
16. $11m^4n^5 + 121m^3n^2$ — $11m^3n^2(mn^3+11)$
17. $13a^5b^5 - 169a^4b^3$ — $13a^4b^3(ab^2-13)$
18. $x^{19} + x^{27} + x^{13}$ — $x^{13}(x^6+x^{14}+1)$
19. $147 - 36x^5 + 288x^7$ — $3(49-12x^5+96x^7)$
20. $76x^3y^5 - 95x^2y^4z^2 + 133x^4y^3z$ — $19x^2y^3(4xy^2-5yz^2+7x^2z)$
21. $189x^9 + 270x^4 + 144$ — $9(21x^9+30x^4+16)$
22. $a^5b^3c^3 + a^4b^3c^4 + a^5b^2c^4$ — $a^4b^2c^3(ab+bc+ac)$
23. $26a^3b^2 + 39a^2bc + 65ab^2c^2$ — $13ab(2a^2b+3ac+5bc^2)$
24. $p^6q^3r^4 - p^5q^3r^5 + p^6q^2r^5$ — $p^5q^2r^4(pq-qr+pr)$
25. $32x^5y^3 + 40x^3y^4 + 48x^2y^5$ — $8x^2y^3(4x^3+5xy+6y^2)$
26. $49xyz - 56x^2z^3 + 147xy^2z$ — $7xz(7y-8xz^2+21y^2$

*Use with Lesson 15-6, text pages 424–425.

Copyright © Sadlier-Oxford

Monomial Factors of Polynomials (con't)

Name ______________________
Date ______________________

Factor.

27. $40c^4d^2 - 50c^2d^3 + 10cd^3$ $10cd^2(4c^3 - 5cd + d)$

28. $1.5m^3n - 4.5mn^2 + 6mn$ $1.5mn(m^2 - 3n + 4)$

29. $-10x^5y - 75x^4y^2 - 45x^3y^3$ $5x^3y(-2x^2 - 15xy - 9y^2)$

30. $1.3c^3d^2 + 2.6cd^3 - 6.5cd^2$ $1.3cd^2(c^2 + 2d - 5)$

31. $-33a^5b^3c^2 - 44a^4b^2c^3 - 22a^5bc^4$ $11a^4bc^2(-3ab^2 - 4bc - 2ac^2)$

32. $90m^5n^5c^6 - 60m^2n^4c^3 - 50m^5n^4c^5$ $10m^2n^4c^3(9m^3nc^3 - 6 - 5m^3c^2)$

33. $0.2x^3y^5z^2 - 0.8x^2y^4z^3 + 1.2x^4y^2z^4$ $0.2x^2y^2z^2(xy^3 - 4y^2z + 6x^2z^2)$

34. $120x^3y^5z - 75x^2y^6z^2 + 135x^3y^3z^4$ $15x^2y^3z(8xy^2 - 5y^3z + 9xz^3)$

35. $2.7a^4b^3c + 0.3a^3b^3c^2 - 0.6a^5b^2c^2$ $0.3a^3b^2c(9ab + bc - 2a^2c)$

36. $119p^6q^8r^2 + 68p^8q^4r^4 + 170p^5q^4r^6$ $17p^5q^4r^2(7pq^4 + 4p^3r^2 + 10r^4)$

Solve.

37. The area of a parallelogram is represented by $(2x^2y - 2xy^2)$ in.². Express the area as a product of two factors.

$(2xy)(x - y)$, $(2x)(xy - y^2)$, and so

38. The area of a rectangle is $(8a^2bc - 4abc^2)$ cm². Express the area as a product of two factors.

$(4abc)(2a - c)$, $(4ab)(2ac - c^2)$, and so

39. Jessica uses $4c^4 + 96$ to represent the area of a rectangle and 4 to represent its length. What expression represents its width? $4(\_\_\_) = 4c^4 + 96$

$c^4 + 24$

40. Charlene uses $48b^2 - 32b^2c^2$ to represent the area of a parallelogram. If the GCF of $48b^2 - 32b^2c^2$ is the base, what is the base and the height of the parallelogram?

base (GCF) $= 16b^2$; height $= 3 - 2c^2$

*Use with Lesson 15-6, text pages 424–425.

Copyright © Sadlier-Oxford

Factoring Trinomials*

Name ____________________

Date ____________________

$x^2 - x - 6 = \underline{\ ?\ }$
Factors of 6: {1, 2, 3, 6}
Factors of −6 whose sum is −1: 2 and −3
$x^2 - x - 6 = (x + 2)(x - 3)$

Factor.

1. $x^2 + 6x + 5$ $(x+5)(x+1)$
2. $a^2 + 12a + 27$ $(a+9)(a+3)$
3. $y^2 - 20y + 19$ $(y-19)(y-1)$
4. $x^2 + 7x + 12$ $(x+4)(x+3)$
5. $b^2 - 20b + 64$ $(b-4)(b-16)$
6. $y^2 - 38y - 39$ $(y-39)(y+1)$
7. $y^2 - 11y + 24$ $(y-3)(y-8)$
8. $b^2 + 11b - 102$ $(b+17)(b-6)$
9. $a^2 + 17a + 16$ $(a+16)(a+1)$
10. $y^2 - 10y + 21$ $(y-3)(y-7)$
11. $x^2 - 15x - 54$ $(x-18)(x+3)$
12. $a^2 - 24a + 44$ $(a-22)(a-2)$
13. $a^2 - 3a - 10$ $(a-5)(a+2)$
14. $x^2 - 19x - 42$ $(x-21)(x+2)$
15. $x^2 - 41x + 180$ $(x-36)(x-5)$
16. $a^2 + 3a - 28$ $(a+7)(a-4)$
17. $y^2 + 22y + 120$ $(y+10)(y+12)$
18. $x^2 - 7x - 144$ $(x+9)(x-16)$
19. $m^2 - 5m - 36$ $(m-9)(m+4)$
20. $y^2 + 26y + 153$ $(y+9)(y+17)$
21. $c^2 - 15cd + 44d^2$ $(c-4d)(c-11d)$
22. $n^2 + 9n - 52$ $(n+13)(n-4)$
23. $y^2 - 26y + 144$ $(y-8)(y-18)$
24. $x^4 - 16x^2y^2 + 55y^4$ $(x^2-5y^2)(x-11y^2)$
25. $n^2 - 10n + 9$ $(n-9)(n-1)$
26. $m^2 - 2m - 143$ $(m+11)(m-13)$
27. $m^4 + 8m^2n^2 - 105n^4$ $(m^2-7n^2)(m^2+15n^2)$
28. $c^2 - 12c + 11$ $(c-11)(c-1)$
29. $x^2 + 23x + 120$ $(x+15)(x+8)$
30. $a^4 - 19a^2b^2 + 34b^4$ $(a^2-17b^2)(a^2-2b^2)$
31. $d^2 + 18d + 65$ $(d+13)(d+5)$
32. $n^2 - 13n + 42$ $(n-7)(n-6)$
33. $c^4 - 22c^2d^2 - 23d^4$ $(c^2+d^2)(c^2-23d^2)$
34. $r^2 - 19r + 70$ $(r-14)(r-5)$
35. $x^2 - 17x + 60$ $(x-12)(x-5)$
36. $p^4 + 14p^2q^2 - 32q^4$ $(p^2+16q^2)(p^2-2q^2)$

*Use with Lesson 15-7, text pages 426–427.

Copyright © Sadlier-Oxford

Factoring Trinomials* (con't)

Name ______________________

Date ______________________

Factor.

37. $a^2 + 6ab + 8b^2$

$(a+4b)(a+2b)$

38. $m^4 - 9m^2n^2 - 70n^4$

$(m^2+5n^2)(m^2-14n^2)$

39. $x^2 - 12xy + 32y^2$

$(x-8y)(x-4y)$

40. $x^2y^2 + 17xy + 66$

$(xy+6)(xy+11)$

41. $b^2 - 8bc - 20c^2$

$(b-10c)(b+2c)$

42. $x^2y^2 + 15xy - 34$

$(xy+17)(xy-2)$

43. $y^2 + 13yz - 48z^2$

$(y+16z)(y-3z)$

44. $a^2b^2 + 19ab + 70$

$(ab+14)(ab+5)$

45. $m^2 + 9mn + 14n^2$

$(m+7n)(m+2n)$

46. $c^2d^2 - 22cd - 75$

$(cd-25)(cd+3)$

47. $r^2 - 15rs + 50s^2$

$(r-5s)(r-10s)$

48. $x^4y^4 - 3x^2y^2 - 108$

$(x^2y^2+9)(x^2y^2-12)$

49. $a^2 + 16ab + 63b^2$

$(a+9b)(a+7b)$

50. $a^4b^4 - 11a^2b^2 - 60$

$(a^2b^2-15)(a^2b^2+4)$

Solve.

51. The area of a rectangle is $(x^2 - 7x + 12)$ cm^2. Find the binomials that represent the dimensions of the rectangle.

$A = lw$

$(x-4)(x-3)$

52. The distance traveled by a bus is $(x^2 - 5x - 24)$ mi. Find the binomials that represent the rate of the bus per hour, and the time in hours the bus travels to cover the given distance.

$d = rt$

$(x+3)(x-8)$

53. The area of a parallelogram is $(x^2 + 17x + 42)$ $in.^2$. Find the binomials that represent the dimensions of the parallelogram.

$A = bh$

$(x+14)(x+3)$

*Use with Lesson 15-7, text pages 426–427.

Copyright © Sadlier-Oxford

Factoring More Polynomials*

Name ______________________

Date ______________________

$10x^2 + 3x - 7 = \underline{\ ?\ }$

Factors of 10: {1, 2, 5, 10} and factors of 7: {1, 7}
Work out possible combinations of factors to find $3x$ as the middle term.

$10x^2 - 7x + 10x - 7 = (x + 1)(10x - 7)$

Factor.

1. $3x^2 + 4x + 1$ $(3x+1)(x+1)$
2. $4x^2 - x - 3$ $(4x+3)(x-1)$
3. $60 - 11x - 14x^2$ $(12-7x)(5+2x)$
4. $14x^2 - 9x + 1$ $(7x-1)(2x-1)$
5. $6x^2 - 7x - 10$ $(6x+5)(x-2)$
6. $72 + 13x - 15x^2$ $(9+5x)(8-3x)$
7. $15a^2 - 11a + 2$ $(3a-1)(5a-2)$
8. $2a^2 + a - 10$ $(2a+5)(a-2)$
9. $24r^2 + 38rs + 15s^2$ $(4r+3s)(6r+5s)$
10. $12a^2 - a - 6$ $(4a-3)(3a+2)$
11. $30a^2 - 17a + 2$ $(5a-2)(6a-1)$
12. $35x^2 - 48xy - 27y^2$ $(5x-9y)(7x+3y)$
13. $35x^2 + 31x + 6$ $(7x+2)(5x+3)$
14. $4x^2 + x - 14$ $(4x-7)(x+2)$
15. $21a^2 - 58ab - 40b^2$ $(7a+4b)(3a-10b)$
16. $10x^2 + 13x - 3$ $(5x-1)(2x+3)$
17. $9x^2 - 9x - 4$ $(3x+1)(3x-4)$
18. $15m^2 - 106mn + 7n^2$ $(15m-n)(m-7n)$
19. $16x^2 + 6x - 1$ $(8x-1)(2x+1)$
20. $22x^2 - 17x + 3$ $(11x-3)(2x-1)$
21. $24c^2 - 19cd - 9d^2$ $(8c-9d)(3c+d)$
22. $8x^2 + 22x + 15$ $(4x+5)(2x+3)$
23. $20x^2 - 32x + 3$ $(10x-1)(2x-3)$
24. $15x^2 - 34xy + 15y^2$ $(3x-5y)(5x-3y)$
25. $5x^2 + 4x - 1$ $(5x-1)(x+1)$
26. $11x^2 - 9x - 2$ $(11x+2)(x-1)$
27. $45a^2 + 56ab - 45b^2$ $(9a-5b)(5a+9b)$
28. $5x^2 + 21x + 4$ $(5x+1)(x+4)$
29. $12x^2 - 20x + 7$ $(2x-1)(6x-7)$
30. $24x^4 + 26x^2y + 5y^2$ $(6x^2+5y)(4x^2+y)$
31. $15x^2 - 26x + 8$ $(5x-2)(3x-4)$
32. $6x^2 - 13x - 63$ $(3x+7)(2x-9)$
33. $6x^6 + 7x^3y - 55y^2$ $(2x^3-5y)(3x^3+11y)$

*Use with Lesson 15-8, text pages 428–429.

Copyright © Sadlier-Oxford

Factoring Polynomials* (con't)

Name ______________________

Date ______________________

34. $132r^2 - 101rs + 14s^2$

$(11r-2s)(12r-7s)$

35. $77x^2 - 170xy + 77y^2$

$(7x-11y)(11x-7y)$

36. $36s^2 + 23st - 3t^2$

$(9s-t)(4s+3t)$

37. $6a^2 + 5ab - 6b^2$

$(3a-2b)(2a+3b)$

38. $39a^2 + 19ab + 2b^2$

$(13a+2b)(3a+b)$

39. $15x^4 - 22x^2y + 8y^2$

$(5x^2-4y)(3x^2-2y)$

40. $84m^2 + 16mn - 5n^2$

$(14m+5n)(6m-n)$

41. $19x^6 - 59x^3y + 6y^2$

$(19x^3-2y)(x^3-3y)$

42. $2c^2 + 13cd - 45d^2$

$(2c-5d)(c+9d)$

43. $12x^4 - 40x^2y^2 + 25y^4$

$(6x^2-5y^2)(2x^2-5y^2)$

44. $8x^4 + 26x^2y^2 + 21y^4$

$(4x^2+7y^2)(2x^2+3y^2)$

45. $6x^6 + 7x^3y^3 - 10y^6$

$(6x^3-5y^3)(x^3+2y^3)$

46. $6x^4 + 43x^2y^2 + 77y^4$

$(3x^2+11y^2)(2x^2+7y^2)$

47. $18h^4 + 23h^2b^2 - 6b^4$

$(9h^2-2b^2)(2h^2+3b^2)$

48. $15x^6 + 41x^3y^3 + 14y^6$

$(3x^3+7y^3)(5x^3+2y^3)$

49. $35a^6 - 33a^3b^3 - 8b^6$

$(5a^3+b^3)(7a^3-8b^3)$

Solve.

50. The area of a rectangle is $(6x^2 - 7x - 5)$ cm^2. Find the binomials that represent the dimensions of the rectangle.

$A = lw$

$(3x-5)(2x+1)$

51. The area of a rhombus is $(2x^2 + 13x + 21)$ in.^{2}. Find the binomials that represent the dimensions of the rhombus.

$A = bh$

$(2x+7)(x+3)$

*Use with Lesson 15-8, text pages 428–429.

Copyright © Sadlier-Oxford

Perfect Square Trinomials*

Name ______________________

Date ______________________

Simplify.

1. $(x + 5)^2$ $x^2 + 10x + 25$

2. $(4c + 5d)^2$ $16c^2 + 40cd + 25d^2$

3. $(3a - 2)^2$ $9a^2 - 12a + 4$

4. $(y - 8)^2$ $y^2 - 16y + 64$

5. $(m + 2n)^2$ $m^2 + 4mn + 4n^2$

6. $(7c - 3d)^2$ $49c^2 - 42cd + 9d^2$

7. $(2a + 3)^2$ $4a^2 + 12a + 9$

8. $(x + 7)^2$ $x^2 + 14x + 49$

9. $(m - 9n)^2$ $m^2 - 18mn + 81n^2$

$4x^2 - 20x + 25 = \underline{\ ?\ }$

- 1st term: $4x^2 \longrightarrow$ perfect square
- 3rd term: $25 \longrightarrow$ perfect square
- middle term: $20x \longrightarrow 20x = 2 \cdot \sqrt{4x^2} \cdot \sqrt{25} = 2 \cdot 2x \cdot 5$

Factors are: $(2x - 5)(2x - 5) = (2x - 5)^2$

Factor.

10. $x^2 + 22x + 121$ $(x + 11)^2$

11. $x^2 + 14x + 49$ $(x + 7)^2$

12. $y^2 - 24y + 144$ $(y - 12)^2$

13. $y^2 - 20y + 100$ $(y - 10)^2$

14. $9x^2 - 30x + 25$ $(3x - 5)^2$

15. $4x^2 - 28x + 49$ $(2x - 7)^2$

16. $16x^2 + 40xy + 25y^2$ $(4x + 5y)^2$

17. $9a^2 - 66ab + 121b^2$ $(3a - 11b)^2$

18. $a^2b^2 - 10ab + 25$ $(ab - 5)^2$

19. $0.04x^2 + 1.2xy + 0.09y^2$ $(0.2x + 0.3y)^2$

20. $1.21x^2 - 1.1xy + 0.25y^2$ $(1.1x - 0.5y)^2$

Solve.

21. The area of a square is $(121x^2 + 22x + 1)$ cm^2. Find the binomial that represents the length of a side of the square. $A = s^2$

$A = (11x + 1)^2;\ s = 11x + 1$

22. The area of a circle is $(9x^2 + 24x + 16)\ \pi$ cm^2. Find the binomial that represents the radius of the circle. $A = \pi r^2$

$A = (3x + 4)^2 \pi;\ r = 3x + 4$

*Use with Lesson 15-9, text page 430.

Copyright © Sadlier-Oxford

Difference of Two Squares*

Name ______________________

Date ______________________

$(x + 4)(x - 4) = \underline{\ ?\ }$

$(x + 4)(x - 4) = x^2 - 4x + 4x - 16$

$= x^2 - 16$

Multiply.

1. $(x - 5)(x + 5)$ $x^2 - 25$
2. $(x + 13)(x - 13)$ $x^2 - 169$
3. $(14a + 1)(14a - 1)$ $196a^2 - 1$
4. $(x + 4y)(x - 4y)$ $x^2 - 16y^2$
5. $(x - 7y)(x + 7y)$ $x^2 - 49y^2$
6. $(\frac{2}{3}a + \frac{1}{2}b)(\frac{2}{3}a - \frac{1}{2}b)$ $\frac{4}{9}a^2 - \frac{1}{4}b^2$
7. $(3a + 5b)(3a - 5b)$ $9a^2 - 25b^2$
8. $(2a - 13b)(2a + 13b)$ $4a^2 - 169b^2$
9. $(\frac{4}{7}c + \frac{2}{3}d)(\frac{4}{7}c - \frac{2}{3}d)$ $\frac{16}{49}c^2 - \frac{4}{9}d^2$

$4x^2 - 25 = \underline{\ ?\ }$

$\sqrt{4x^2} = 2x$ and $\sqrt{25} = 5$

Factors are: $(2x + 5)(2x - 5)$

Factor.

10. $x^2 - 81$ $(x+9)(x-9)$
11. $x^2 - 16$ $(x+4)(x-4)$
12. $m^2 - n^2$ $(m+n)(m-n)$
13. $9 - 25a^2$ $(3+5a)(3-5a)$
14. $25 - 121b^2$ $(5+11b)(5-11b)$
15. $\frac{1}{4}x^2 - \frac{1}{9}y^2$ $(\frac{1}{2}x + \frac{1}{3}y)(\frac{1}{2}x - \frac{1}{3}y$
16. $64x^2 - 9y^2$ $(8x+3y)(8x-3y)$
17. $169x^2 - 25y^2$ $(13x+5y)(13x-5y)$
18. $0.36x^2 - y^2$ $(0.6x+y)(0.6x-y)$
19. $a^2b^2 - c^2$ $(ab+c)(ab-c)$
20. $\frac{16}{25}m^2 - \frac{4}{9}n^2$ $(\frac{4}{5}m + \frac{2}{3}n)(\frac{4}{5}m - \frac{2}{3}n)$
21. $1.21c^2 - 0.09d^2$ $(1.1c + 0.3d)(1.1c - 0.3$

Solve.

22. The area of a rectangle is $(9x^2 - 16y^2)$ cm^2. Express the area as a product of two binomials. $A = lw$ $(3x+4y)(3x-4y)$
23. The area of a rhombus is $(169x^2 - 4y^2)$ cm^2. Express the area as a product of two binomials. $A = bh$ $(13x+2y)(13x-2y)$
24. The average mark of a class is represented by the expression $(144a^2 - 225b^2)$. Express the average mark as a product of two binomials. $(12a+15b)(12a-15b)$

*Use with Lesson 15-10, text page 431.

Copyright © Sadlier-Oxford

Complete Factorization*

Name ______________________

Date ______________________

To factor a polynomial completely:

- Factor out any GCF.
- Divide each term by the GCF.
- Factor, if possible, the new polynomial.
- Rewrite the original polynomial as a product of the GCF and these factors.

Factor completely.

1. $14x + 35y$

   $7(2x+5y)$

2. $18x + 27y$

   $9(2x+3y)$

3. $15ab + 35bc$

   $5b(3a+7c)$

4. $20mn + 50np$

   $10n(2m+5p)$

5. $5x^2 - 20y^2$

   $5(x+2y)(x-2y)$

6. $3x^2y - 27y$

   $3y(x+3)(x-3)$

7. $m^3 - mn^4$

   $m(m+n^2)(m-n^2)$

8. $x^3y^5 - xy$

   $xy(xy^2+1)(xy^2-1)$

9. $4x^2y - 8xy + 4y$

   $4y(x-1)^2$

10. $2a^2x^2 - 8a^2x + 8a^2$

    $2a^2(x-2)^2$

11. $3x^3 - 3x^2 - 6x$

    $3x(x-2)(x+1)$

12. $2x^2y - 10xy + 12y$

    $2y(x-3)(x-2)$

13. $5ax^2y^2 - 5az^2$

    $5a(xy+z)(xy-z)$

14. $28a^3x^2y^2 - 7a^3c^2$

    $7a^3(2xy+c)(2xy-c)$

15. $5m^2 - 30mn + 45n^2$

    $5(m-3n)^2$

16. $7a^2 - 70ab + 175b^2$

    $7(a-5b)^2$

17. $2a^3 - a^2 - a$

    $a(2a+1)(a-1)$

18. $15b^2 - 5b - 10$

    $5(3b+2)(b-1)$

19. $18b + 21b^2 + 6b^3$

    $3b(3+2b)(2+b)$

20. $50ab - 5ab^2 - 15ab^3$

    $5ab(5-3b)(2+b)$

21. $24x^3y - 28x^2y^2 + 8xy^3$

    $4xy(2x-y)(3x-2y)$

22. $10x^3y^2 + 34x^2y^3 + 12xy^4$

    $2xy^2(5x+2y)(x+3y)$

*Use with Lesson 15-11, text pages 432–433.

Copyright © Sadlier-Oxford

Complete Factorization* (con't)

Name ______________________

Date ______________________

Factor completely.

23. $3y^2 + 6$ — $3(y^2+2)$

24. $r + 2sr$ — $r(1+2s)$

25. $mx^2 - mx - 2m$ — $m(x-2)(x+1)$

26. $8x + 24$ — $8(x+3)$

27. $mn^2 - m^2n$ — $mn(n-m)$

28. $15a^2 + 10a - 5$ — $5(3a-1)(a+1)$

29. $x^2 + x$ — $x(x+1)$

30. $6b^2 - 30b$ — $6b(b-5)$

31. $2\pi r - \pi r^2$ — $\pi r(2-r)$

Factor completely. If the polynomial cannot be factored, label it prime.
(Hint: $5c^2 + 8e^2$ is prime.)

32. $98x^3y - 28x^3y^2 + 2x^3y^3$ — $2x^3y(7-y)^2$

33. $243x^2y^2 - 54x^2y^3 + 3x^2y^4$ — $3x^2y^2(9-y)^2$

34. $a^4 - b^4$ — $(a^2+b^2)(a+b)(a-b)$

35. $36x^2y^2 + 84xyz + 49z^2$ — $(6xy+7z)^2$

36. $81x^4 - y^4$ — $(9x^2+y^2)(3x+y)(3x-y)$

37. $81a^2c^2 + 72abc + 64b^2$ — Prime

38. $36a^4 - 13a^2 + 1$ — $(3a+1)(3a-1)(2a+1)(2a-1)$

39. $4m^4 + 144n^6$ — $4(m^4+36n^6)$

40. $100a^4 - 29a^2 + 1$ — $(5a+1)(5a-1)(2a+1)(2a-1)$

41. $36a^4 - 225b^4$ — $9(2a^2+5b^2)(2a^2-5b^2)$

42. $6a^4b^4 - 17a^2b^2 + 7$ — $(2a^2b^2-1)(3a^2b^2-7)$

43. $44x^2y^2 - 3xyz - 65z^2$ — $(11xy+13z)(4xy-5z)$

44. $72c^4d^4 + 35c^2d^2 + 3$ — $(9c^2d^2+1)(8c^2d^2+3)$

45. $42a^2b^2 + 25abc - 28c^2$ — $(6ab+7c)(7ab-4c)$

46. $6x^4y^4 - x^2y^2 - 77$ — $(3x^2y^2-11)(2x^2y^2+7)$

47. $6r^2p^2 + rpt + 40t^2$ — Prime

48. $121a^2b^2 - 264abc + 144c^2$ — $(11ab-12c)^2$

49. $6a^3r^2s^2 - 54a^3t^4$ — $6a^3(rs+3t^2)(rs-3t^2)$

50. $90c^2d^2 + 129cde + 28e^2$ — $(15cd+4e)(6cd+7e)$

51. $6n^6y + 216y$ — $6y(n^6+36)$

*Use with Lesson 15-11, text pages 432–433.

Copyright © Sadlier-Oxford

Complete Factorization* (con't)

Name ______________________

Date ______________________

Factor. Rearrange terms if necessary.

52. $x^2 + 6 + 5x$ $(x+3)(x+2)$

53. $-3y + y^2 - 4$ $(y-4)(y+1)$

54. $a^2 - 5a - 6$ $(a-6)(a+1)$

55. $3y + y^2 - 4$ $(y+4)(y-1)$

56. $y^2 + 4 - 5y$ $(y-4)(y-1)$

57. $x^2 - 9x + 14$ $(x-7)(x-2)$

58. $-8c - 9 + c^2$ $(c-9)(c+1)$

59. $x^2 + 5x - 14$ $(x+7)(x-2)$

60. $9 + d^2 + 6d$ $(3+d)^2$

61. $x^2 - 5x - 14$ $(x-7)(x+2)$

62. $10r + 24 + r^2$ $(r+6)(r+4)$

63. $y^2 + 48y - 100$ $(y+50)(y-2)$

64. $16 + 10m + m^2$ $(8+m)(2+m)$

65. $x^2 - 12x + 20$ $(x-10)(x-2)$

66. $x^4 + 2x^2 + 1$ $(x^2+1)^2$

67. $y^2 + 100 + 29y$ $(y+25)(y+4)$

68. $x^6 + 1 + 2x^3$ $(x^3+1)^2$

69. $2 - y - y^2$ $(2+y)(1-y)$

70. $6y^3 + 3y^2 - 3y$ $3y(2y-1)(y+1)$

71. $x^4 - 8x^2 - 9$ $(x^2+1)(x+3)(x-3)$

72. $100x^2 - 4y^2$ $4(5x+y)(5x-y)$

Factor completely.

73. $3a - a^2$ $a(3-a)$

74. $x^3 - x^2 - 2x$ $x(x-2)(x+1)$

75. $2m^3 - 11$ Prime

76. $r^2 + 11r$ $r(r+11)$

77. $9x^5 + 27x^3 - 45x^2$ $9x^2(x^3+3x-5)$

78. $4x^2 - 36y^2$ $4(x+3y)(x-3y)$

79. $x^2y^2 + y$ $y(x^2y+1)$

80. $14a^2c - 7a^2$ $7a^2(2c-1)$

81. $3x^4 + 11x^2 + 13x$ $x(3x^3+11x+13)$

82. $16c^4 - 81$ $(4c^2+9)(2c+3)(2c-3)$

83. $8n^2 + 2nr - r^2$ $(4n-r)(2n+r)$

84. $(a+b)^2 - (c+d)^2$ $[(a+b)+(c+d)][(a+b)-(c+d)]$

85. $(e+f)^2 + 6(e+f) + 9$ $[(e+f)+3]^2$

86. $576a^2 - 1$ $(24a+1)(24a-1)$

87. $9r^2 - 9m^2$ $9(r+m)(r-m)$

*Use with Lesson 15-11, text pages 432–433.

Copyright © Sadlier-Oxford

Complete Factorization* (con't)

Name ______________________

Date ______________________

Solve. Show your work.

88. The volume of a rectangular prism is $(6x^3y - 6x^2y - 120xy)$ cm^3. Write in factored form the expression that represents the dimensions of the rectangular solid.

$6xy(x-5)(x+4)$

$V = lwh$

$V = 6xy(x^2 - x - 20)$

$V = 6xy(x-5)(x+4)$

89. The volume of a right cylinder is $(3x^3y + 12x^2y + 12xy)\pi$ cm^3. Write in factored form the expression that represents the dimensions of the right cylinder.

$3xy(x+2)^2$

$V = \pi r^2 h$

$V = \pi(3xy)(x^2 + 4x + 4)$

$V = \pi(3xy)(x+2)^2$

90. If the product of three factors is $(6x^3 + 12x^2 - 48x)$, what are the factors?

$6x(x+4)(x-2)$

$6x(x^2 + 2x - 8)$

$6x(x+4)(x-2)$

91. What are the factors representing three consecutive numbers if the product is $x^3 + 3x^2 + 2x$?

$x(x+1)(x+2)$

$x(x^2 + 3x + 2)$

$x(x+1)(x+2)$

92. What factor, when squared, equals one half of $(2x^2 + 4x + 2)$?

$x+1$

$2(x^2 + 2x + 1) \div 2;\ x^2 + 2x + 1 = (x+1)^2$

*Use with Lesson 15-11, text pages 432–433.

Copyright © Sadlier-Oxford

Division of Polynomials*

Name ______________________

Date ______________________

$$\frac{a^7}{a^5} = \underline{\ ?\ } = a^{7-5} = a^2$$

Divide.

1. $\frac{a^{10}}{a^6}$ a^4

2. $\frac{x^{12}y^6}{x^4y^2}$ x^8y^4

3. $\frac{6x^3y}{2xy}$ $3x^2$

4. $\frac{39a^2bc}{13abc}$ $3a$

5. $\frac{-24x^3y}{6x^2y}$ $-4x$

6. $\frac{35a^4b^2}{-7a^3b}$ $-5ab$

7. $\frac{22.5m^5n^4}{1.5m^2n^3}$ $15m^3n$

8. $\frac{1.69c^6d^4}{1.3c^3}$ $1.3c^3d^4$

9. $\frac{-336c^5d^7}{-16c^2d^5}$ $21c^3d^2$

10. $\frac{-495e^8f^3}{-45e^3f}$ $11e^5f^2$

11. $\frac{a^3b^3 + a^2b^2}{a^2b^2}$ $ab+1$

12. $\frac{27c^3d^5 - 18c^2d^6}{9c^2d^3}$ $3cd^2 - 2d^3$

13. $\frac{-136x^2y^3 + 187xy}{17xy}$ $-8xy^2 + 11$

14. $\frac{x^4y^5 + x^3y^2}{x^2y^2}$ $x^2y^3 + x$

15. $\frac{-196a^7 + 126a^6}{14a^5}$ $-14a^2 + 9a$

16. $\frac{3\pi r^2h - 9\pi rh}{-3\pi rh}$ $-r+3$

17. $\frac{-75x^{10} + 90x^{12}}{-15x^9}$ $5x - 6x^3$

18. $\frac{x^3y^4z^2 + x^5y^3z^3 - x^4y^5z^4}{x^3y^3z^2}$ $y + x^2z - xy^2z^2$

19. $\frac{-209r^3s^2 + 95r^5s^2}{19rs^2}$ $-11r^2 + 5r^4$

*Use with Lesson 15-12, text pages 434–435.

Copyright © Sadlier-Oxford

Division of Polynomials* (con't)

Name ______________________

Date ______________________

$(x^2 - x - 20) \div (x + 4) = \underline{\ ?\ }$

$$\begin{array}{r} x \quad -5 \\ x+4 \overline{) x^2 \quad -x \quad -20} \\ \underline{-x^2 \quad -4x} \\ -5x \quad -20 \\ \underline{+5x \quad +20} \end{array}$$

Check:

$(x - 5)(x + 4) = x^2 - x - 20$

Divide and check.

20. $(a^2 + 5a + 6) \div (a + 3)$

$a+2$

21. $(10 - 11b + 3b^2) \div (5 - 3b)$

$2-b$

22. $(r^2 + 7r + 12) \div (r + 4)$

$r+3$

23. $(56 - 3m - 20m^2) \div (8 - 5m)$

$7+4m$

24. $(2x^2 - 13x - 7) \div (2x + 1)$

$x-7$

25. $(m^3 + 9m^2 + 19m + 10) \div (m + 2)$

m^2+7m+5

26. $(6x^2 - 7x - 20) \div (3x + 4)$

$2x-5$

27. $(r^3 - 10r^2 + 25r + 12) \div (r - 3)$

$r^2-7r+4+\frac{24}{r-3}$

28. $(3x^2 - 11x - 30) \div (x - 6)$

$3x+7+\frac{12}{x-6}$

29. $(9x^3 - 9x^2y + 17xy^2 - 5y^3) \div (3x - y)$

$3x^2-2xy+5y^2$

30. $(10x^2 - 19x + 12) \div (2x - 3)$

$5x-2+\frac{6}{2x-3}$

31. $(4a^3 + 12a^2b + ab^2 - 12b^3) \div (2a + 3b)$

$2a^2+3ab-4b^2$

Solve.

32. The area of a rectangle is represented by $(16r^2 + 34r - 15)$ cm^2. If the length of the rectangle is represented by $(8r - 3)$ cm, what is the width of the rectangle? $w=\frac{A}{l}$

$(16r^2+34r-15)\div(8r-3)$

$(2r+5)$ cm

33. The distance traveled by a car is $(2x^2 - 7x + 6)$ miles. If the car travels $(2x - 3)$ miles per hour, how much time did the car travel to cover the distance? $t=\frac{d}{r}$

$(2x^2-7x+6)\div(2x-3)$

$(x-2)$ hr

*Use with Lesson 15-12, text pages 434–435.

Copyright © Sadlier-Oxford

Multiplication and Division of Rational Expressions*

Name ____________________

Date ____________________

Simplify $\frac{5x^2}{20x^3}$. $\frac{5x^2}{20x^3} = \frac{(\not{5})(\not{x})(\not{x})}{(4)(\not{5})(\not{x})(\not{x})(x)} = \frac{1}{4x}$

Simplify.

1. $\frac{6ab}{24ac}$ $\frac{b}{4c}$

2. $\frac{^-15x^2y}{25x^3y^2}$ $\frac{-3}{5xy}$

3. $\frac{25 - x^2}{2x - 10}$ $\frac{5+x}{-2}$

4. $\frac{2a + 6}{4}$ $\frac{a+3}{2}$

5. $\frac{3b + 9}{-15}$ $\frac{b+3}{-5}$

6. $\frac{b - a}{a - b}$ -1

7. $\frac{12xy - 3y^2}{3xy}$ $\frac{4x-y}{x}$

8. $\frac{14a^2b + 21ab^2}{28ab}$ $\frac{2a+3b}{4}$

9. $\frac{x^2 - 5x - 6}{x^2 + 2x + 1}$ $\frac{x-6}{x+1}$

10. $\frac{5m^2}{15m^2 - 5mn}$ $\frac{m}{3m-n}$

11. $\frac{9d}{9d + 18}$ $\frac{d}{d+2}$

12. $\frac{3y^2 - 10y + 3}{9y^2 - 6y + 1}$ $\frac{y-3}{3y-1}$

$$\frac{5}{2x - 12} \cdot \frac{x - 6}{x^2 - 10} = \frac{5}{2(\not{x - 6})} \cdot \frac{(\not{x - 6})}{(x^2 - 10)} = \frac{5}{2(x^2 - 10)} = \frac{5}{2x^2 - 20}$$

Multiply

13. $\frac{7x^2}{9y^2} \cdot \frac{18xy^2}{7x^3}$ $\frac{7x^2}{7x^2 \cdot x} \cdot \frac{9y^2 \cdot 2x}{9y^2}$ 2

14. $\frac{36a^2}{15b} \cdot \frac{3b}{6a}$ $\frac{6a \cdot 6a}{6a} \cdot \frac{3b}{3b \cdot 5}$ $\frac{6a}{5}$

15. $\frac{7}{8} \cdot \frac{2a + 4}{21}$ $\frac{7}{7 \cdot 3} \cdot \frac{2(a+2)}{2 \cdot 4}$ $\frac{a+2}{12}$

16. $\frac{4a + 12}{16a} \cdot \frac{a^3}{24}$ $\frac{4(a+3)}{4 \cdot 4a} \cdot \frac{a \cdot a^2}{24}$ $\frac{a^3 + 3a^2}{96}$

17. $\frac{a^2 - 1}{a^2} \cdot \frac{15}{3a^2 - 3a}$ $\frac{(a+1)(a-1)(3)(5)}{(a^2)(3a)(a-1)}$ $\frac{5a+5}{a^3}$

18. $\frac{x^2 - 9}{2x^2 \; 3} \cdot \frac{12}{2x^2 - 6}$ $\frac{(x+3)(x-3)}{2(x^2-3)} \cdot \frac{3 \cdot 4^2}{3}$ $\frac{2x^2 \; 3 \; 18}{x^2 - 3}$

*Use with Lesson 15-13, text pages 436–437.

Copyright © Sadlier-Oxford

Multiplication and Division of Rational Expressions* (con't)

Name ____________________

Date ____________________

Multiply.

19. $\frac{5x + 10}{15x + 30} \cdot \frac{6x + 12}{x^2 - 4}$ $\frac{2}{x-2}$

20. $\frac{y^2 - 3y + 2}{2y^3} \cdot \frac{4y^2}{2y - 4}$ $\frac{y-1}{y}$

21. $\frac{x^2 + 2x - 15}{x^2 + 9x + 20} \cdot \frac{x^2 + 3x - 4}{x^2 - 4x + 3}$ 1

22. $\frac{6x^2 - 7x - 3}{10x^2 - 17x + 3} \cdot \frac{3x^2 + 16x + 16}{3x^2 + 13x + 4}$ $\frac{3x+4}{5x-1}$

$$\frac{5x}{8} \div \frac{6x}{x + 2} = \frac{5\cancel{x}}{8} \cdot \frac{x + 2}{6\cancel{x}} = \frac{5x + 10}{48}$$

Divide.

23. $\frac{4x}{7y} \div \frac{10x^3}{28y^2}$ $\frac{8y}{5x^2}$

24. $\frac{7xy^2}{10ab} \div \frac{14y^3}{5a^2b^2}$ $\frac{abx}{4y}$

25. $\frac{5x^2y^2}{15z} \div 10xy$ $\frac{xy}{30z}$

26. $\frac{14x^3y^3}{7z^3} \div 28x^2y^2$ $\frac{xy}{14z^3}$

27. $\frac{a^2 - 1}{7} \div \frac{a + 1}{14}$ $2a-2$

28. $\frac{a^2 - 2a + 1}{6a} \div \frac{a - 1}{15a^2}$ $\frac{5a^2-5a}{2}$

29. $\frac{a^2 - 2a - 15}{3a} \div \frac{a^2 - 9}{a^2}$ $\frac{a^2-5a}{3a-9}$

30. $\frac{2b^2 - b - 1}{b^2 - 2b + 1} \div \frac{4b^2 + 4b + 1}{2b^2 + 7b + 3}$ $\frac{b+3}{b-1}$

31. $\frac{x^2 - 6x + 9}{4x - 12} \div (3 - x)$ $-\frac{1}{4}$

32. $(16 - y^2) \div \frac{y^2 + 9y + 20}{2y + 10}$ $8-2y$

Simplify.

33. $\frac{2x + 6}{x^2 - 9} \div \frac{x + 3}{3 - x} \cdot \frac{x + 3}{4}$ $-\frac{1}{2}$

34. $\frac{x^2 + 2xy + y^2}{x^2 - y^2} \div \frac{x + y}{y^2 - x^2} \cdot \frac{x - y}{x^2 - 2xy + y^2}$ $\frac{x+y}{y-x}$

35. For what value(s) of x is $\frac{x^2 - 49}{7} \cdot \frac{14}{2x - 14}$ undefined? 7

36. For what value(s) of y is $\frac{y^2 - 4y + 4}{y^2} \div \frac{y^2 - 4}{y}$ undefined? $0, \pm 2$

*Use with Lesson 15-13, text pages 436–437.

Copyright © Sadlier-Oxford

Addition and Subtraction with Like Denominators*

Name ______________________

Date ______________________

To add or subtract rational expressions with *like* denominators:

- Add or subtract the numerators.
- Write the sum or difference over the like denominator.
- Simplify.

Add or subtract. Simplify answers where possible.

1. $\frac{9}{4x} + \frac{5}{4x}$ $\quad \frac{14}{4x} = \frac{7}{2x}$

2. $\frac{2a}{5x} + \frac{8a}{5x}$ $\quad \frac{10a}{5x} = \frac{2a}{x}$

3. $\frac{11x}{x - y} - \frac{11y}{x - y}$ $\quad \frac{11(x-y)}{x-y} = 11$

4. $\frac{6x}{x - 3} - \frac{18}{x - 3}$ $\quad \frac{6(x-3)}{x-3} = 6$

5. $\frac{8}{5y} + \frac{4}{5y} - \frac{7}{5y}$ $\quad \frac{5y}{5} = \frac{1}{y}$

6. $\frac{6}{9c} + \frac{7}{9c} - \frac{4}{9c}$ $\quad \frac{9}{9c} = \frac{1}{c}$

7. $\frac{x^2 + 4x}{x^2 - 4} + \frac{4}{x^2 - 4}$ $\quad \frac{x+2}{x-2}$

8. $\frac{6x - 5}{x^2 - 1} - \frac{5x - 6}{x^2 - 1}$ $\quad \frac{1}{x-1}$

9. $\frac{x^2 + 3xy}{x + y} + \frac{y^2 - xy}{x + y}$ $\quad x + y$

10. $\frac{a^2 - 2ab}{a - 2b} - \frac{ab - 2b^2}{a - 2b}$ $\quad a - b$

11. $\frac{x + 4y}{x^2 - y^2} + \frac{4x - 7y}{x^2 - y^2} - \frac{3x - y}{x^2 - y^2}$ $\quad \frac{2}{x+y}$

12. $\frac{7 + 3x}{x^2 - 4} - \frac{8 + 4x}{x^2 - 4} + \frac{3 + 2x}{x^2 - 4}$ $\quad \frac{1}{x-2}$

13. $\frac{3a^2 - 2b^2}{a^2 + y^2} - \frac{2a^2 - 3y^2}{a^2 + y^2}$ $\quad \frac{a^2 - 2b^2 + 3y^2}{a^2 + y^2}$

14. $\frac{5c - 2}{3c - 4} - \frac{16c - 26}{3c - 4}$ $\quad \frac{-11c + 24}{3c - 4}$

*Use with Lesson 15-14, text page 438.

Copyright © Sadlier-Oxford

Addition and Subtraction with Like Denominators* (con't)

Name ______________________

Date ______________________

Add or subtract. Simplify answers.

15. $\frac{a^2 + 4a}{a^2 - a - 6} + \frac{8 - a^2}{a^2 - a - 6}$

$\frac{4(a+2)}{(a-3)(a+2)} = \frac{4}{a-3}$

16. $\frac{4b^2 + 7b}{2b^2 + 5b + 2} - \frac{1 + 7b}{2b^2 + 5b + 2}$

$\frac{(2b+1)(2b-1)}{(2b+1)(b+2)} = \frac{2b-1}{b+2}$

17. $\frac{7x^2 + 12x}{4x^2 + 3x} - \frac{5x^2 + 3x}{4x^2 + 3x}$

$\frac{x(2x+9)}{x(4x+3)} = \frac{2x+9}{4x+3}$

18. $\frac{3r + 1}{r^2 - 7r + 12} + \frac{r + 17}{r^2 - 7r + 12}$

$\frac{2(2r+9)}{(r-4)(r-3)}$ or $\frac{4r+18}{r^2-7r+12}$

Solve. Show your work.

19. What is the average rate of speed for a 6-hour trip where the first 160 miles are by car and the next 110 miles are by bus?

45 mph

$\frac{d}{r} = t$

$\frac{160}{r} + \frac{110}{r} = 6;\ \frac{270}{r} = 6;\ 6r = 270;\ r = 45$

20. Find the perimeter of a triangle whose sides are represented by $\frac{4x + 1}{x + 6}$, $\frac{2 - 3x}{x + 6}$, and $\frac{9 + x}{x + 6}$.

2

$P = \frac{4x+1}{x+6} + \frac{2-3x}{x+6} + \frac{9+x}{x+6};\ \frac{2x+12}{x+6};\ \frac{2(x+6)}{x+6}$

21. The perimeter of a triangle is represented by $\frac{6a - 7}{6}$, and the two sides are represented by $\frac{2a - 6}{6}$ and $\frac{a + 1}{6}$. Find the representation of the third side.

$\frac{3a-2}{6}$

$\frac{6a-7}{6} - \frac{2a-6}{6} - \frac{a+1}{6};\ \frac{6a-7-2a+6-a-1}{6};\ \frac{3a-2}{6}$

*Use with Lesson 15-14, text page 438.

Copyright © Sadlier-Oxford

Least Common Denominator of Rational Expressions*

Name ______________________

Date ______________________

To find the Least Common Denominator (LCD) of two or more rational expressions:

- Completely factor each denominator.
- Express every prime factor with the greatest exponent it has in any denominator.
- Multiply these prime factors with their greatest exponents. This product is the LCD of the given expressions.

Find the LCD.

1. $\frac{1}{x}, \frac{3}{4x}$

   $4x$

2. $\frac{2}{15a}, \frac{4}{30a^2}$

   $30a^2$

3. $\frac{3}{7x^2y}, \frac{5}{14xy^2}$

   $14x^2y^2$

4. $\frac{9}{3x + 2}, \frac{7}{3x^2 + 5x + 2}$

   $(3x+2)(x+1) = 3x^2+5x+2$

5. $\frac{14}{2x - 7}, \frac{8x}{4x^2 - 28x + 49}$

   $(2x-7)(2x-7) = 4x^2-28x+49$

6. $\frac{4}{5x + 10z}, \frac{7}{3x + 6z}$

   $15(x+2z) = 15x + 30z$

7. $\frac{4x}{x - 3y}, \frac{9}{3y - x}$

   $x-3y$ or $3y-x$

8. $\frac{5a}{a + 1}, \frac{2a}{a + 5}$

   $(a+1)(a+5) = a^2+6a+5$

9. $\frac{8}{x - 5}, \frac{4}{x}$

   $x(x-5) = x^2-5x$

10. $\frac{7}{x^2 - xy}, \frac{10}{xy - y^2}$

    $xy(x-y) = x^2y - xy^2$

Find the LCD and complete the fraction.

11. $\frac{4}{x - 4} = \frac{\quad}{x^2 - 16}$ $4x+16$

12. $\frac{2}{3xy} = \frac{\quad}{9x^3y^2}$ $6x^2y$

13. $\frac{2a + b}{a - b} = \frac{\quad}{ab - b^2}$ $2ab+b^2$

14. $\frac{7}{r^3} = \frac{\quad}{t^2r^3}$ $7t^2$

15. $\frac{3}{x - 5} = \frac{\quad}{x^2 - 7x + 10}$ $3x-6$

16. $\frac{5}{2a - 4} = \frac{\quad}{2a^2 - 8}$ $5a+10$

*Use with Lesson 15-15, text page 439.

Copyright © Sadlier-Oxford

Addition and Subtraction with Unlike Denominators*

Name ______________________

Date ______________________

To add and subtract rational expressions with *unlike* denominators:

- Find the LCD.
- Change each rational expression to an equivalent fraction with the LCD as the denominator.
- Add or subtract.
- Simplify, if necessary.

Add or subtract.

1. $\frac{9x}{8y} - \frac{3x}{4y}$ $\frac{9x-6x}{8y} = \frac{3x}{8y}$

2. $\frac{2}{5x} + \frac{3}{10x}$ $\frac{4+3}{10x} = \frac{7}{10x}$

3. $\frac{4}{x^2} - \frac{7}{x}$ $\frac{4}{x^2} - \frac{7x}{x^2} = \frac{4-7x}{x^2}$

4. $\frac{1}{xy} + \frac{1}{yz}$ $\frac{z}{xyz} + \frac{x}{xyz} = \frac{z+x}{xyz}$

5. $\frac{7}{ab} - \frac{9}{ac}$ $\frac{7c}{abc} - \frac{9b}{abc} = \frac{7c-9b}{abc}$

6. $\frac{a}{3xy} - \frac{b}{2yz}$ $\frac{2az}{6xyz} - \frac{3bx}{6xyz} = \frac{2az-3bx}{6xyz}$

7. $\frac{a+5}{2a} + \frac{2a-1}{4a}$ $\frac{2a+10}{4a} + \frac{2a-1}{4a} = \frac{4a+9}{4a}$

8. $\frac{m+6}{m} + \frac{m-3}{4m}$ $\frac{4m+24}{4m} + \frac{m-3}{4m} = \frac{5m+21}{4m}$

9. $\frac{3d-7}{2d} - \frac{3d-2}{3d^2}$ $\frac{9d^2-21d}{6d^2} - \frac{6d-4}{6d^2} = \frac{9d^2-27d+4}{6d^2}$

10. $\frac{9}{xy} + \frac{2}{yz} - \frac{3}{xz}$ $\frac{9z}{xyz} + \frac{2x}{xyz} - \frac{3y}{xyz} = \frac{9z+2x}{xy}$

11. $x + \frac{1}{x}$ $\frac{x^2}{x} + \frac{1}{x} = \frac{x^2+1}{x}$

12. $x + 1 + \frac{1}{x+1}$ $\frac{(x+1)(x+1)+1}{x+1} = \frac{x^2+2x+2}{x+1}$

13. $x - 4 - \frac{x}{x+2}$ $\frac{(x-4)(x+2)-x}{x+2} = \frac{x^2-3x-8}{x+2}$

14. $x - \frac{1}{x-3}$ $\frac{x(x-3)-1}{x-3} = \frac{x^2-3x-1}{x-3}$

15. $\frac{6}{3x-5y} + \frac{9}{5y-3x}$ $\frac{6}{3x-5y} - \frac{9}{3x-5y} = \frac{-3}{3x-5y}$

16. $\frac{4}{x-4} + \frac{8}{2x-8}$ $\frac{8+8}{2(x-4)} = \frac{16}{2(x-4)} = \frac{8}{x-}$

17. $\frac{5}{4a-3} + \frac{8}{8a-6}$ $\frac{10+8}{8a-6} = \frac{18}{2(4a-3)} = \frac{9}{4a-3}$

18. $\frac{1}{x-3} + \frac{1}{x+3}$ $\frac{x+3+x-3}{(x-3)(x+3)} = \frac{2x}{x^2-9}$

*Use with Lesson 15-16, text pages 440–441.

Copyright © Sadlier-Oxford

Addition and subtraction with Unlike Denominators* (con't)

Name ______________________

Date ______________________

Add or subtract.

19. $\frac{9}{y+5} - \frac{6}{y-5}$

$\frac{3(y-25)}{(y+5)(y-5)} = \frac{3y-75}{y^2-25}$

20. $\frac{x^2}{x^2-y^2} - \frac{xy}{y-x}$

$\frac{x^2}{x^2-y^2} + \frac{xy}{x-y} = \frac{x^2+x^2y+xy^2}{x^2-y^2}$

21. $\frac{7}{x^2-xy} + \frac{5}{xy-y^2}$

$\frac{7y+5x}{xy(x-y)} = \frac{7y+5x}{x^2y-xy^2}$

22. $\frac{7a}{a^2+2a-3} - \frac{3a+4}{a^2+5a+6}$

$\frac{4a^2+13a+4}{(a+3)(a-1)(a+2)} = \frac{4a^2+13a+4}{a^3+4a^2+a-6}$

23. $\frac{4}{x^2-9} - \frac{7}{x^2-5x+6}$

$\frac{-3x-29}{(x+3)(x-3)(x-2)} = \frac{-3x-29}{x^3-2x^2-9x+18}$

24. $\frac{3x}{x^2-4} + \frac{4x-3}{x^2+2x-8}$

$\frac{7x^2+17x-6}{(x+2)(x-2)(x+4)} = \frac{7x^2+17x-6}{x^3+4x^2-4x-16}$

25. $\frac{1}{x^2-x-2} + \frac{2}{3x^2+2x-1} - \frac{1}{3x^2-7x+2}$

$\frac{2(2x-3)}{(x-2)(x+1)(3x-1)}$

$\frac{4x-6}{3x^3-4x^2-5x+2}$

26. $\frac{2x}{4x^2+x-3} - \frac{1}{x^2+6x+5} + \frac{x+1}{4x^2+17x-15}$

$\frac{(3x+2)(x+2)}{(4x-3)(x+1)(x+5)}$

$\frac{3x^2+8x+4}{4x^3+21x^2+2x-15}$

Solve.

$\frac{(x-3)(x+5)+(x-2)(x+5)+(x-2)(x-3)}{(x-2)(x-3)(x+5)}$

27. Find the perimeter of a triangle if the lengths of its sides are represented by $\frac{1}{x-2}$, $\frac{1}{x-3}$, and $\frac{1}{x+5}$.

$P = \frac{3x^2-19}{x^3-19x+30}$

$\frac{1}{2} \cdot \frac{4x^2+4}{(x-7)(x+3)} - \frac{x+1}{x+3}; \frac{2(x^2+1)}{(x-7)(x+3)} - \frac{(x+1)(x-7)}{(x-7)(x+3)}; \frac{(x+3)^2}{(x-7)(x+3)}$

28. The perimeter of a rectangle is represented by $\frac{4x^2+4}{x^2-4x-21}$ and its length by $\frac{x+1}{x+3}$. Find its width.

$\frac{1}{2}P - \ell = w$

$w = \frac{x+3}{x-7}$

*Use with Lesson 15-16, text pages 440–441.

Copyright © Sadlier-Oxford

Linear Equations and Slope*

Name ______________________

Date ______________________

Remember: To find the slope of a line represented by a linear equation:

- Choose any 2 points, P_1 and P_2, on the line. Name their coordinates, $P_1(x_1, y_1)$ and $P_2(x_2, y_2)$.
- Substitute the value of these coordinates in the slope formula:

$$m = \frac{(y_2 - y_1)}{(x_2 - x_1)}$$

Find the slope of each line (1–4) in the given graph.

1. $\frac{^-4-6}{0-2} = 5$
2. $\frac{0-3}{2-(^-4)} = \frac{^-1}{2}$
3. $\frac{^-8-(^-2)}{8-(^-5)} = \frac{^-6}{13}$
4. $\frac{^-5-7}{7-0} = \frac{^-12}{7}$

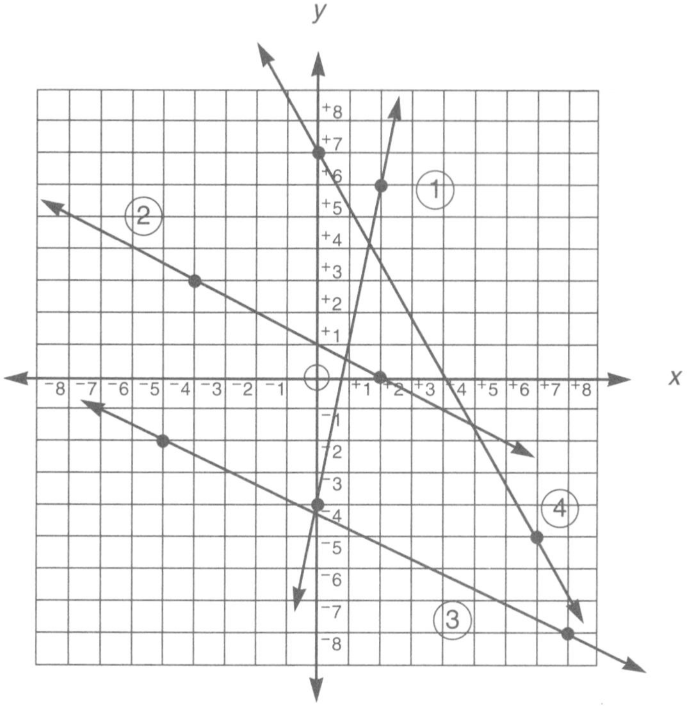

Find the slope of the line that passes through each pair of points.

5. (2, 5) and (6, 10) $\frac{10-5}{6-2} = \frac{5}{4}$
6. ($^-3$, 7) and (4, $^-5$) $\frac{^-5-7}{4-(^-3)} = \frac{^-12}{7}$
7. ($^-1$, $^-8$) and ($^-9$, $^-2$) $\frac{^-2-(^-8)}{^-9-(^-1)} = -\frac{6}{8} = \frac{^-3}{4}$
8. (0, 7) and (14, 0) $\frac{0-7}{14-0} = \frac{^-7}{14} = \frac{^-1}{2}$
9. (0, 0) and (8, 16) $\frac{16-0}{8-0} = \frac{16}{8} = 2$
10. (1, $^-6$) and ($^-8$, $^-9$) $\frac{-9-(^-6)}{-8-1} = \frac{^-3}{-9} = \frac{1}{3}$

*Use with Lesson 16-1, text pages 456–457.

Copyright © Sadlier-Oxford

Linear Equations and Slope* (cont'd)

Name ____________________

Date ____________________

Find the slope of each line.

11. $2x + 3y = 5$ $\frac{-2}{3}$

12. $5x - y = 0$ 5

13. $7x + y = 1$ $^-7$

14. $y = 3$ 0

15. $x + 8 = 0$ undefined

16. $x - 11y = 4$ $\frac{1}{11}$

Tell whether the line (17–22) in the given graph has positive, negative, zero, or undefined slope.

17. positive

18. undefined

19. negative

20. zero

21. negative

22. positive

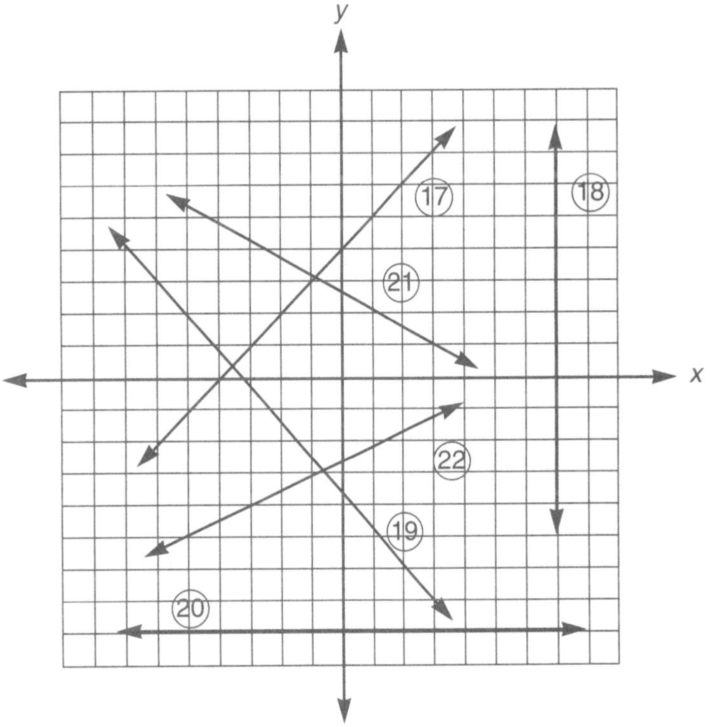

Solve.

23. The vertices of a triangle are $A(2, 3)$, $B(5, ^-2)$, and $C(^-1, ^-4)$. Find the slope of each side of triangle ABC.

$\overline{AB} = \frac{-2-3}{5-2}$; $\frac{-5}{3}$ $\overline{AC} = \frac{-4-3}{-1-2}$; $\frac{7}{3}$ $\overline{BC} = \frac{-4-^-2}{-1-5}$; $\frac{1}{3}$

24. Without drawing the graph, tell which of these equations have graphs that pass through the point $(0, 0)$.

a. $y = 2x$ **b.** $y = 4$ **c.** $x = 6y$ **d.** $x = ^-3$

a and c

25. Tell which lines have a slope equal to 5.

a. $2y + 5x = 1$ **b.** $3y - 15x = 9$

c. $\frac{y}{5} = x - 2$ **d.** $y = \frac{x}{5} + 5$

b and c

*Use with Lesson 16-1, text pages 456–457.

Copyright © Sadlier-Oxford

Slope-Intercept Form*

Name ______________________

Date ______________________

Remember: Slope-Intercept Form of a linear equation is represented by:

$$y = mx + b$$

m = slope; b = point at which the line intersects the y-axis and is called the y intercept.

Find the slope and y-intercept of the line that is the graph of the equation.

1. $2x - 5y = 3$ $m = \frac{2}{5}; b = \frac{^-3}{5}$
2. $x + y = 0$ $m = ^-1; b = 0$
3. $^-4x + y = 7$ $m = 4; b = 7$
4. $y + 5 = 0$ $m = 0; b = ^-5$
5. $y = ^-2x$ $m = ^-2; b = 0$
6. $2x - 3 = 0$ m = undefined; no y-interc
7. $\frac{1}{3}x + \frac{3}{4}y = \frac{1}{2}$ $m = \frac{^-4}{9}; b = \frac{2}{3}$
8. $\frac{1}{5}x - \frac{1}{3} = \frac{2}{7}y$ $m = \frac{7}{10}; b = \frac{^-7}{6}$
9. $\frac{x}{4} + 2y = 5$ $m = \frac{^-1}{8}; b = \frac{5}{2}$
10. $\frac{x}{7} - 4y = ^-2$ $m = \frac{1}{28}; b = \frac{1}{2}$

Write an equation of the line whose slope and y-intercept are:

11. $m = \frac{1}{3}$; $b = 3$ $y = \frac{1}{3}x + 3$ or $3y - x = 9$
12. $m = 0$; $b = ^-7$ $y = ^-7$
13. $m = ^-4$; $b = 5$ $y = ^-4x + 5$ or $4x + y = 5$
14. $m = \frac{^-2}{3}$; $b = ^-1$ $y = \frac{^-2}{3}x - 1$ or $2x + 3y = ^-3$
15. $m = ^-2$; $b = 0$ $y = ^-2x$ or $2x + y = 0$
16. $m = \frac{2}{7}$; $b = \frac{1}{3}$ $y = \frac{2}{7}x + \frac{1}{3}$ or $21y - 6x = 7$

State whether the lines are parallel, perpendicular or neither.

17. $2x + 5y = 6$; $y = \frac{^-2}{5}x + 3$ parallel
18. $y + 4x + 5 = 0$; $y = 4x + 5$ neither
19. $y = 7x$; $7y + x = 1$ perpendicular
20. $y = \frac{1}{2}x + 5$; $y = \frac{^-1}{2}x - 3$ neither

*Use with Lesson 16-2, text pages 458–459.

Copyright © Sadlier-Oxford

Finding the Equation of a Line*

Name ______________________

Date ______________________

Given: $P_1 = (2, ^-3)$ and $P_2 = (6, ^-1)$

Equation of line through P_1 and P_2 = ?

- $m = \frac{^-1 - ^-3}{6 - 2} = \frac{2}{4} = \frac{1}{2}$
- $y = mx + b \longrightarrow {^-3} = \frac{1}{2}(2) + b;\ b = {^-4}$
- Slope-Intercept Form: $y = \frac{1}{2}x - 4$

  or $x - 2y - 8 = 0$ (Equation of line)

Given: $m = \frac{1}{4}$ and $P = (^-8, 1)$

Equation of line through P = ?

- $y = mx + b \longrightarrow 1 = \frac{1}{4}(^-8) + b;\ b = 3$
- Slope-Intercept Form: $y = \frac{1}{4}x + 3$

  or $x - 4y + 12 = 0$ (Equation of line)

Write the equation of the line that passes through the given points.

1. $(3, 6)$ and $(7, 9)$ $3x - 4y + 15 = 0$
2. $(0, 0)$ and $(^-5, ^-8)$ $8x - 5y = 0$
3. $(^-1, ^-5)$ and $(^-4, ^-9)$ $4x - 3y - 11 = 0$
4. $(4, 0)$ and $(0, ^-7)$ $7x - 4y - 28 = 0$
5. $(4, ^-9)$ and $(^-5, 11)$ $20x + 9y + 1 = 0$
6. $(5, 9)$ and $(7, ^-3)$ $6x + y - 39 = 0$
7. $(^-3, ^-3)$ and $(6, 6)$ $x - y = 0$
8. $(^-7, 3)$ and $(2, 5)$ $2x - 9y + 41 = 0$

Write the equation of the line that has the given slope and passes through the given point.

9. $m = 3;\ (4, 1)$ $3x - y - 11 = 0$
10. $m = {^-6};\ (^-2, ^-3)$ $6x + y + 15 = 0$
11. $m = -\frac{1}{2};\ (1, ^-3)$ $x + 2y + 5 = 0$
12. $m = -\frac{9}{5};\ (0, ^-5)$ $9x + 5y + 25 = 0$
13. $m = \frac{3}{5};\ (^-5, 0)$ $3x - 5y + 15 = 0$
14. $m = 2;\ (3, 4)$ $2x - y - 2 = 0$

Write the equation of the line that is:

15. parallel to the line $y = 5x - 3$ and passes through the point $(^-1, 2)$. $m = 5$ and $(^-1, 2)$

    $2 = 5(^-1) + b;\ b = 7$

    $5x - y + 7 = 0$

16. parallel to the line $3x - 5y = 2$ and passes through the point $(5, 3)$. $m = \frac{3}{5}$ and $(5, 3)$

    $3 = \frac{3}{5}(5) + b;\ b = 0$

    $3x - 5y = 0$

17. perpendicular to the line $2x - 3y = 12$ and has the same y-intercept. $m = -\frac{3}{2};\ b = {^-4}$

    $3x + 2y + 8 = 0$

*Use with Lesson 16-3, text pages 460–461.

Copyright © Sadlier-Oxford

Finding the Equation of a Line*
(cont'd)

Name ______________________

Date ______________________

Write the equation of the line that is:

16. perpendicular to the line $3x + 4y = 7$ and has the same y-intercept.

$m = \frac{4}{3}$

$b = \frac{7}{4}$

$16x - 12y + 21 = 0$

17. parallel to the line $x + y = {}^{-}2$ and passes through the origin.

$m = {}^{-}1$ and $(0,0)$

$x + y = 0$

18. perpendicular to the line $2x + y = 5$ and passes through the origin.

$m = \frac{1}{2}$ and $(0,0)$

$x - 2y = 0$

19. parallel to the line $y = {}^{-}2x + 7$ and has the same y-intercept as the line $y = 2x - 4$.

$m = {}^{-}2$ and $b = {}^{-}4$

$2x + y + 4 = 0$

20. parallel to the line $y = -\frac{2}{5}x$ and has the same y-intercept as the line $2y - 3x = 5$.

$m = \frac{{}^{-}2}{5}$ and $b = \frac{5}{2}$

$4x + 10y - 25 = 0$

Find the equation of each line (21–26) indicated in the graphs.

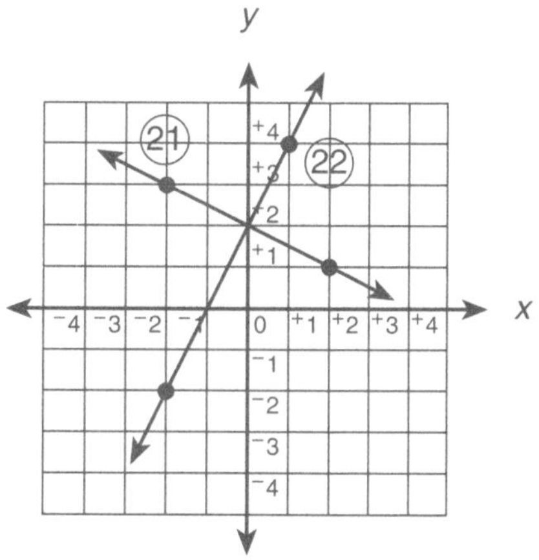

21. $m = \frac{{}^{-}1}{2}$; $b = 2$; $x + 2y - 4 = 0$

22. $m = 2$; $b = 2$; $2x - y + 2 = 0$

23. $m = 0$; $b = 2$; $y - 2 = 0$

24. $m =$ undefined; $x + 3 = 0$

25. $m = \frac{3}{4}$; $b = \frac{{}^{-}13}{4}$; $3x - 4y - 13 = 0$

26. $m = {}^{-}1$; $b = {}^{-}2$; $x + y + 2 = 0$

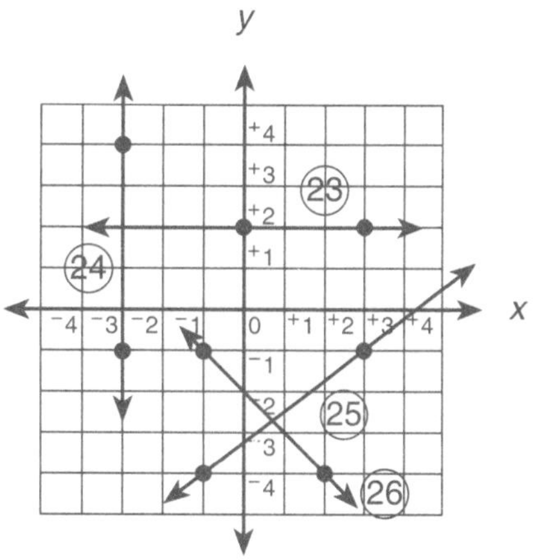

*Use with Lesson 16-3, text pages 460–461.

Copyright © Sadlier-Oxford

Equations, Slopes, and Lines*

Name ______________________

Date ______________________

Solve.

1. What is the slope of the line passing through the points (3,11) and (7, 2)?

   $\frac{11-2}{3-7}$; $m = \frac{-9}{4}$

2. Write an equation of the line whose slope is $^-2$ and y-intercept is 9.

   $y = {^-2}x + 9$ or $2x + y - 9 = 0$

3. What is the slope of the line whose equation is $\frac{1}{2}x + \frac{1}{4}y = \frac{1}{3}$?

   $y = {^-2}x + \frac{4}{3}$; $m = {^-2}$

4. What is the y-intercept of the line whose equation is $\frac{3}{5}x + \frac{1}{2} = \frac{1}{6}y$?

   $y = \frac{18}{5}x + 3$; $b = 3$

5. Find the equation of the line that passes through $(^-2, 5)$ and has slope of $-\frac{1}{5}$.

   $5 = \frac{^-1}{5}(^-2) + b$; $b = \frac{23}{5}$;
   $y = \frac{^-1}{5}x + \frac{23}{5}$; $x + 5y - 23 = 0$

6. Find the equation of the line that passes through the origin and is parallel to $y = -\frac{1}{3}x + 2$.

   $m = \frac{^-1}{3}$
   $y = \frac{^-1}{3}x + 0$; $x + 3y = 0$

7. What is the slope and y-intercept of the line whose equation is $5(x - y) = {^-4}$?

   $x - y = \frac{^-4}{5}$; $y = x + \frac{4}{5}$;
   $m = 1$ and $b = \frac{4}{5}$

8. Find the slope and y-intercept of the line whose equation is $\frac{2x + 3y}{7} = 2$.

   $2x + 3y = 14$; $y = \frac{^-2}{3}x + \frac{14}{3}$;
   $m = \frac{^-2}{3}$ and $b = \frac{14}{3}$

9. Find the equation of the line passing through $(^-3, 5)$ and is perpendicular to the line $2y - 5x + 2 = 0$.

   $m = \frac{^-2}{5}$; $5 = \frac{^-2}{5}(^-3) + b$; $b = \frac{19}{5}$;
   $y = \frac{^-2}{5}x + \frac{19}{5}$; $2x + 5y - 19 = 0$

10. Find the equation of the line that passes through the origin and is perpendicular to the line $3y + x - 12 = 0$.

    $m = 3$; $y = 3x + 0$; $3x - y = 0$

11. Write the equation of the line passing through $(^-2, ^-2)$ and $(7, 11)$.

    $m = \frac{13}{9}$; $^-2 = \frac{13}{9}(^-2) + b$; $b = \frac{8}{9}$;
    $y = \frac{13}{9}x + \frac{8}{9}$; $13x - 9y + 8 = 0$

12. Write the equation of the line passing through $\left(\frac{1}{2}, \frac{1}{2}\right)$ and $\left(\frac{-3}{4}, \frac{-1}{8}\right)$.

    $m = \frac{1}{2}$; $\frac{1}{2} = \frac{1}{2}\left(\frac{1}{2}\right) + b$; $b = \frac{1}{4}$;
    $y = \frac{1}{2}x + \frac{1}{4}$; $2x - 4y + 1 = 0$

13. A quadrilateral has vertices $A(^-2, 2)$, $B(5, 8)$, $C(7, ^-1)$, and $D(0, ^-4)$. Find the slopes of its diagonals.

    $\overline{AC} = \frac{2 - {^-1}}{^-2 - 7}$; $m = \frac{^-1}{3}$

    $\overline{BD} = \frac{8 - {^-4}}{5 - 0}$; $m = \frac{12}{5}$

*Use with Lessons 16-1, 16-2, 16-3, text pages 456–461.

Copyright © Sadlier-Oxford

Simplifying Radical Expressions*

Name ____________________

Date ____________________

Product Property of Square Roots:

$\sqrt{ab} = \sqrt{a} \cdot \sqrt{b}$ and $\sqrt{a} \cdot \sqrt{b} = \sqrt{ab}$

Quotient Property of Square Roots:

$\sqrt{\frac{a}{b}} = \frac{\sqrt{a}}{\sqrt{b}}$ and $\frac{\sqrt{a}}{\sqrt{b}} = \sqrt{\frac{a}{b}}$

Simplify.

1. $\sqrt{32}$ $\quad \sqrt{16\cdot 2} = 4\sqrt{2}$

2. $\sqrt{250}$ $\quad \sqrt{25\cdot 10} = 5\sqrt{10}$

3. $\sqrt{128x^3}$ $\quad \sqrt{64x^2\cdot 2x} = 8x\sqrt{2x}$

4. $\sqrt{75y^4}$ $\quad \sqrt{25y^4\cdot 3} = 5y^2\sqrt{3}$

5. $\sqrt{288a^3b^2}$ $\quad \sqrt{144a^2b^2\cdot 2a} = 12ab\sqrt{2a}$

6. $\sqrt{243ab^3}$ $\quad \sqrt{81b^2\cdot 3ab} = 9b\sqrt{3ab}$

7. $\sqrt{450x^2}$ $\quad \sqrt{225x^2\cdot 2} = 15x\sqrt{2}$

8. $\sqrt{625x^3y^2}$ $\quad \sqrt{625x^2y^2\cdot x} = 25xy\sqrt{x}$

9. $\sqrt{512x^2y}$ $\quad \sqrt{256x^2\cdot 2y} = 16x\sqrt{2y}$

10. $\sqrt{120x}$ $\quad \sqrt{4\cdot 30x} = 2\sqrt{30x}$

11. $\sqrt{\frac{1}{2}}$ $\quad \frac{\sqrt{1}}{\sqrt{2}}\cdot\frac{\sqrt{2}}{\sqrt{2}} = \frac{\sqrt{2}}{2}$

12. $\sqrt{\frac{4}{5}}$ $\quad \frac{\sqrt{4}}{\sqrt{5}} = \frac{2}{\sqrt{5}}\cdot\frac{\sqrt{5}}{\sqrt{5}} = \frac{2\sqrt{5}}{5}$

13. $\sqrt{\frac{7x}{3y}}$ $\quad \frac{\sqrt{7x}}{\sqrt{3y}}\cdot\frac{\sqrt{3y}}{\sqrt{3y}} = \frac{\sqrt{21xy}}{3y}$

14. $\sqrt{\frac{5x}{6y}}$ $\quad \frac{\sqrt{5x}}{\sqrt{6y}} = \frac{\sqrt{5x}}{\sqrt{6y}}\cdot\frac{\sqrt{6y}}{\sqrt{6y}} = \frac{\sqrt{30xy}}{6y}$

15. $\sqrt{\frac{24a^7}{5c}}$ $\quad \frac{\sqrt{4a^6\cdot 6a}}{\sqrt{5c}} = \frac{2a^3\sqrt{6a}}{\sqrt{5c}}\cdot\frac{\sqrt{5c}}{\sqrt{5c}} = \frac{2a^3\sqrt{30ac}}{5c}$

16. $\sqrt{\frac{x}{7y}}$ $\quad \frac{\sqrt{x}}{\sqrt{7y}}\cdot\frac{\sqrt{7y}}{\sqrt{7y}} = \frac{\sqrt{7xy}}{7y}$

17. $\sqrt{\frac{3a}{242}}$ $\quad \frac{\sqrt{3a}}{\sqrt{121.2}} = \frac{\sqrt{3a}}{11\sqrt{2}}\cdot\frac{\sqrt{2}}{\sqrt{2}} = \frac{\sqrt{6a}}{22}$

18. $\sqrt{\frac{a^3bc^2}{3d}}$ $\quad \frac{\sqrt{a^2c^2\cdot ab}}{\sqrt{3d}} = \frac{ac\sqrt{ab}}{\sqrt{3d}}\cdot\frac{\sqrt{3d}}{\sqrt{3d}} = \frac{ac\sqrt{3a}}{3}$

19. $\sqrt{\frac{x^2y^4}{z^3}}$ $\quad \frac{\sqrt{x^2y^4}}{\sqrt{z^2\cdot z}} = \frac{xy^2}{z\sqrt{z}}\cdot\frac{\sqrt{z}}{\sqrt{z}} = \frac{xy^2\sqrt{z}}{z^2}$

20. $\sqrt{\frac{3y^4}{5z^3}}$ $\quad \frac{\sqrt{y^4\cdot 3}}{\sqrt{z^2\cdot 5z}} = \frac{y^2\sqrt{3}}{z\sqrt{5z}}\cdot\frac{\sqrt{5z}}{\sqrt{5z}} = \frac{y^2\sqrt{15z}}{5z^2}$

21. $\frac{4}{\sqrt{5a}}$ $\quad \frac{4}{\sqrt{5a}}\cdot\frac{\sqrt{5a}}{\sqrt{5a}} = \frac{4\sqrt{5a}}{5a}$

22. $\frac{6\sqrt{18}}{\sqrt{2}}$ $\quad 6\sqrt{\frac{18}{2}} = 6\sqrt{9} = 6(3) = 18$

23. $\frac{4\sqrt{20}}{\sqrt{5}}$ $\quad 4\sqrt{\frac{20}{5}} = 4\sqrt{4} = 4(2) = 8$

24. $\sqrt{\frac{81}{50c^2}}$ $\quad \frac{\sqrt{81}}{\sqrt{25c^2\cdot 2}} = \frac{9}{5c\sqrt{2}}\cdot\frac{\sqrt{2}}{\sqrt{2}} = \frac{9\sqrt{2}}{10c}$

*Use with Lesson 16-4, text pages 462–463.

Copyright © Sadlier-Oxford

Simplifying Radical Expressions* (cont'd)

Name ______________________

Date ______________________

Simplify.

25. $\frac{5}{\sqrt{a+b}}$ $\frac{5}{\sqrt{a+b}} \cdot \frac{\sqrt{a+b}}{\sqrt{a+b}} = \frac{5\sqrt{a+b}}{a+b}$

26. $\sqrt{\frac{15c^3d^4e^3}{3ce^4}}$ $\frac{\sqrt{5c^2d^4}}{\sqrt{e}} \cdot \frac{\sqrt{e}}{\sqrt{e}} = \frac{cd^2\sqrt{5e}}{e}$

27. $\frac{3}{\sqrt{x-y}}$ $\frac{3}{\sqrt{x-y}} \cdot \frac{\sqrt{x-y}}{\sqrt{x-y}} = \frac{3\sqrt{x-y}}{x-y}$

28. $\sqrt{\frac{98a^3bc^2}{2ab^2}}$ $\frac{\sqrt{49a^2c^2}}{\sqrt{b}} \cdot \frac{\sqrt{b}}{\sqrt{b}} = \frac{7ac\sqrt{b}}{b}$

29. $3x\sqrt{\frac{x}{3}}$ $\frac{3x\sqrt{x}}{\sqrt{3}} \cdot \frac{\sqrt{3}}{\sqrt{3}} = \frac{3x\sqrt{3x}}{3} = x\sqrt{3x}$

30. $5y\sqrt{\frac{2x}{5x^3}}$ $\frac{5y\sqrt{2}}{\sqrt{5x^2}} \cdot \frac{\sqrt{5}}{\sqrt{5}} = \frac{5y\sqrt{10}}{5x} = \frac{y\sqrt{10}}{x}$

31. $\sqrt{\frac{3x^3}{363y^3}}$ $\frac{\sqrt{x^2 \cdot x}}{\sqrt{121y^2 \cdot y}} = \frac{x\sqrt{x}}{11y\sqrt{y}} \cdot \frac{\sqrt{y}}{\sqrt{y}} = \frac{x\sqrt{xy}}{11y^2}$

32. $\frac{\sqrt{128a^3}}{\sqrt{2a}}$ $\sqrt{\frac{128a^3}{2a}} = \sqrt{64a^2} = 8a$

33. $xy\sqrt{\frac{x}{5y}}$ $\frac{xy\sqrt{x}}{\sqrt{5y}} \cdot \frac{\sqrt{5y}}{\sqrt{5y}} = \frac{xy\sqrt{5xy}}{5y} = \frac{x\sqrt{5xy}}{5}$

34. $xy\sqrt{\frac{x^3}{7x}}$ $\frac{xy\sqrt{x^2}}{\sqrt{7}} \cdot \frac{\sqrt{7}}{\sqrt{7}} = \frac{x^2y\sqrt{7}}{7}$

35. $8\sqrt{\frac{4a^4}{6b}}$ $\frac{8 \cdot 2a^2}{\sqrt{6b}} \cdot \frac{\sqrt{6b}}{\sqrt{6b}} = \frac{16a^2\sqrt{6b}}{6b} = \frac{8a^2\sqrt{6b}}{3b}$

36. $6\sqrt{\frac{24x^5}{18x}}$ $\frac{6\sqrt{4x^4}}{\sqrt{3}} \cdot \frac{\sqrt{3}}{\sqrt{3}} = \frac{6(2x^2\sqrt{3})}{3} = 4x^2\sqrt{3}$

Tell whether each is rational or irrational.

37. $\sqrt{225}$ rational

38. $\sqrt{12}$ irrational

39. $\sqrt{169}$ rational

40. $\sqrt{20}$ irrational

41. $\sqrt{\frac{4}{16}}$ rational

42. $\sqrt{\frac{5}{25}}$ irrational

43. $\frac{1}{2}\sqrt{8}$ irrational

44. $\frac{1}{3}\sqrt{9}$ rational

*Use with Lesson 16-4, text pages 462–463.

Copyright © Sadlier-Oxford

Addition and Subtraction of Radical Expressions*

Name ______________________

Date ______________________

Remember: Simplify the radicals if possible.
Add only like terms.

Simplify if possible.

1. $5\sqrt{3} + 6\sqrt{3}$ $11\sqrt{3}$

2. $9\sqrt{7} + \sqrt{7}$ $10\sqrt{7}$

3. $15\sqrt{x} - 13\sqrt{x}$ $2\sqrt{x}$

4. $7a\sqrt{2b} - 4a\sqrt{2b}$ $3a\sqrt{2b}$

5. $5\sqrt{2} + \sqrt{2} - 2\sqrt{2}$ $4\sqrt{2}$

6. $4\sqrt{6} - \sqrt{6} - 5\sqrt{6}$ $-2\sqrt{6}$

7. $\sqrt{27} + \sqrt{12}$ $3\sqrt{3} + 2\sqrt{3} = 5\sqrt{3}$

8. $\sqrt{20} + \sqrt{45}$ $2\sqrt{5} + 3\sqrt{5} = 5\sqrt{5}$

9. $3\sqrt{8} - \sqrt{32}$ $6\sqrt{2} - 4\sqrt{2} = 2\sqrt{2}$

10. $5\sqrt{50} - 7\sqrt{18}$ $25\sqrt{2} - 21\sqrt{2} = 4\sqrt{2}$

11. $16x^2\sqrt{98} - 15x^2\sqrt{128}$ $-8x^2\sqrt{2}$
 $112x^2\sqrt{2} - 120x^2\sqrt{2}$

12. $5\sqrt{108x^3} - 4x\sqrt{243x}$ $-6x\sqrt{3x}$
 $30x\sqrt{3x} - 36x\sqrt{3x}$

13. $\sqrt{100xy} - \sqrt{64xy} + \sqrt{25xy}$ $7\sqrt{xy}$
 $10\sqrt{xy} - 8\sqrt{xy} + 5\sqrt{xy}$

14. $\sqrt{300} - \sqrt{108} + 5\sqrt{48}$ $24\sqrt{3}$
 $10\sqrt{3} - 6\sqrt{3} + 20\sqrt{3}$

15. $\sqrt{8ab^2c} + 3b\sqrt{2ac}$ $5b\sqrt{2ac}$
 $2b\sqrt{2ac} + 3b\sqrt{2ac}$

16. $\sqrt{27a^3} + 5\sqrt{3a} - 4\sqrt{12a}$ $3a\sqrt{3a} - 3\sqrt{a}$ or $(3a-3)\sqrt{3a}$
 $3a\sqrt{3a} + 5\sqrt{3a} - 8\sqrt{3a}$

17. $\sqrt{\frac{11}{25}} - \sqrt{\frac{11}{49}}$ $\frac{2\sqrt{11}}{35}$
 $\frac{\sqrt{11}}{5} - \frac{\sqrt{11}}{7}$

18. $3\sqrt{\frac{5}{x^2}} + 7\sqrt{\frac{20}{x^2}}$ $\frac{17\sqrt{5}}{x}$
 $\frac{3\sqrt{5}}{x} + \frac{14\sqrt{5}}{x}$

19. $5\sqrt{\frac{54}{3x^4}} - 2\sqrt{\frac{216}{3x^4}}$ $\frac{3\sqrt{2}}{x^2}$
 $\frac{15\sqrt{2}}{x^2} - \frac{12\sqrt{2}}{x^2}$

20. $5\sqrt{\frac{15}{5x^2}} - \sqrt{\frac{135}{5x^2}}$ $\frac{2\sqrt{3}}{x}$
 $\frac{5\sqrt{3}}{x} - \frac{3\sqrt{3}}{x}$

*Use with Lesson 16-5, text pages 464–465.

Copyright © Sadlier-Oxford

Addition and Subtraction of Radical Expressions* (cont'd)

Name ______________________

Date ______________________

Simplify.

21. $\sqrt{72x^3} + 8x\sqrt{2x} - 7x\sqrt{18x}$

$6x\sqrt{2x} + 8x\sqrt{2x} - 21x\sqrt{2x}$; $^-7x\sqrt{2x}$

22. $4\sqrt{50} - 2\sqrt{98} + \frac{1}{2}\sqrt{72}$

$20\sqrt{2} - 14\sqrt{2} + 3\sqrt{2}$; $9\sqrt{2}$

Solve. Show your work.

23. Find the perimeter of a rectangle if the length is $\sqrt{363}$ inches and width is $\sqrt{48}$ inches.

$P = 2(\sqrt{363} + \sqrt{48})$; $2(11\sqrt{3} + 4\sqrt{3})$; $30\sqrt{3}$ in.

24. What is the length of the longer leg of a right triangle if the shorter leg is 8 cm and the hypotenuse is 16 cm?

$16^2 = 8^2 + a^2$; $8\sqrt{3}$ cm

25. Find the diagonal of a rectangle 9 meters wide and 12 meters long.

$c^2 = 9^2 + 12^2$; 15 m

26. Find the hypotenuse of an isosceles right triangle if each leg is 8 inches long.

$c^2 = 8^2 + 8^2$; $8\sqrt{2}$ in.

27. If the hypotenuse of a right triangle is 25 cm and one leg is 24 cm, what would be the length of the other leg?

$25^2 = 24^2 + b^2$; 7 cm

28. If the hypotenuse of a right triangle is 41 inches and one leg is 9 inches long, what would be the length of the other leg?

$41^2 = 9^2 + b^2$; 40 in.

*Use with Lesson 16-5, text pages 464–465.

Copyright © Sadlier-Oxford

Multiplication and Division of Radical Expressions*

Name ______________________

Date ______________________

To multiply radical expressions:

- Cluster similar terms.
- Simplify.
- Use the Product Rule for Radicals.

Multiply.

1. $3\sqrt{5x} \cdot 2\sqrt{5x}$ $30x$

2. $4\sqrt{7} \cdot 8\sqrt{7}$ 224

3. $5x\sqrt{2} \cdot 6x\sqrt{6}$ $30x^2\sqrt{12} = 30x^2(2)\sqrt{3} = 60x^2\sqrt{3}$

4. $4\sqrt{2x} \cdot 8\sqrt{3x}$ $32x\sqrt{6}$

5. $^-7a\sqrt{a^3} \cdot 2a\sqrt{a}$ $^-14a^2\sqrt{a^4} = {}^-14a^4$

6. $\frac{1}{4}\sqrt{2b} \cdot {}^-20\sqrt{2b^3}$ $^-10b^2$

7. $\frac{-1}{2}\sqrt{5x} \cdot {}^-10\sqrt{10x}$ $5\sqrt{50x^2} = 25x\sqrt{2}$

8. $^-6y\sqrt{xy} \cdot {}^-2y\sqrt{x^2y}$ $12y^2\sqrt{x^3y^2} = 12xy^3\sqrt{x}$

9. $\sqrt{2} \cdot \sqrt{3} \cdot \sqrt{4}$ $2\sqrt{6}$

10. $\sqrt{3} \cdot \sqrt{5} \cdot \sqrt{6}$ $\sqrt{90} = 3\sqrt{10}$

11. $\sqrt{27x} \cdot \sqrt{3x}$ $9x$

12. $\sqrt{25a} \cdot \sqrt{ab}$ $5a\sqrt{b}$

13. $\sqrt{xyz} \cdot \sqrt{4x^3yz^5}$ $2x^2yz^3$

14. $\sqrt{a^2b^3c} \cdot \sqrt{27abc}$ $\sqrt{27a^3b^4c^2} = 3ab^2c\sqrt{3a}$

15. $9\sqrt{32} \cdot 3\sqrt{2}$ 216

16. $10\sqrt{5} \cdot \frac{1}{2}\sqrt{10}$ $5\sqrt{50} = 25\sqrt{2}$

17. $7\sqrt{50x^3} \cdot 2\sqrt{6x}$ $14\sqrt{300x^4} = 140x^2\sqrt{3}$

18. $10x\sqrt{48} \cdot 3x\sqrt{15}$ $40x\sqrt{3} \cdot 3x\sqrt{15} = 120x^2\sqrt{4}$[illegible] $= 360x^2\sqrt{5}$

19. $9a\sqrt{a^2b} \cdot 4b\sqrt{bc}$ $36ab\sqrt{a^2b^2c} = 36a^2b^2\sqrt{c}$

20. $7xy\sqrt{xy^2} \cdot 3y\sqrt{xy^3}$ $21xy^2\sqrt{x^2y^5} = 21x^2y^4\sqrt{y}$

21. $\sqrt{3} \cdot (\sqrt{6} - \sqrt{15})$ $\sqrt{18} - \sqrt{45} = 3\sqrt{2} - 3\sqrt{5}$

22. $\sqrt{ab} \cdot (\sqrt{2ab} + \sqrt{3b})$ $ab\sqrt{2} + b\sqrt{3a}$

*Use with Lesson 16-6, text pages 466–467.

Copyright © Sadlier-Oxford

Multiplication and Division of Radical Expressions* (cont'd)

Name ______________________

Date ______________________

$$\frac{\sqrt{5}}{\sqrt{15}} = \frac{\sqrt{5}}{\sqrt{15}} \cdot \frac{\sqrt{15}}{\sqrt{15}} = \frac{\sqrt{75}}{15} = \frac{\sqrt{25 \cdot 3}}{15}$$

$$= \frac{\sqrt{25} \cdot \sqrt{3}}{15} = \frac{5\sqrt{3}}{15} = \frac{\sqrt{3}}{3}$$

$(2 + \sqrt{3}) \cdot (5 + \sqrt{3}) = \underline{\ ?\ }$

$10 + 2\sqrt{3} + 5\sqrt{3} + \sqrt{9}$

$10 + 7\sqrt{3} + 3 = 10 + 3 + 7\sqrt{3} = 13 + 7\sqrt{3}$

Compute.

23. $\frac{\sqrt{98}}{\sqrt{2}}$ $\sqrt{49}; 7$

24. $\frac{\sqrt{75}}{\sqrt{3}}$ $\sqrt{25}; 5$

25. $\frac{\sqrt{15}}{\sqrt{5}}$ $\sqrt{3}$

26. $\frac{\sqrt{42}}{\sqrt{7}}$ $\sqrt{6}$

27. $\frac{\sqrt{3x}}{\sqrt{2}}$ $\frac{\sqrt{3x}}{\sqrt{2}} \cdot \frac{\sqrt{2}}{\sqrt{2}}; \frac{\sqrt{6x}}{2}$

28. $\frac{\sqrt{5y}}{\sqrt{3}}$ $\frac{\sqrt{5y}}{\sqrt{3}} \cdot \frac{\sqrt{3}}{\sqrt{3}}; \frac{\sqrt{15y}}{3}$

29. $\frac{\sqrt{5xy}}{\sqrt{2x}}$ $\frac{\sqrt{5y}}{\sqrt{2}} \cdot \frac{\sqrt{2}}{\sqrt{2}}; \frac{\sqrt{10y}}{2}$

30. $\frac{\sqrt{7ab}}{\sqrt{3a}}$ $\frac{\sqrt{7b}}{\sqrt{3}} \cdot \frac{\sqrt{3}}{\sqrt{3}}; \frac{\sqrt{21b}}{3}$

31. $\frac{x\sqrt{216}}{\sqrt{3x}}$ $\frac{x\sqrt{36 \cdot 2}}{\sqrt{x}} \cdot \frac{\sqrt{x}}{\sqrt{x}}; \frac{6x\sqrt{2x}}{x}; 6\sqrt{2x}$

32. $\frac{y\sqrt{125}}{\sqrt{5y}}$ $\frac{y\sqrt{25}}{\sqrt{y}} \cdot \frac{\sqrt{y}}{\sqrt{y}}; \frac{5y\sqrt{y}}{y}; 5\sqrt{y}$

33. $\frac{\sqrt{3} + \sqrt{2}}{\sqrt{5}}$ $\frac{\sqrt{5}(\sqrt{3}+\sqrt{2})}{\sqrt{5} \cdot \sqrt{5}}; \frac{\sqrt{15}+\sqrt{10}}{5}$

34. $\frac{\sqrt{7} - \sqrt{3}}{\sqrt{2}}$ $\frac{\sqrt{2}(\sqrt{7}-\sqrt{3})}{\sqrt{2} \cdot \sqrt{2}}; \frac{\sqrt{14}-\sqrt{6}}{2}$

35. $\frac{6\sqrt{12x} \cdot 3\sqrt{18y}}{2\sqrt{2}}$ $54\sqrt{3xy}$

$\frac{18\sqrt{4 \cdot 3x \cdot 9 \cdot 2y}}{2\sqrt{2}} \cdot \frac{\sqrt{2}}{\sqrt{2}}; \frac{216\sqrt{3xy}}{4}$

36. $\frac{7\sqrt{10a} \cdot 4\sqrt{27b}}{3\sqrt{3}}$ $28\sqrt{10ab}$

$\frac{28\sqrt{10a \cdot 9 \cdot 3b}}{3\sqrt{3}} \cdot \frac{\sqrt{3}}{\sqrt{3}}; \frac{28 \cdot 9\sqrt{10ab}}{9}$

37. $(7 + \sqrt{3})(2 - \sqrt{3})$ $11 - 5\sqrt{3}$

$14 - 7\sqrt{3} + 2\sqrt{3} - 3$

38. $(x + \sqrt{3y})(2x + \sqrt{3y})$ $2x^2 + 3x\sqrt{3y} + 3y$

$2x^2 + x\sqrt{3y} + 2x\sqrt{3y} + 3y$

39. $(2\sqrt{2} + 5\sqrt{3})(2\sqrt{2} - 5\sqrt{3})$ -67

$4(2) - 25(3)$

40. $(4\sqrt{x} + 5\sqrt{y})(4\sqrt{x} - 5\sqrt{y})$ $16x - 25y$

*Use with Lesson 16-6, text pages 466–467.

Copyright © Sadlier-Oxford

Solving Quadratic Equations by Factoring*

Name ______________________

Date ______________________

Find the solution set.

$x^2 - 9x = {}^-20$	Let $(x - 4) = 0$	Let $(x - 5) = 0$
$x^2 - 9x + 20 = 0$	$x = 4$	$x = 5$
$(x - 4)(x - 5) = 0$	**SS:** $\{4, 5\}$ or $x = 4$ or 5	

1. $x^2 + 9x + 14 = 0$ $\{^-7, ^-2\}$
   $(x+7)(x+2) = 0$

2. $6x^2 - 24 = 0$ $\{^-2, 2\}$
   $6(x+2)(x-2) = 0$

3. $x^2 - 9x + 18 = 0$ $\{6, 3\}$
   $(x-6)(x-3) = 0$

4. $3x^2 - 75 = 0$ $\{^-5, 5\}$
   $3(x+5)(x-5) = 0$

5. $x^2 + 3x - 28 = 0$ $\{^-7, 4\}$
   $(x+7)(x-4) = 0$

6. $x^2 + 12x = 0$ $\{0, ^-12\}$
   $x(x+12) = 0$

7. $x^2 - 6x - 55 = 0$ $\{11, ^-5\}$
   $(x-11)(x+5) = 0$

8. $x^2 - 8x = 0$ $\{0, 8\}$
   $x(x-8) = 0$

9. $x^2 + 9x = 0$ $\{0, ^-9\}$
   $x(x+9) = 0$

10. $x^2 - 7x + 24 = 2x^2 - 2x$ $\{^-8, 3\}$
    $(x+8)(x-3) = 0$

11. $x^2 - 15x = 0$ $\{0, 15\}$
    $x(x-15) = 0$

12. $3x^2 - 4x - 81 = 2x^2 - 4$ $\{11, ^-7\}$
    $(x-11)(x+7) = 0$

13. $x^2 + 56 = 15x$ $\{8, 7\}$
    $(x-8)(x-7) = 0$

14. $\frac{y + 5}{5} = \frac{10}{y}$ $\{^-10, 5\}$
    $(y+10)(y-5) = 0$

15. $x^2 + 48 = {}^-16x$ $\{^-12, ^-4\}$
    $(x+12)(x+4) = 0$

16. $\frac{y - 7}{6} = \frac{13}{y}$ $\{13, ^-6\}$
    $(y-13)(y+6) = 0$

17. $6x^2 - x - 1 = 0$ $\{^-\frac{1}{3}, \frac{1}{2}\}$
    $(3x+1)(2x-1) = 0$

18. $\frac{x}{75} = \frac{3}{x}$ $\{15, ^-15\}$
    $(x+15)(x-15) = 0$

19. $32x^2 - 20x - 3 = 0$ $\{^-\frac{1}{8}, \frac{3}{4}\}$
    $(8x+1)(4x-3) = 0$

20. $\frac{x}{8} = \frac{32}{x}$ $\{^-16, 16\}$
    $(x+16)(x-16) = 0$

21. $x(x + 3) = 54$ $\{^-9, 6\}$
    $(x+9)(x-6) = 0$

22. $18x^2 - 15x + 2 = 0$ $\{\frac{1}{6}, \frac{2}{3}\}$
    $(3x-2)(6x-1) = 0$

23. $x(x + 7) = 60$ $\{^-12, 5\}$
    $(x+12)(x-5) = 0$

24. $50x^2 - 25x + 2 = 0$ $\{\frac{1}{10}, \frac{2}{5}\}$
    $(10x-1)(5x-2) = 0$

*Use with Lesson 16-7, text pages 468–469.

Copyright © Sadlier-Oxford

Solving Quadratic Equations by Factoring* (cont'd)

Name ______________________

Date ______________________

Solve. Show your work.

25. The square of a positive number is 22 more than 9 times the number. Find the number.

Answer: 11

Let x = the number

$x^2 = 9x + 22$; $x^2 - 9x - 22 = 0$;

$(x-11)(x+2) = 0$

26. The sum of the squares of 2 consecutive positive integers is 145. Find the integers.

Answer: 8 and 9

Let x = the first integer and

$x+1$ = the next consecutive positive integer

$x^2 + (x+1)^2 = 145$; $x^2 + x - 72 = 0$;

$(x-8)(x+9) = 0$

27. The length of a rectangle is 5 meters more than its width. The area of the rectangle is 84 sq meters. Find the dimensions of the rectangle.

Answer: 7 m and 12 m

Let w = width and $w+5$ = length

$w(w+5) = 84$; $w^2 + 5w - 84 = 0$

$(w+12)(w-7) = 0$

28. The perimeter of a rectangle is 30 inches and its area is 54 square inches. Find the dimensions of the rectangle.

Answer: 9 in. and 6 in.

$30 \div 2 = \ell + w$; Let x = length and

$15 - x$ = width

$x(15-x) = 54$; $x^2 - 15x + 54 = 0$;

$(x-9)(x-6) = 0$

29. The square of a number decreased by 27 is equal to 6 times the number. Find the number.

Answer: 9 or $^-3$

Let n = the number

$n^2 - 27 = 6n$; $n^2 - 6n - 27 = 0$;

$(n-9)(n+3) = 0$

30. Find three consecutive positive integers if the product of the second and third integers is 90.

Answer: 8, 9, and 10

Let n = first, $n+1$ = the second, $n+2$ = the third

$(n+1)(n+2) = 90$; $n^2 + 3n - 88 = 0$;

$(n+11)(n-8) = 0$

*Use with Lesson 16-7, text pages 468–469.

Copyright © Sadlier-Oxford

Completing the Square*

Name ____________________

Date ____________________

Remember: To solve an equation by completing the square:

- The coefficient of x^2 must be equal to 1.
- Set all terms containing x on one side of the equation.
- Take $\frac{1}{2}$ of the coefficient of x, square it, and add it to both sides of the equation.
- Factor. Then take the square root of both sides to solve for x.

Solve by completing the square.

1. $x^2 + x - 1 = 0$ $\frac{-1 \pm \sqrt{5}}{2}$

2. $x^2 - 3 = 5x$ $\frac{5 \pm \sqrt{37}}{2}$

3. $2x^2 + 8x - 12 = 0$ $-2 \pm \sqrt{10}$

4. $x^2 + 2x = 4$ $-1 \pm \sqrt{5}$

5. $3x^2 + 9x - 6 = 0$ $\frac{-3 \pm \sqrt{17}}{2}$

6. $x^2 - 4x + 1 = 0$ $2 \pm \sqrt{3}$

7. $9x^2 + 3 = 36x$ $\frac{6 \pm \sqrt{33}}{3}$ or $2 \pm \frac{\sqrt{33}}{3}$

8. $7x^2 - 49 = 21x$ $\frac{3 \pm \sqrt{37}}{2}$

9. $4x^2 = 8x + 1$ $\frac{2 \pm \sqrt{5}}{2}$ or $1 \pm \frac{\sqrt{5}}{2}$

10. $11x^2 - 121 = 22x$ $1 \pm 2\sqrt{3}$

Solve. Check students' "Let statements." Solve by completing the square or by factoring.

11. The difference between a positive number and its reciprocal is $\frac{5}{6}$. Find the number.

$x - \frac{1}{x} = \frac{5}{6}$; $6x^2 - 5x - 6 = 0$; $(2x-3)(3x+2) = 0$

$\frac{3}{2}$

12. The square of a number decreased by 7 is equal to 1 more than 7 times the number. Find the number.

$x^2 - 7 = 7x + 1$; $x^2 - 7x - 8 = 0$; $(x+1)(x-8) = 0$

8 or -1

13. The length of the base of a parallelogram is twice its height. The area of the parallelogram is 36 square centimeters. Find the length of its base and its height.

$36 = x(2x)$; $2x^2 - 36 = 0$; $x^2 - 18 = 0$; $x = \pm 3\sqrt{2}$

height $= 3\sqrt{2}$ cm; base $= 6\sqrt{2}$ cm

14. The height of a triangle measures 3 cm less than its base. The area of the triangle is 20 cm^2. Find the lengths of its base and height.

$20 = \frac{1}{2}x(x-3)$; $x^2 - 3x - 40 = 0$; $(x-8)(x+5) = 0$

base = 8 cm; height = 5 cm

*Use with Lesson 16-8, text pages 470–471.

Copyright © Sadlier-Oxford

Quadratic Formula*

Name ______________________

Date ______________________

Remember:

If $ax^2 + bx + c = 0$, and a, b, and c are real numbers and $a \neq 0$, then:

$$x = \frac{-b \pm \sqrt{b^2 - 4ac}}{2a}$$

Solve. Use the Quadratic Formula.

1. $x^2 - 2x - 10 = 0$ $1 \pm \sqrt{11}$
2. $x^2 + 14 = 8x$ $4 \pm \sqrt{2}$
3. $x^2 + 6x + 2 = 0$ $^-3 \pm \sqrt{7}$
4. $x^2 + 19 = 10x$ $5 \pm \sqrt{6}$
5. $4x^2 - 4x - 1 = 0$ $\frac{1 \pm \sqrt{2}}{2}$
6. $4x^2 + x = 3x^2 + x + 21$ $\pm\sqrt{21}$
7. $9x^2 + 12x + 1 = 0$ $\frac{^-2 \pm \sqrt{3}}{3}$
8. $5x^2 + x - 20 = 4x^2 + x + 5$ ± 5
9. $16x^2 - 24x - 4 = 0$ $\frac{3 \pm \sqrt{13}}{4}$
10. $2x^2 + 5x = 1$ $\frac{^-5 \pm \sqrt{33}}{4}$

Solve. (Hint: Some problems may have more than one answer.) Check students' "Let statements."

Solve by quadratic formula or factoring

11. One positive number is 3 more than twice another. Their product is 119. Find the numbers. 7 and 17

$x(2x+3) = 119;\ 2x^2 + 3x - 119 = 0$

$(x-7)(2x+17) = 0$

12. One positive number is 9 less than another. The sum of the squares of these numbers is 153. Find the numbers. 12 and 3

$x^2 + (x-9)^2 = 153;$

$2x^2 - 18x - 72 = 0;\ 2(x-12)(x+3) = 0$

13. The sum of a number and the square of its additive inverse is 72. Find the number. 8 or $^-9$

$x + (^-x)^2 = 72;\ x^2 + x - 72 = 0;$

$(x+9)(x-8) = 0$

14. The sides of a rectangle are represented by x and $4x + 3$. The area of the rectangle is 76 cm^2. Find the lengths of the sides. 4 cm and 19 cm

$x(4x+3) = 76;\ 4x^2 + 3x - 76 = 0;\ (4x+19)(x-4) = 0$

*Use with Lesson 16-9, text pages 472–473.

Copyright © Sadlier-Oxford

Solving Quadratic Equations*

Name ______________________

Date ______________________

Solve. (Use any method.)

1. $x^2 - 4x - 21 = 0$ $x = -3;\ x = 7$

$(x-7)(x+3) = 0$

2. $x^2 + 5x - 66 = 0$ $x = 6;\ x = -11$

$(x-6)(x+11) = 0$

3. $10x^2 - 11x + 3 = 0$ $x = \frac{3}{5};\ x = \frac{1}{2}$

$(2x-1)(5x-3) = 0$

4. $6x^2 - 19x + 10 = 0$ $x = \frac{2}{3};\ x = \frac{5}{2}$

$(3x-2)(2x-5) = 0$

5. $x^2 - 6x - 5 = 0$ $x = 3 \pm \sqrt{14}$

(Quadratic Formula or completing the square)

6. $x^2 - 10x + 14 = 0$ $x = 5 \pm \sqrt{11}$

(Quadratic Formula or completing the square)

7. $3x^2 - 2 = x$ $x = 1;\ x = \frac{-2}{3}$

$(x-1)(3x+2) = 0$

8. $4x^2 + 9x = 9$ $x = -3;\ x = \frac{3}{4}$

$(x+3)(4x-3) = 0$

9. $2x^2 - 12x = 0$ $x = 6;\ x = 0$

$2x(x-6) = 0$

10. $3x^2 = 72$ $x = \pm 2\sqrt{6}$

$x^2 = 24$

11. $4x^2 - 12x = 112$ $x = 7;\ x = -4$

$4(x-7)(x+4) = 0$

12. $5x^2 - 175 = 10x$ $x = -5;\ x = 7$

$5(x+5)(x-7) = 0$

13. $8x^2 + 12 = -20x$ $x = \frac{-3}{2};\ x = -1$

$4(2x+3)(x+1) = 0$

14. $12x^2 + 30 = 39x$ $x = \frac{5}{4};\ x = 2$

$3(4x-5)(x-2) = 0$

15. $20x^2 - 10x = 5$ $x = \frac{1 \pm \sqrt{5}}{4}$

(Quadratic Formula or completing the square)

16. $18x^2 + 2 = 24x$ $x = \frac{2 \pm \sqrt{3}}{3}$

(Quadratic Formula or completing the square)

17. $\frac{2x}{3} = \frac{150}{x}$ $x = \pm 15$

$2x^2 = 450;\ x^2 = 225$

18. $\frac{x}{10} = \frac{32}{5x}$ $x = \pm 8$

$5x^2 = 320;\ x^2 = 64$

*Use with Lesson 16-9, text pages 472–473.

Copyright © Sadlier-Oxford

Solving Quadratic Equations* (cont'd)

Name ______________________

Date ______________________

Remember: Quadratic equations are not always expressed in terms of *x*.

19. $\frac{c+3}{5} = \frac{2}{c}$ $c = {}^-5;\ c = 2$

$c^2 + 3c - 10 = 0;\ (c+5)(c-2) = 0$

20. $\frac{2r+15}{2} = \frac{4}{r}$ $r = \frac{1}{2};\ r = {}^-8$

$2r^2 + 15r - 8 = 0;\ (2r-1)(r+8) = 0$

21. $4n^2 + 1 = {}^-4n$ $n = \frac{-1}{2}$

$4n^2 + 4n + 1 = 0;\ (2n+1)^2$

22. $e^2 + 1 = 3e$ $e = \frac{3 \pm \sqrt{5}}{2}$

(Quadratic Formula or completing the square.)

23. $30y^2 = 2 + 7y$ $y = \frac{2}{5};\ y = \frac{-1}{6}$

$(6y+1)(5y-2) = 0$

24. $21y^2 + 5y - 6 = 0$ $y = \frac{3}{7};\ y = \frac{-2}{3}$

$(7y-3)(3y+2) = 0$

25. $y^2 = 4y + 14$ $y = 2 \pm 3\sqrt{2}$

(Quadratic Formula or completing the square)

26. $2y^2 - 6y + 3 = 0$ $y = \frac{3 \pm \sqrt{3}}{2}$

(Quadratic Formula or completing the square)

Solve. Check students' "Let statements."

27. Twice the square of a number decreased by three times the number is 9. Find the number.

$2x^2 - 3x = 9;\ (2x+3)(x-3) = 0$

$\frac{-3}{2}$ or 3

28. The larger of two positive numbers is 4 more than the smaller. The product of the numbers is 5. Find the numbers.

$x(x+4) = 5;\ (x-1)(x+5) = 0$

1 and 5

29. 16 times a certain number is 5 more than 3 times the square of the number. Find the number.

$16n = 3n^2 + 5;\ (3n-1)(n-5) = 0$

$\frac{1}{3}$ or 5

30. The sum of two numbers is 4 and their product is $^-45$. Find the numbers.

$x(4-x) = {}^-45;\ (x-9)(x+5) = 0$

9 and $^-5$

31. One leg of a right triangle is 7 inches longer than the other leg. The hypotenuse is 17 in. Find the length of each leg of the triangle.

$17^2 = x^2 + (x+7)^2;\ (x+15)(x-8) = 0$

8 in. and 15 in.

32. A rectangle has an area of 25 square units. The sides of the rectangle are represented by x and $4x - 15$. Find the lengths of these sides.

$x(4x-15) = 25;\ (4x+5)(x-5) = 0$

5 units each

*Use with Lesson 16-9, text pages 472–473.

Copyright © Sadlier-Oxford

Advanced Placement Review*

Name ______________________

Date ______________________

Circle the correct answer.

1. The value of $16a^2b^2 - 9b$ when $a = -1$ and $b = 2$ is:
   a. -82 b. -78 (c.) 46 d. 42

2. Subtract the sum of $5a^2 + 14$ and $-9a + 7$ from $7a^2 - 4a - 3$. The result is:
   (a.) $2a^2 + 5a - 24$ b. $-2a^2 - 5a + 24$ c. $2a^2 - 5a - 24$ d. $-2a^2 + 5a - 24$

3. $x^2y(3x^2 - 5y^2)$ is equal to:
   a. $3x^4 - 5xy^3$ (b.) $3x^4y - 5x^2y^3$ c. $3x^4y - 5xy^3$ d. $3x^4 - 5xy^3$

4. Which of the following is prime?
   a. $16x^2 + 64y^2$ b. $16x^2 - 64y^2$ c. $9x^2 - 24xy + 16y^2$ (d.) $9x^2 - 12xy + 16y^2$

5. The least common denominator of $\frac{7x + 2}{3x - 6}$ and $\frac{5x - 1}{2x - 4}$ is:
   a. $(3x - 6)(2x - 4)$ (b.) $6(x - 2)$ c. $3(x - 2)$ d. $2(x - 2)$

6. If $m = \frac{-1}{3}$ and $b = 2$, the equation of the line is:
   a. $x + 3y - 2 = 0$ (b.) $x + 3y - 6 = 0$ c. $x - 3y + 2 = 0$ d. $x - 3y - 6 = 0$

7. $\frac{3}{a^2 + 6a} \div \frac{9}{a + 6}$ is equal to:
   (a.) $\frac{1}{3a}$ b. $\frac{1}{9a}$ c. $\frac{a + 6}{3}$ d. $\frac{a + 6}{9}$

8. Which of the following is an irrational number?
   a. $\sqrt{400}$ b. $\sqrt{625}$ (c.) $-\sqrt{54}$ d. $-\sqrt{36}$

9. $4\sqrt{48} - 8\sqrt{12}$ is equal to:
   a. $8\sqrt{3}$ (b.) 0 c. $-4\sqrt{3}$ d. $-2\sqrt{3}$

10. $\frac{16\sqrt{21}}{2\sqrt{7}}$ is equal to:
    a. $24\sqrt{3}$ b. $8\sqrt{7}$ (c.) $8\sqrt{3}$ d. 24

11. The solution set of the equation $x^2 - 15x + 56 = 0$ is:
    a. $\{-7, -8\}$ (b.) $\{7, 8\}$ c. $\{7, -8\}$ d. $\{-7, 8\}$

12. The solution set of the equation $x^2 - 2x - 2 = 0$ is:
    (a.) $\{1 \pm \sqrt{3}\}$ b. $\{^-1 \pm \sqrt{3}\}$ c. $\left\{\frac{2 \pm \sqrt{3}}{2}\right\}$ d. $\left\{\frac{^-2 \pm \sqrt{3}}{2}\right\}$

13. The diagonal of a square whose side is 5 cm is:
    (a.) $5\sqrt{2}$ cm b. 10 cm c. $25\sqrt{2}$ cm d. $2\sqrt{10}$ cm

Solve. $\frac{1}{x} + \frac{1}{x-3} = \frac{5}{18}$; $5x^2 - 51x + 54 = 0$; $(5x-6)(x-9) = 0$

14. The sum of the reciprocals of two numbers is $\frac{5}{18}$. If one number is three less than the other, find the numbers. 9 and 6 or $\frac{6}{5}$ and $\frac{-9}{5}$

15. A 25 ft-ladder leaning against the wall reaches a point 15 ft above the ground. How far is the foot of the ladder from the foot of the wall? $a^2 + b^2 = c^2$; $x^2 + 15^2 = 25^2$; 2

*Use to review Chapters 15 and 16.

Copyright © Sadlier-Oxford

Nonroutine Problems*

Name ______________________

Date ______________________

Solve. Strategies may vary.

1. Speedy Spike and Motor Mike are racers who are racing in the same direction. Speedy Spike left 2 hours before Motor Mike and is going 70 mph. Motor Mike is going 80 mph. How many miles apart will they be 30 minutes before the faster one catches the slower one?

Combining strategies: $d = rt$

$70(t+2) = 80t$; $t = 14$ hr

SS: $14 + 2 = 16$ hr; MM: 14 hr; hidden fact: 30 min = $\frac{1}{2}$ hr

$70(15\frac{1}{2}) - 80(13\frac{1}{2}) = 1085 - 1080$; 5 mi

2. A swimmer does 40 laps (down and back) in a square pool 2025 square feet in area. How many yards does the swimmer swim?

Using drawings; finding hidden facts: 1 yd = 3 ft

$s = \sqrt{A}$; $s = \sqrt{2025}$; $s = 45$ ft or 15 yd;

$40(30) = 1200$ yd

3. Directions on a frozen-juice can 6.2 cm in diameter and 10.5 cm deep recommend adding 2 cans of water to the concentrate. To the nearest milliliter, what will the total volume of juice be when this is done?

Using volume formulas; finding hidden facts: $1\ cm^3 = 1$ mL

$V = \frac{22}{7}(3.1)^2(10.5)$; 317.13 mL; $3(317.13) = 951.39$ mL

or

$V = 3.14(3.1)^2(10.5)$; 316.8417 mL; $3(316.8417) = 950.5251$ mL

4. A baby looks up a flight of stairs. His toy is on the fifth step. Each step is 12 inches deep and 9 inches high. If the baby could travel in a straight line, what is the distance he would travel from the floor to the bottom of the fifth step?

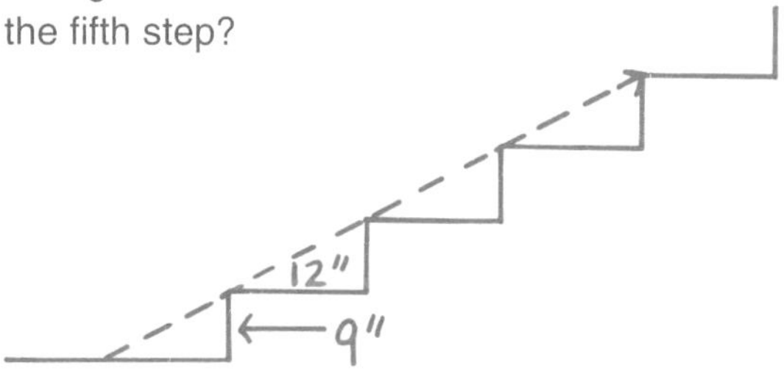

Combining strategies:

$c^2 = 12^2 + 9^2$; $c = 15$

$4(15) = 60$ in.

5. The perimeter of a rectangle is 72 feet. If the length exceeds 4 times the width by 1 foot, what are the dimensions of the rectangle?

Writing and using systems of equations:

Let w = width: $4w + 1$ = length

$P = 2(\ell + w)$; $72 = 2(4w + 1 + w)$; $w = 7$ ft; $\ell = 29$ ft

*Use for Chapters 11 through 16.

Copyright © Sadlier-Oxford

Advanced Placement-Type Test*

Name ______________________

Date ______________________

Circle the correct answer.

1. $(3x^2)^3$ is equivalent to:
   a. $3x^5$ b. $27x^5$ (c.) $27x^6$ d. $3x^6$

2. The sum of $x^2 + 5x - 24$ and $-4x^2 - 12x + 5$ is:
   (a.) $-3x^2 - 7x - 19$ b. $3x^2 - 7x - 16$ c. $-3x^2 + 17x - 18$ d. $3x^2 + 17x - 29$

3. Subtract $2a^2 - 3a + 7$ from $a^2 + 6a - 12$. The result is:
   a. $3a^2 - 3a - 5$ b. $a^2 + 3a - 5$ c. $-a^2 + 9a + 19$ (d.) $-a^2 + 9a - 19$

4. $^-x^3y^3(6x^4y - 3y^4)$ is equal to:
   (a.) $-6x^7y^4 + 3x^3y^7$ b. $-6x^{12}y^3 + 3x^3y^{12}$ c. $6x^7y^4 + 3x^3y^7$ d. $6x^{12}y^3 + 3x^3y^{12}$

5. $(5a + 2b)(3a + 4b)$ is equal to:
   a. $15a^2 + 26ab + 6b^2$ b. $8a^2 + 26ab + 8b^2$ c. $15a^2 + 15ab + 8b^2$ (d.) $15a^2 + 26ab + 8b^2$

6. Evaluate $6a^4b - 5a^2b^3$ when **a** = −1 and **b** = 2. The result is:
   a. 28 (b.) −28 c. −42 d. 30

7. $(9x^3 - 6x^2 + 3x) \div 3x$ is equal to:
   a. $3x^2 + 2x + 1$ (b.) $3x^2 - 2x + 1$ c. $3x^3 + 2x + 1$ d. $3x^3 - 2x + 1$

8. $xy - [x^2 - x(y + x)]$ is equal to:
   a. $2x^2 - 2xy$ b. $2x^2 - xy$ (c.) $2xy$ d. $2x^2$

9. In factored form, $8x^3y^2z^3 + 12x^2y^2z^2$ is:
   a. $2x^2y^2z(4z^2 + 3x)$ b. $2x^2y^2z^2(4xz + 3)$ c. $4xyz^2(2x^2y + 3z)$ (d.) $4x^2y^2z^2(2xz + 3)$

10. As a product of 2 binomials, $2x^2 - 9xy - 5y^2$ is equal to:
    (a.) $(2x + y)(x - 5y)$ b. $(2x - y)(x + 5y)$ c. $(2x + 5y)(x - y)$ d. $(2x - 5y)(x + y)$

11. If the measure of a side of a square is $3x - 2y$, the trinomial that represents the area of the square is:
    a. $9x^2 + 4xy + 4y^2$ b. $9x^2 - 6xy + 4y^2$ c. $9x^2 + 6xy + 4y^2$ (d.) $9x^2 - 12xy + 4y^2$

12. Which of the following is prime?
    a. $x^2 - y^2$ b. $8x^2 + 16y^2$ (c.) $x^2 - xy + y^2$ d. $x^2 + 2xy + y^2$

13. When factored completely, $x^4 + x^2 - 2$ is equal to:
    (a.) $(x^2 + 2)(x + 1)(x - 1)$ b. $(x^2 + 2)(x^2 - 1)$
    c. $(x^2 + 1)(x^2 - 2)$ d. $(x^2 + 1)(x + 2)(x - 2)$

*Use after Chapters 15, 16.

Copyright © Sadlier-Oxford

Advanced Placement-Type Test*

Name ____________________

Date ____________________

14. For what value of x is $\frac{x + 5}{x + 2}$ undefined?

a. $^{-}5$ **(b.)** $^{-}2$ **c.** 0 **d.** no value

15. The sides of a triangle are represented by $\frac{x}{2}$, $\frac{4x}{5}$, and $\frac{5x}{6}$. Find the perimeter of the triangle.

a. $\frac{63x}{64}$ **b.** $\frac{31x}{15}$ **c.** $\frac{x}{2}$ **(d.)** $\frac{32x}{15}$

16. $\frac{a^2 - 5a}{a^2} \cdot \frac{a}{2a - 10}$ is equal to:

(a.) $\frac{1}{2}$ **b.** $\frac{a}{2}$ **c.** $\frac{a - 5}{2}$ **d.** $\frac{a}{a - 5}$

17. The least common denominator of $\frac{3x - 2}{2x + 2}$ and $\frac{4x - 1}{3x + 3}$ is:

a. $(2x + 2)(3x + 3)$ **b.** $3(x + 1)$ **(c.)** $6(x + 1)$ **d.** $2(x + 1)$

18. What value of k will complete the square of the equation $x^2 - 18x + k = 0$?

a. 9 **(b.)** 81 **c.** $^{-}81$ **d.** 36

19. The slope of the line passing through $\left(\frac{^{-}1}{2}, \frac{^{-}1}{3}\right)$, and $\left(\frac{1}{4}, \frac{^{-}5}{6}\right)$ is:

a. $\frac{^{-}7}{9}$ **b.** $\frac{^{-}1}{8}$ **(c.)** $\frac{^{-}2}{3}$ **d.** $\frac{^{-}3}{8}$

20. The y-intercept of the line $5x + 3y - 9 = 0$ is:

(a.) 3 **b.** $\frac{5}{3}$ **c.** $^{-}3$ **d.** $\frac{^{-}3}{8}$

21. The equation of the line passing through the origin and has slope $\frac{2}{5}$ is:

a. $2x + 5y = 0$ **(b.)** $2x - 5y = 0$ **c.** $5x - 2y = 0$ **d.** $5x + 2y = 0$

22. Which line is parallel to $7x - 9y + 1 = 0$?

a. $x + 9y - 7 = 0$ **b.** $7x + y - 9 = 0$ **(c.)** $7x - 9y = 0$ **d.** $7x + 9y + 2 = 0$

23. $\sqrt{125} + 8\sqrt{5}$ can be written in the form of $x\sqrt{5}$. Find the value of x.

(a.) 13 **b.** 33 **c.** 10 **d.** 23

24. The product of $\sqrt{7xy}$ and $\sqrt{28xy}$ is:

a. $7xy\sqrt{2}$ **(b.)** $14xy$ **c.** $2xy\sqrt{7}$ **d.** $8xy$

***Use after Chapters 15, 16.**

Copyright © Sadlier-Oxford

Advanced Placement-Type Test*

Name ____________________

Date ____________________

25. The solution set of $3x^2 = 7 - 4x$ is:

a. $\left\{1, \frac{7}{3}\right\}$ **b.** $\left\{^-1, \frac{^-7}{3}\right\}$ **c.** $\left\{^-1, \frac{7}{3}\right\}$ **(d.)** $\left\{1, \frac{^-7}{3}\right\}$

26. $\sqrt{\frac{x + y}{x - y}}$ is equivalent to:

(a.) $\frac{\sqrt{x^2 - y^2}}{x - y}$ **b.** $\sqrt{\frac{x + y}{x - y}}$ **c.** $\frac{(x + y)\sqrt{x - y}}{x - y}$ **d.** $\sqrt{\frac{x - y}{x + y}}$

27. The solution set of $x^2 = 2x + 6$ is:

a. $\left\{\frac{1 \pm \sqrt{7}}{2}\right\}$ **b.** $\left\{\frac{^-1 \pm \sqrt{7}}{2}\right\}$ **(c.)** $\left\{1 \pm \sqrt{7}\right\}$ **d.** $\left\{^-1 \pm \sqrt{7}\right\}$

28. Between what two positive numbers does $2\sqrt{13}$ lie?

a. 6 and 7 **(b.)** 7 and 8 **c.** 8 and 9 **d.** 9 and 10

29. The sum of the square of a positive integer and 5 is 230. Find the positive integer.

a. 5 **b.** 12 **c.** 23 **(d.)** 15

30. What is the square root of $81x^2 - 144xy + 64y^2$?

(a.) $9x - 8y$ **b.** $9x + 8y$ **c.** $9x^2 - 8y^2$ **d.** $9x^2 + 8y^2$

31. Which points form a line that has a slope that is undefined?

a. (4, 7) and ($^-3$, 7) **(b.)** (3, $^-2$) and (3, $^-5$)
c. ($^-1$, $^-1$) and ($^-2$, $^-2$) **d.** (2, 2) and (5, 5)

32. What is the height of an equilateral triangle that has 12 cm as the length of its side?

a. $6\sqrt{2}$ cm **(b.)** $6\sqrt{3}$ cm **c.** 6 **d.** $12\sqrt{3}$ cm

33. The lengths of the legs of a right triangle are both 5 cm. Find the length of the hypotenuse.

(a.) $5\sqrt{2}$ cm **b.** $10\sqrt{2}$ cm **c.** $\frac{5\sqrt{2}\text{ cm}}{2}$ **d.** 10 cm

34. Which of the following is a Pythagorean triple?

a. 4, 5, 6 **b.** 4, $4\sqrt{2}$, 8 **(c.)** $3\sqrt{2}$, $4\sqrt{2}$, $5\sqrt{2}$ **d.** 6, 6, $6\sqrt{3}$

35. If $5a + b$ represents the width of a rectangle and $7a + 2b$ represents the length, then which of the following represents the perimeter?

a. $13a + 3b$ **b.** $12a + 3b$ **c.** $26a + 6b$ **(d.)** $24a + 6b$

*Use after Chapters 15, 16.

Copyright © Sadlier-Oxford

Advanced Placement-Type Test*

Name ______________________

Date ______________________

36. If $9x - y$ represents the radius of a circle, which of the following represents the circumference?

a. $(9x^2 - y^2)\pi$ **b.** $(18x - y)\pi$ **(c.)** $(18x - 2y)\pi$ **d.** $(9x - y)\pi$

37. If x represents the second of 3 consecutive integers, which expression represents the largest integer?

(a.) $x + 1$ **b.** $x - 1$ **c.** $x + 2$ **d.** $x - 2$

38. If one factor of the product $4x^2 - 5xy - 6y^2$ is $x - 2y$, then the other factor is:

a. $2x + 6y$ **b.** $2x - 6y$ **(c.)** $4x + 3y$ **d.** $4x - 3y$

39. $81x^2 + 18x + 1$ represents the area of a square. The binomial that represents the length of a side is:

a. $9x - 1$ **(b.)** $9x + 1$ **c.** $81x + 1$ **d.** $81x - 1$

40. Which line is perpendicular to $7x - 5y = 0$?

a. $5x - 7y = 0$ **b.** $^{-}7x - 5y = 0$ **(c.)** $5x + 7y = 0$ **d.** $7x + 5y = 0$

Compute.

41. $\frac{6}{x^2y} + \frac{3}{xy^2} + \frac{4}{xy}$ $\frac{6y+3x+4xy}{x^2y^2}$

42. $\frac{6x + 18}{x^2 - 9} \div \frac{x + 3}{x - 3} \cdot \frac{x + 3}{6}$ 1

43. $\frac{\sqrt{6x} \cdot \sqrt{2x}}{\sqrt{x^3 + 3x}}$ $\frac{2\sqrt{3x^3+9x}}{x^2+3}$

44. $(5\sqrt{7} + 4\sqrt{3})(6\sqrt{7} - 2\sqrt{3})$ $186+14\sqrt{21}$

45. $\frac{a + 2}{a^2 - 2a - 15} - \frac{4a - 3}{a^2 - 7a + 10} + \frac{2a - 1}{a^2 + a - 6}$ $\frac{-a^2-20a+10}{(a-5)(a+3)(a-2)} = \frac{-a^2-20a+10}{a^3-4a^2-11a+30}$

Solve. Check students' "Let statements."

46. The sum of the reciprocals of two positive numbers is $\frac{1}{2}$. One number is 3 more than the other. Find the numbers.

$\frac{1}{x} + \frac{1}{x+3} = \frac{1}{2}$; $x^2 - x - 6 = 0$; $(x-3)(x+2) = 0$; 3 and 6

47. Ann has \$1.70 in dimes and nickels. There are 8 more dimes than nickels. Find the number of each kind of coin that she has.

6 nickels; 14 dimes

$5n + 10(n+8) = 170$; $n = 6$

48. The numerator of a fraction is 12 less than the denominator of the fraction. The value of the fraction is $\frac{7}{11}$. Find the fraction.

$\frac{x-12}{x} = \frac{7}{11}$; $x = 33$; $\frac{21}{33}$

49. The hypotenuse of a right triangle is 4 cm longer than one leg and 18 cm longer than the other leg. Find the length of each side of the triangle.

$(x-4)^2 + (x-18)^2 = x^2$; $x^2 - 44x + 340 = 0$ → $(x-34)(x-10) = 0$; $x = 34$

34 cm, 30 cm, 16 cm

50. The smaller of two pipes takes 5 hours longer than the larger to fill a tank. If both pipes are used, the job can be done in $3\frac{1}{3}$ hours. How long will it take each pipe to fill the tank alone?

$\frac{1}{x} + \frac{1}{x+5} = \frac{3}{10}$; $3x^2 - 5x - 50 = 0$; → $(3x+10)(x-5) = 0$; $x = 5$

larger: 5 hr; smaller: 10 hr

Copyright © Sadlier-Oxford

Tables for Measures

Metric Units

Length

1 millimeter (mm) = 0.001 meter (m)
1 centimeter (cm) = 0.01 meter
1 decimeter (dm) = 0.1 meter

1 dekameter (dam) = 10 meters
1 hectometer (hm) = 100 meters
1 kilometer (km) = 1000 meters

Mass

1 milligram (mg) = 0.001 gram (g)
1 kilogram (kg) = 1000 grams
1 metric ton (t) = 1000 kilograms

Capacity

1 milliliter (mL) = 0.001 liter (L)
1 kiloliter (kL) = 1000 liters

Temperature

0° Celsius (C) .... Water freezes.
100° Celsius (C) .... Water boils.

Customary Units

Length

1 foot (ft) = 12 inches (in.)
1 yard (yd) = 36 inches
1 yard (yd) = 3 feet
1 mile (mi) = 5280 feet
1 mile (mi) = 1760 yards

Weight

1 pound (lb) = 16 ounces (oz)
1 ton = 2000 pounds

Capacity

3 teaspoons (tsp) = 1 tablespoon (tbsp)
1 cup (c) = 8 fluid ounces (fl oz)
1 pint (pt) = 2 cups
1 quart (qt) = 2 pints
1 quart (qt) = 4 cups
1 gallon (gal) = 4 quarts

Temperature

32° Fahrenheit (F) ... Water freezes.
212° Fahrenheit (F) ... Water boils.

Mathematical Symbols

$=$	is equal to
$\neq$	is not equal to
$>$	is greater than
$<$	is less than
$\geq$	is greater than or equal to
$\leq$	is less than or equal to
ϕ, { }	the empty set
...	continues without end
$\subset$	is a subset of
$\cup$	union
$\cap$	intersection
$\wedge$	conjunction
$\vee$	disjunction
$n!$	factorial $n \cdot (n-1) \cdot (n-2) \cdot \ldots \cdot 1$
10^2	ten squared
$0.\overline{3}$	0.333 ... (repeating decimals)
%	percent
$^\circ$	degree
$\cdot$	times
$\overleftrightarrow{AB}$	line AB
$\overline{AB}$	segment AB
$\overrightarrow{AB}$	ray AB
$\angle ABC$	angle ABC
ABC	plane ABC
$\sim$	is similar to
$\cong$	is congruent to
$\parallel$	is parallel to
$\perp$	is perpendicular to
2 : 3	two to three (ratio)
π	pi
$\approx$	is approximately equal to
(3, 4)	ordered pair
P(E)	probability of an event
$\frown{AB}$	arc AB

Geometric Formulas

Perimeter

Rectangle: $P = 2(\ell + w)$

Square: $P = 4s$

Area

Rectangle: $A = \ell w$

Square: $A = s^2$

Parallelogram: $A = bh$

Triangle: $A = \frac{1}{2}bh$

Trapezoid: $A = \frac{1}{2}(b_1 + b_2)h$

Circle: $A = \pi r^2$

Pythagorean Theorem: $c^2 = a^2 + b^2$

Circumference of Circle

$C = \pi d$ or $2\pi r$

Surface Area

Rectangular Prism:

$S = 2(\ell w + \ell h + wh)$

Cube: $S = 6s^2$

Volume

Prism: $V = Bh$

Cube: $V = e^3$

Pyramid: $V = \frac{1}{3}Bh$

Other Formulas

Distance = Rate × Time: $d = r \times t$

Discount = List Price × Rate of Discount: $D = LP \times R$ of D

Sales Tax = Marked Price × Rate of Sales Tax: $T = MP \times R$ of T

Commission = Total Sales × Rate of Commission: $C = TS \times R$ of C

Interest = Principal × Rate × Time: $I = P \times R \times T$

Slope: $(y_2 - y_1) \div (x_2 - x_1)$

Table of Trigonometric Ratios

Angle	Sin	Cos	Tan	Angle	Sin	Cos	Tan
0°	0.000	1.000	0.000	**45°**	0.707	0.707	1.000
1°	0.017	1.000	0.017	**46°**	0.719	0.695	1.036
2°	0.035	0.999	0.035	**47°**	0.731	0.682	1.072
3°	0.052	0.999	0.052	**48°**	0.743	0.669	1.111
4°	0.070	0.998	0.070	**49°**	0.755	0.656	1.150
5°	0.087	0.996	0.087	**50°**	0.766	0.643	1.192
6°	0.105	0.995	0.105	**51°**	0.777	0.629	1.235
7°	0.122	0.993	0.123	**52°**	0.788	0.616	1.280
8°	0.139	0.990	0.141	**53°**	0.799	0.602	1.327
9°	0.156	0.988	0.158	**54°**	0.809	0.588	1.376
10°	0.174	0.985	0.176	**55°**	0.819	0.574	1.428
11°	0.191	0.982	0.194	**56°**	0.829	0.559	1.483
12°	0.208	0.978	0.213	**57°**	0.839	0.545	1.540
13°	0.225	0.974	0.231	**58°**	0.848	0.530	1.600
14°	0.242	0.970	0.249	**59°**	0.857	0.515	1.664
15°	0.259	0.966	0.268	**60°**	0.866	0.500	1.732
16°	0.276	0.961	0.287	**61°**	0.875	0.485	1.804
17°	0.292	0.956	0.306	**62°**	0.883	0.469	1.881
18°	0.309	0.951	0.325	**63°**	0.891	0.454	1.963
19°	0.326	0.946	0.344	**64°**	0.899	0.438	2.050
20°	0.342	0.940	0.364	**65°**	0.906	0.423	2.145
21°	0.358	0.934	0.384	**66°**	0.914	0.407	2.246
22°	0.375	0.927	0.404	**67°**	0.921	0.391	2.356
23°	0.391	0.921	0.424	**68°**	0.927	0.375	2.475
24°	0.407	0.914	0.445	**69°**	0.934	0.358	2.605
25°	0.423	0.906	0.466	**70°**	0.940	0.342	2.747
26°	0.438	0.899	0.488	**71°**	0.946	0.326	2.904
27°	0.454	0.891	0.510	**72°**	0.951	0.309	3.078
28°	0.469	0.883	0.532	**73°**	0.956	0.292	3.271
29°	0.485	0.875	0.554	**74°**	0.961	0.276	3.487
30°	0.500	0.866	0.577	**75°**	0.966	0.259	3.732
31°	0.515	0.857	0.601	**76°**	0.970	0.242	4.011
32°	0.530	0.848	0.625	**77°**	0.974	0.225	4.332
33°	0.545	0.839	0.649	**78°**	0.978	0.208	4.705
34°	0.559	0.829	0.675	**79°**	0.982	0.191	5.145
35°	0.574	0.819	0.700	**80°**	0.985	0.174	5.671
36°	0.588	0.809	0.727	**81°**	0.988	0.156	6.314
37°	0.602	0.799	0.754	**82°**	0.990	0.139	7.115
38°	0.616	0.788	0.781	**83°**	0.993	0.122	8.144
39°	0.629	0.777	0.810	**84°**	0.995	0.105	9.514
40°	0.643	0.766	0.839	**85°**	0.996	0.087	11.430
41°	0.656	0.755	0.869	**86°**	0.998	0.070	14.301
42°	0.669	0.743	0.900	**87°**	0.999	0.052	19.081
43°	0.682	0.731	0.933	**88°**	0.999	0.035	28.636
44°	0.695	0.719	0.966	**89°**	1.000	0.017	57.290
45°	0.707	0.707	1.000	**90°**	1.000	0.000	———

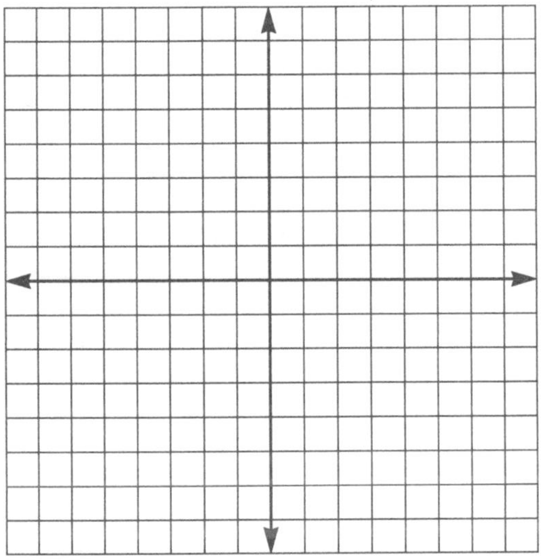

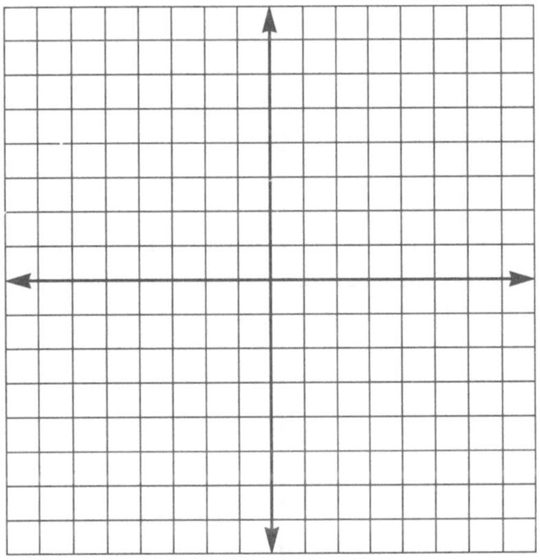

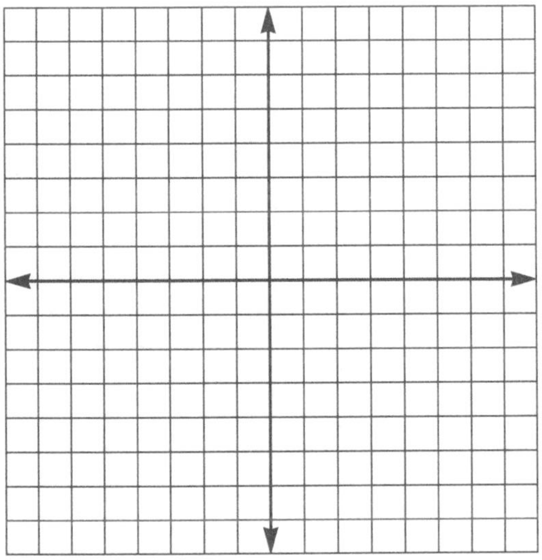

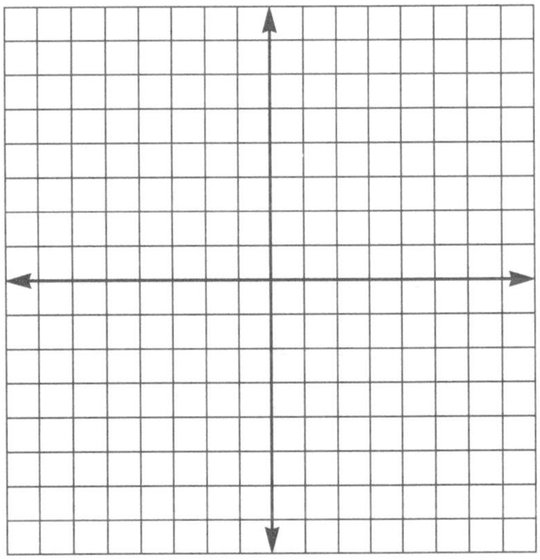

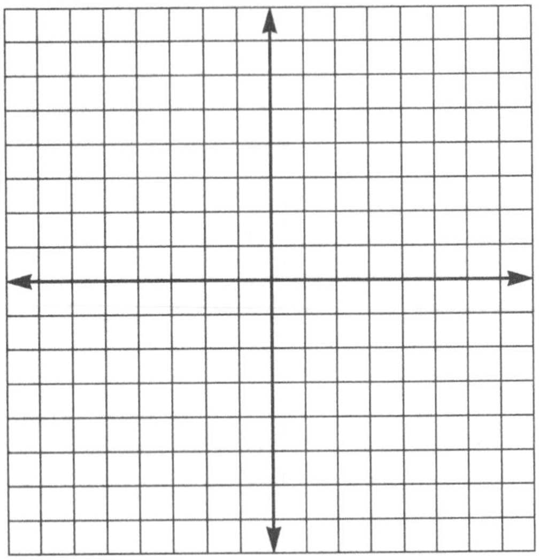

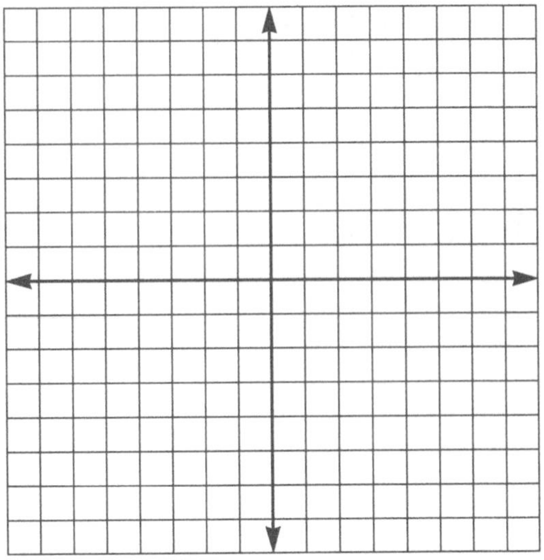

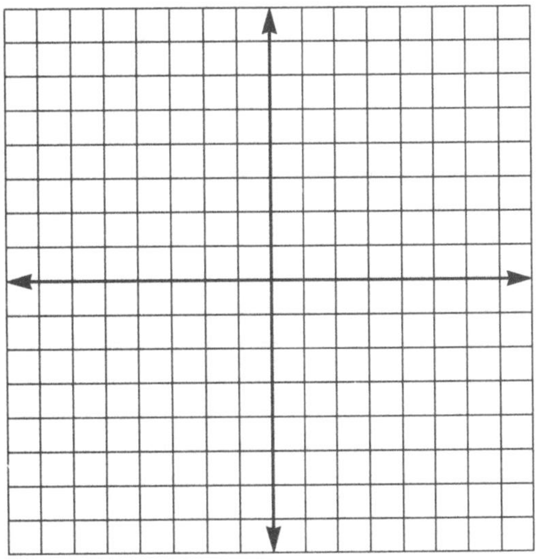

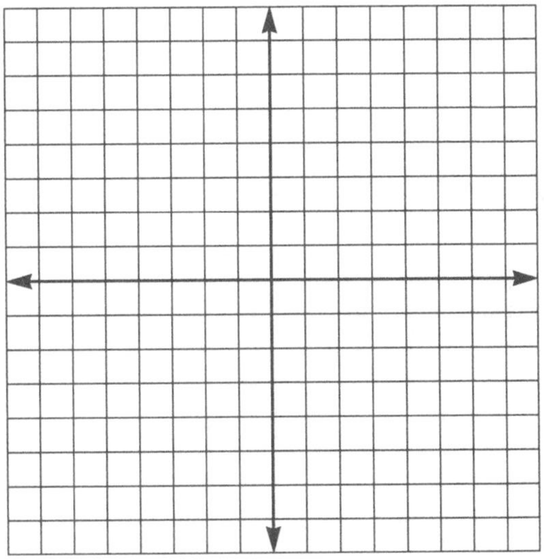

Answers to Selected Odd-Numbered Exercises

Page 3: **1.** 11,640,018 **3.** 10,000,500,002,000 **5.** ten millions; zero ten million **7.** ten thousands; 7 ten thousands **9.** billions; 2 billions **11.** hundred billions; 9 hundred billions **13.** one billion times greater **15.** 10 billion times greater **17.** 114,000,000; no; no

Page 4: **1.** zero hundredths **3.** 7 tenths **5.** 7 millionths **7.** 80,402 **9.** 0.7008 **11.** 6,000,000 **13.** 7,000,000,000 **15.** 4,200,000,000.2 **17.** 3,800,000,000,000 **19.** 3.600508 **21.** 0.022908006 **23.** 98,760 **25.** 1.083052

Page 5: **1.** 1.6987 **3.** 2.4614 **5.** 5.89 **7.** 38.421 **9.** 1.8015 **11.** 2.7038 **13.** 14.9693 **15.** 2.2 **17.** 1.9 **19.** 402

Page 6: **1.** 3,618,318 **3.** 1,330,596 **5.** 2,976,137 **7.** 1,943,980 **9.** 1,877,720 **11.** 4,206,736 **13.** 5,400,000 **15.** 32,000 **17.** 90,000 **19.** 15,000,000 **21.** 30,000,000

Page 7: **1.** 201.24 **3.** 32.0492 **5.** 731.3141 **7.** 1.72414 **9.** 12.714 **11.** 15.0627 **13.** 74.9115 **15.** 27.9097 **17.** 360 **19.** 0.36 **21.** 160 **23.** $8.14

Page 8: **1.** 780 **3.** 9020 R30 **5.** 407 R10 **7.** 600 R9 **9.** 951 **11.** 680 **13.** 36 R12 **15.** 68 **17.** 463 R67 **19.** 50 R23 **21.** 50 **23.** 800 **25.** 20

Page 9: **1.** 0.16 **3.** 3.4 **5.** 20.3 **7.** 16.87 **9.** 20.03 **11.** 1.86 **13.** 0.05 **15.** 50 **17.** 2 **19.** 0.41L

Page 10: **1.** = **3.** > **5.** = **7.** 107,500 **9.** 30.2 **11.** 560,000 **13.** 200 **15.** 9 **17.** R **19.** R

Page 11: **1.** e **3.** h **5.** g **7.** j **9.** i **11.** 490 **13.** 8.7 **15.** 300 **17.** = **19.** = **21.** <

Page 12: **1.** $\frac{16}{3}$ **3.** $\frac{73}{9}$ **5.** $\frac{11}{3}$ **7.** $\frac{17}{8}$ **9.** $\frac{71}{5}$ **11.** $\frac{48}{5}$ **13.** $\frac{67}{5}$ **15.** $\frac{50}{3}$ **17.** $\frac{125}{6}$ **19.** $\frac{64}{5}$ **21.** $\frac{84}{5}$ **23.** $\frac{99}{8}$ **25.** $9\frac{2}{3}$ **27.** $5\frac{2}{3}$ **29.** $5\frac{1}{7}$ **31.** $11\frac{5}{7}$ **33.** $5\frac{1}{6}$ **35.** $9\frac{4}{5}$ **37.** $7\frac{3}{7}$ **39.** $9\frac{1}{3}$ **41.** $22\frac{3}{4}$ **43.** $12\frac{1}{3}$ **45.** $40\frac{1}{2}$ **47.** $14\frac{1}{3}$ **49.** $\frac{15}{4}$ **51.** $\frac{8}{3}$

Page 13: **1.** 2, 4, 6, 40 **3.** 4, 10, 72, 18 **5.** 6, 65, 24, 130 **7.** 64 **9.** 24 **11.** 7 **13.** 3 **15.** 5 **17.** 3 **19.** $\frac{5}{7}$ **21.** $\frac{2}{5}$ **23.** $\frac{1}{3}$ **25.** $\frac{3}{4}$ **27.** $\frac{1}{4}$ **29.** $\frac{7}{10}$ **31.** $\frac{7}{9}$ **33.** $\frac{1}{3}$ **35.** $\frac{6}{7}$ **37.** $\frac{9}{14}$

Page 14: **1.** 1,2,7,14 **3.** 1,5,7,35 **5.** 1,2,4,8 **7.** 1,3,5,15 **9.** 1,2,3,5,6,10,15,30 **11.** 1,2,3,4,5,6,10,12,15,20,30,60 **13.** 1,2,3,4,5,6,8,10,12,15,20,24,30,40,60,120 **15.** 5 + 7 **17.** prime numbers: 101,103,107,109,113,127,131,137,139,149,151, 157,163,167,173,179,181,191,193,197,199

Page 15: **1.** $2^3 \times 7$;

56
8 × 7
4 × 2 × 7
2 × 2 × 2 × 7

3. 11×2^2 **5.** $3^2 \times 2$ **7.** $2^3 \times 3 \times 5$ **9.** $2^2 \times 5$ **11.** $2 \times 3^2 \times 5$ **13.** $2^4 \times 3$ **15.** 216 **17.** 99 **19.** 1512 **21.** 1617 **23.** 75 **25.** 585

Page 16: **1.** 3 **3.** 21 **5.** 28 **7.** 14 **9.** 4 **11.** 3^2; $2^2 \times 3$; 3 **13.** 2^3; $2^2 \times 5$; 4 **15.** 24 **17.** 18 **19.** 30 **21.** 40 **23.** 45 **25.** 2×3; 2^3; 24 **27.** 2^3; $2^2 \times 3$; $2^3 \times 5$; 120

Page 17: **1.** 0.08 **3.** 0.95 **5.** 2.5 **7.** 6.2 **9.** 0.4 **11.** 0.625 **13.** 0.3125 **15.** 0.16 **17.** $0.\overline{7}$ **19.** 0.75 **21.** 2.125 **23.** $1.\overline{3}$ **25.** $9.1\overline{3}$ **27.** $7.1\overline{6}$ **29.** $2.\overline{1}$ **31.** $6.\overline{4}$ **33.** 2.875 **35.** 10.3

Page 18: **1.** < **3.** < **5.** < **7.** > **9.** < **11.** < **13.** > **15.** > **17.** > **19.** > **21.** < **23.** = **25.** $\frac{2}{3}, \frac{4}{5}, \frac{6}{7}$ **27.** $\frac{2}{3}, \frac{7}{10}, \frac{3}{4}$ **29.** $\frac{1}{5}, \frac{2}{7}, \frac{3}{10}$ **31.** 0.472 < 0.857 **33.** 0.657 < 0.662 **35.** 0.349 > 0.289

Page 19: **1.** $1\frac{1}{2}$ **3.** $\frac{23}{33}$ **5.** $1\frac{7}{40}$ **7.** $1\frac{11}{24}$ **9.** 17 **11.** $8\frac{5}{8}$ **13.** $17\frac{11}{36}$ **15.** $19\frac{19}{30}$ **17.** $\frac{1}{3}$ **19.** $\frac{1}{4}$ **21.** $12\frac{1}{2}$ **23.** $12\frac{1}{8}$ **25.** $12\frac{1}{21}$ **27.** $4\frac{7}{18}$ **29.** $13\frac{15}{16}$ lb **31.** $\frac{7}{24}$ yd

Page 20: **1.** $\frac{8}{15}$ **3.** $\frac{3}{35}$ **5.** $1\frac{1}{3}$ **7.** $12\frac{1}{4}$ **9.** $4\frac{1}{12}$ **11.** $23\frac{1}{3}$ **13.** $26\frac{3}{5}$ **15.** 36 **17.** $5\frac{1}{9}$ **19.** $6\frac{7}{15}$ **21.** $82\frac{2}{3}$ **23.** 30 **25.** 20 yd

Page 21: **1.** $\frac{4}{3}$ **3.** $\frac{9}{1}$ **5.** $\frac{9}{4}$ **7.** $\frac{6}{13}$ **9.** $\frac{11}{7}$ **11.** $\frac{3}{25}$ **13.** $\frac{1}{18}$ **15.** $\frac{5}{27}$ **17.** $\frac{9}{10}$ **19.** $\frac{2}{3}$ **21.** $\frac{4}{11}$ **23.** $\frac{1}{20}$ **25.** $2\frac{2}{9}$ **27.** 57 **29.** $3\frac{3}{4}$ **31.** $2\frac{4}{9}$ **33.** $16\frac{1}{2}$ **35.** $1\frac{1}{18}$ **37.** $12\frac{2}{9}$ miles

Page 22: **1.** 11 **3.** 10 **5.** 4 **7.** 6 **9.** 14 **11.** 12 **13.** 56 **15.** 2 **17.** $\frac{2}{3}$ **19.** $\frac{1}{6}$ **21.** $\frac{6}{7}$ **23.** $4\frac{1}{3}$ **25.** $6\frac{4}{21}$ **27.** $9\frac{3}{32}$ **29.** $14\frac{1}{3}$ **31.** $48\frac{32}{45}$ **33.** $27\frac{3}{5}$ **35.** about 50 in.

Page 23: **1.** 10 **3.** 8 **5.** 20 **7.** 19 **9.** 8 **11.** 4 **13.** 35 **15.** 24 **17.** 6 **19.** 7 **21.** 11 **23.** 87 **25.** 14

Page 24: **1.** $n - 8$ **3.** $5n$ **5.** $n - 9$ **7.** $12n$ **9.** $\frac{n}{4}$ **11.** $\frac{n+1}{3}$ or $\frac{n}{3} + 1$ **13.** $7n + 9$ **15.** $5n$

Copyright © Sadlier-Oxford

17. $\frac{1}{2}n$ or $\frac{n}{2}$ **19.** $5n - 4$

Page 25: **1.** $n + 4 = 10$; equation **3.** $\frac{1}{4}n - 5 > 1$; inequality **5.** $5n < 10$; inequality **7.** $3 + n < 6$; inequality **9.** $\frac{1}{2}n - 5 \geq 6$; inequality
11. $A + 6 = 14$

Page 26: **1.** 40 **3.** 23 **5.** 44 **7.** 5 **9.** 2 **11.** 16 **13.** 8 **15.** 80 **17.** 125 **19.** 31 **21.** 25 **23.** 5 **25.** 39 **27.** 50 **29.** 38 **31.** 0 **33.** 112 **35.** 220 **37.** 250

Page 27: **1.** 3 **3.** 14 **5.** 7 **7.** 10 **9.** 9 **11.** 13 **13.** 8 **15.** 7 **17.** 20 **19.** 27 **21.** 50 **23.** 100 **25.** 12 **27.** 84 **29.** 17 **31.** 91 **33.** 60 **35.** 15

Page 28: **1.** 6 **3.** 20 **5.** 20 **7.** 72 **9.** 15 **11.** 16 **13.** 72 **15.** 84 **17.** 98 **19.** 81 **21.** 184 **23.** 125 **25.** 4 **27.** 60 **29.** 65 **31.** 36 **33.** 192

Page 29: **1.** 7 **3.** 72 **5.** 4 **7.** 72 **9.** 7 **11.** 7 **13.** 4 **15.** 65 **17.** 6 **19.** 5 **21.** 16 **23.** 5 **25.** 15 microscopes

Page 30: **1.** 27 **3.** 100 **5.** 8 **7.** 9 **9.** 5 **11.** 6 **13.** 5 **15.** 8 **17.** 373 **19.** 140; 28

Page 31: **1.** $a = 5$ **3.** $y = 1$ **5.** $s = 2$ **7.** $x = 16$ **9.** $s = 13$ **11.** $m = 17$ **13.** $a = 102$ **15.** $n = 16$ **17.** $n = 11$ **19.** $d = 14\frac{3}{5}$ **21.** $d = 83$ **23.** $r = 5$ **25.** $8(n - 9) = 96; n = 21$ **27.** $3(n - 5) = 36; n = 17$

Page 32: **1.** {4} **3.** {10,11,12,...,25} **5.** {25,30,35,...,50} **7.** {17,21,23,...,33} **9.** {0,1,2,3} **11.** {20,10} **13.** $<$ **15.** $\geq$ **17.** $\neq$ **19.** {21,22,23,...,29} **21.** {0,3,6,9,12,15,18}

Page 33: **1.** Area of a Square **3.** Circumference of a Circle **5.** Area of a Triangle **7.** $S = 16$ units **9.** $\ell = 5'$ **11.** $S = 18$ yd **13.** R of $T = T \div MP$ **15.** $D = LP \times R$ of D **17.** $68 \approx (2) \times (3.14) \times r$; $r = 10\frac{9}{11}$ ft or 10.828 ft
19. $V = 20 \times 4 \times 3$; $V = 240$ cu ft

Page 34: **1.** $^{-}5$ **3.** $^{-}4$ **5.** $^{-}17$ **7.** $>$ **9.** $<$ **11.** $<$ **13.** $>$ **15.** $^{-}20, ^{-}15, ^{+}2, ^{+}5, ^{+}20$ **17.** $^{+}15, ^{+}5, 0, ^{-}5, ^{-}19$ **19.** $^{-}$\$31.00 **21.** $^{+}500$ **23.** $^{-}3°C$ **25.** 25;609;14

Page 35: **1.** $^{+}9$ **3.** $^{+}7$ **5.** $^{-}5$ **7.** $^{+}10$ **9.** 0 **11.** $^{-}2$ **13.** $^{+}7$ **15.** $^{-}2$ **17.** $^{+}14$ **19.** $^{-}25$ **21.** $^{+}37$ **23.** $^{+}20$ **25.** 0 **27.** $^{-}33$ **29.** $^{-}22$ **31.** $^{-}18$ **33.** $^{-}2$ **35.** $^{+}11$ **37.** $^{+}15$ **39.** $^{-}1$ **41.** $^{-}3$ **43.** $^{-}3$ **45.** \$84 **47.** $^{-}50$

Page 36: **1.** $^{+}72$ **3.** 0 **5.** $^{+}4$ **7.** $^{+}28$ **9.** $^{+}90$ **11.** $^{-}93$ **13.** $^{+}10$ **15.** $^{-}3$ **17.** $^{-}9$ **19.** $^{-}9$ **21.** $^{-}17$ **23.** $^{+}15$ **25.** $t = {}^{-}12$ **27.** $a = 0$ **29.** $s = {}^{+}36$ **31.** $^{-}6$ **33.** $^{+}32$

Page 37: **1.** $q + 5 + (5 + 1) = 14; q = 3; n = 5; d = 6$; \$1.60 **3.** $8 + 4n = 40; n = 8$ **5.** $6n + 5 = 53; n = 8$ **7.** $120x = 1500; x = 12\frac{1}{2}$ or 12.5 hr **9.** $4w = 34;\ w = 8.5;$ $A = 34 \times 8.5;\ A = 289$ cm^2

Page 38: **1.** $^{+}0.2$ **3.** $^{+}\frac{5}{3}$ **5.** $^{+}8.1$ **7.** 0 **9.** $^{+}\frac{9}{2}$ **11.** $>$ **13.** $<$ **15.** $>$ **17.** $<$ **19.** $<$ **21.** $<$ **23.** $^{-}\frac{7}{2}, ^{-}3, ^{-}0.1, ^{+}2\frac{1}{2}, ^{+}3\frac{2}{3}$
25. $^{-}1.3, ^{-}\frac{1}{3}, ^{-}0.31, ^{+}0.31, ^{+}3.10$ **27.** $^{-}5.03$
29. $^{-}4\frac{2}{3}$

Page 39: **1.** Commutative M **3.** Inverse A **5.** Commutative A **7.** Identity A **9.** $^{-}12$ **11.** $^{+}1$ **13.** $^{-}19$ **15.** 0 **17.** $^{-}92$ **19.** $^{+}9$ **21.** $^{-}3.4$

Page 40: **1.** $^{+}8.1$ **3.** $^{+}7.5$ **5.** $^{+}15.74$ **7.** $^{+}5.59$ **9.** $^{-}1.95$ **11.** $^{-}5$ **13.** $^{-}0.9$ **15.** $^{-}0.07$ **17.** $^{+}2.6$ **19.** $^{-}0.8$ **21.** $^{+}\frac{1}{24}$ **23.** $^{-}2.77$ **25.** $^{-}7.8$
27. $^{+}0.7$ **29.** 0 **31.** $^{-}5.8$ **33.** $^{+}0.7$ **35.** $^{+}2°C$

Page 41: **1.** $^{-}1.5$ **3.** $^{-}3$ **5.** $^{-}2.4$ **7.** $^{+}21.6$ **9.** $^{-}20.4$ **11.** 0 **13.** $^{+}7\frac{1}{2}$ **15.** $^{-}5$ **17.** $^{+}1\frac{1}{2}$
19. $^{+}2.6$ **21.** $^{-}9.5$ **23.** $^{-}3.01$ **25.** $^{-}5.74$ **27.** $^{-}$\$6.94

Page 42: **1.** $^{+}4$ **3.** $^{+}5$ **5.** $^{+}1$ **7.** $^{+}5$ **9.** $^{-}14$ **11.** $^{+}53$ **13.** $^{+}8$ **15.** $^{+}19$ **17.** $^{+}1.3$ **19.** $^{+}3$ **21.** $^{-}26$ **23.** $n + 7 = {}^{-}12, n = {}^{-}19$ **25.** $n + 15 = 41; n = {}^{+}26$

Page 43: **1.** $^{+}6$ **3.** $^{+}36$ **5.** $^{+}16$ **7.** $^{+}28$ **9.** $^{-}12$ **11.** $^{-}20$ **13.** $^{+}63$ **15.** $^{-}27$ **17.** $^{+}0.024$ **19.** $^{-}10.28$ **21.** $^{-}0.0607$ **23.** $^{+}\frac{3}{8}$ **25.** $^{-}\frac{3}{16}$
27. $^{-}\frac{5}{27}$ **29.** $^{-}1\frac{7}{8}$ **31.** $^{-}20$ **33.** $^{-}20$ **35.** $^{-}35$
37. $^{-}18$ **39.** $^{-}200$

Page 44: **1.** $^{+}4; ^{+}4$ **3.** $^{+}63; ^{+}63$ **5.** $^{+}3; ^{+}3$ **7.** $^{-}8$ **9.** $^{-}4$ **11.** $^{+}9$ **13.** $^{+}8$ **15.** $^{-}9$ **17.** $^{+}2$ **19.** $^{-}1$ **21.** $^{-}0.7$ **23.** $^{+}11\frac{3}{5}$ **25.** $^{-}3\frac{1}{2}$ **27.** $^{+}1\frac{1}{2}$ **29.** $^{-}9$

Page 45: **1.** $4n = {}^{-}55; n = {}^{-}13\frac{3}{4}$ or $^{-}13.75$
3. $^{-}9n = {}^{-}36; n = {}^{+}4$ **5.** $^{+}7$ **7.** $^{+}9$ **9.** $^{-}0.08$ **11.** $^{-}35.01$ **13.** $^{-}\frac{1}{63}$ **15.** $^{-}0.9$ **17.** $^{-}1600$
19. $^{-}\frac{3}{4}$ **21.** $^{-}72$ **23.** $^{-}288$ **25.** $^{-}12.5$ **27.** $^{+}5.6$
29. $^{+}13$ **31.** $^{+}192$

Page 46: **1.** $LCM = 10; x = {}^{-}5$ **3.** $LCM = 10; x = 2.4$ **5.** $LCM = 10; y = 120$ **7.** $LCM = 3; s = 90$ **9.** $y = 12$ **11.** $y = 3.5$ **13.** $c = 3\frac{1}{8}$ **15.** $r = {}^{-}5$ **17.** $y = 3\frac{1}{10}$
19. $x = 3.6$ **21.** $t = 11$ **23.** $n = 8$ **25.** $x = 3.6$

Page 47: **1.** 2*C*, 1*A*, 3*B* **3.** Maria: \$108,000; Megan: \$72,000; Ramon: \$144,000; Jeff: \$108,000
5. Moya: 15; Catherine: 15

Page 48: **7.** \$17 **9.** Mighty Mo: \$201.20; Tiny Tim: \$253.24; Sweet Pea: \$239.36

Page 49: **1.** 1000 **3.** 10,000 **5.** 10,000,000,000 **7.** 10^5 **9.** 10^0 **11.** 10^7 **13.** 84 **15.** 948 **17.** 9300 **19.** 384.1 **21.** 643,110 **23.** 0.0793 **25.** 0.5063 **27.** 0.0000106 **29.** 0.0000042 **31.** 0.007009 **33.** 8.22×10^7; 6321.004×10^3;

Copyright © Sadlier-Oxford

5081.426×10^3; 4.321×10^6; 42.21021×10^5
35. $84 \div 10^2$; $8400 \div 10^5$; $8.4 \div 10^3$; $8400 \div 10^7$; $0.84 \div 10^6$

Page 50: **1.** 843.074 **3.** 1204.56 **5.** 0 hundredth **7.** 2 ten thousandths **9.** 1 hundred thousand **11.** 8 hundredths **13.** (9×10^{-2}) **15.** (1×10^{-4}) **17.** $(6 \times 10^1) + (6 \times 10^0) + (3 \times 10^{-1})$ **19.** $(8 \times 10^2) + (3 \times 10^1) + (8 \times 10^0) + (5 \times 10^{-4}) + (2 \times 10^{-5})$ **21.** $(4 \times 10^0) + (8 \times 10^{-4}) \times (4 \times 10^{-5}) + (6 \times 10^{-6})$

Page 51: **1.** 2 **3.** $^{-}5$ **5.** 6.2×10^4 **7.** 6×10^{-6} **9.** 25,200,000,000 **11.** 202,500,000,000 **13.** 0.5985 **15.** 10^3 **17.** 10^3 **19.** 6^4 **21.** 8^1 **23.** 2×10^1 **25.** 1.24×10^{-3} **27.** 1.07×10^8 km **29.** 637,000,000 or 6.37×10^8 m^2

Page 52: **1.** 168; 2514; 217,251 **3.** 948; 66; 27,684; 186,630 **5.** 324; 81,648; 32,166; 386,451 **7.** 247,116; 920,424; 327,164; 367,148 **9.** 112,926; 617,122; 122,221 **11.** No; Yes; No **13.** No; Yes; No **15.** No; Yes; No **17.** Yes; No; Yes **19.** Yes; No; Yes **21.** Yes; Yes; Yes **23.** 18 **25.** Yes; 86

Page 53: **1.** 24; 29; 34 **3.** 46; 44; 42 **5.** 16; 32; 64 **7.** 36; 43; 50 **9.** 12; 12.5; 13 **11.** $\frac{5}{3}$; 2; $\frac{7}{3}$ **13.** 11; 16; 22 **15.** 13.1; 13.3; 13.5 **17.** 17, 18, 23 **19.** 56; 50; 45 **21.** 19; 22; 25 **23.** 81; 243; 729 **25.** 2.2; 2.5; 2.8 **27.** 82; 77; 71 **29.** 10; 11.5; 13 **31.** 12; 6; 9 **33.** 32; 128; 64

Page 54: **1.** $p \wedge q$ **3.** $q \rightarrow r$ **5.** $r \rightarrow (p \wedge q)$
7. Love is everything and silence gives consent.
9. If silence gives consent, then time is a thief.
11. Time is a thief or love is everything.

13.

p	q	$\sim p$	$\sim p \rightarrow q$
T	T	F	F
T	F	F	T
F	T	T	T
F	F	T	F

15.

p	q	$\sim p$	$\sim p \wedge q$
T	T	F	F
T	F	F	F
F	T	T	T
F	F	T	F

17.

p	q	$p \vee q$	$\sim(p \vee q)$
T	T	T	F
T	F	T	F
F	T	T	F
F	F	F	T

Page 55: **1. Converse:** If a number is zero, then it is not divisible by one.
Inverse: If a number is divisible by one, then it is not zero.
Contrapositive: If a number is not zero, then it is divisible by one.
3. Converse: If Stretch is a snake, then Stretch is a python.
Inverse: If Stretch is not a python, then Stretch is not a snake.
Contrapositive: If Stretch is not a snake, then Stretch is not a python.
5. T, F, F, T **7.** F, T, T, F **9.** T, T, T, T

Page 56: **1.** $\frac{9}{10}$ **3.** $\frac{4}{9}$ **5.** $\frac{1}{3}$ **7.** $\frac{3}{5}$ **9.** $\frac{\$450}{1}$ **11.** $\frac{1}{\$6.25}$ **13.** $\frac{25}{2}$ **15.** $\frac{6}{1}$ **17.** $\frac{1}{4}$ **19.** $\frac{5}{9}$ **21.** $\frac{2}{1}$ **23.** $\frac{1}{2}$ **25.** $\frac{6}{5}$ **27.** $\frac{8}{17}$ **29.** $\frac{6}{5}$ **31.** $\frac{4}{1}$ **33.** $\frac{4}{1}$ **35.** $\frac{9}{1}$ **37.** 27:43 or $\frac{27}{43}$

Page 57: **1.** = **3.** ≠ **5.** = **7.** ≠ **9.** = **11.** ≠ **13.** 3 **15.** 6 **17.** 7 **19.** $1\frac{1}{2}$ **21.** 4 **23.** 0.4 **25.** $1\frac{1}{4}$ **27.** 5 **29.** 0.4 **31.** 19.2 km

Page 58: **1.** \$1.25 **3.** 215 plates **5.** \$1.26 **7.** 30¢ **9.** 520 Kilometers **11.** \$2365

Page 59: **1.** 10 km **3.** 30 cm **5.** 16 cm **7.** 44 cm **9.** 2.1 cm **11.** 0.075 cm **13.** 12.24 cm

Page 60: **1.** 2 **3.** 2 **5.** 10 **7.** 6 people **9.** $10\frac{1}{2}$ hr **11.** 1 hr **13.** 4 hr

Page 61: **1.** 16; 48 **3.** 60; 90; 120 **5.** 120; 150; 180 **7.** 15; 60; 90 **9.** John: \$45, Martin: \$30 **11.** 312 birthday cards; 156 anniversary cards; 52 get-well cards; **13.** Ms. Wayne: 1680 votes; Mr. Edwards: 960 votes.

Page 62: **1.** $x = 6.8$; $y = 5.1$ **3.** $\overline{HK}$ **5.** 73° **7.** 0.75; 37° **9.** 0.8; 37° **11.** 0.6; 53° **13.** 37.6 **15.** 82.41

Page 63: **1.** 0.3; 30% **3.** 25: 100; 0.25; 25% **5.** 80: 100: $\frac{4}{5}$; 80% **7.** 42: 100; $\frac{21}{50}$; 42% **9.** $\frac{5}{8}$; 0.625; 62.5% **11.** 6: 10; $\frac{3}{5}$; 60% **13.** 12: 5: 100; 0.125; $12\frac{1}{2}$% **15.** 2.5 **17.** 10: 100 **19.** 4.5 **21.** 37:100 **23.** $\frac{2}{50}$ **25.** 0.15 **27.** 87:100

Page 64: **1.** $\frac{2}{5}$ **3.** $\frac{8}{25}$ **5.** $\frac{1}{8}$ **7.** $\frac{1}{6}$ **9.** $\frac{1}{7}$ **11.** $\frac{5}{8}$ **13.** $1\frac{1}{4}$ **15.** $2\frac{3}{4}$ **17.** $\frac{9}{200}$ **19.** $\frac{7}{200}$ **21.** $\frac{1}{250}$ **23.** $1\frac{1}{20}$ **25.** 0.65 **27.** 0.98 **29.** 0.24 **31.** 0.04 **33.** 0.355 **35.** 0.751 **37.** 0.0225 **39.** 0.074 **41.** 1 **43.** 2.5 **45.** 0.006 **47.** 0.004 **49.** $83\frac{1}{3}$%

Page 65: **1.** 4 **3.** 21 **5.** 3.5 **7.** 8 **9.** 28.08 **11.** 0.34 **13.** 7 **15.** 41 **17.** 28 **19.** 20.15 **21.** 0.225 **23.** 1404 cars **25.** 15 students

Page 66: **1.** 25% **3.** 20% **5.** 24% **7.** $66\frac{2}{3}$% **9.** $11\frac{1}{9}$% **11.** 350% **13.** $8\frac{1}{3}$% **15.** 225% **17.** 40% **19.** $66\frac{2}{3}$%

Page 67: **1.** 1400 **3.** 32 **5.** 15 **7.** 24 **9.** 51 **11.** 52 **13.** 264 **15.** 500 **17.** 5 **19.** 6 **21.** $14\frac{2}{7}$% **23.** 54 **25.** 24

Page 68: **1.** $\frac{1}{3}$ **3.** $\frac{1}{8}$ **5.** $\frac{1}{3}$ **7.** $\frac{2}{5}$ **9.** $\frac{1}{5}$ **11.** 7 **13.** 16 **15.** 27 **17.** $33\frac{1}{3}$; b **19.** 60; b **21.** 112 **23.** 147 **25.** 480

Copyright © Sadlier-Oxford

Page 69: **1.** 5; 11.1% **3.** 8; 13.3% **5.** 7; 12.1% **7.** 6; 8.1% **9.** 6; 10.7% **11.** 36.4% **13.** 33.3% **15.** 6.7% increase

Page 70: **1.** *b* **3.** *c* **5.** *c* **7.** *c* **9.** *d* **11.** *c* **13.** *c* **15.** *d*

Page 71: **17.** = **19.** 6.675 **21.** $^-7.4$ **23.** $n + 15 = 41$; 26 **25.** $4n + 5 = 17$; $n = 3$ **27.** 555 **29.** If it is spring, then it is raining.

Page 72: **1.** $10 **3.** $65.33 **5.** $20.13 **7.** $6.91 **9.** $33.83 **11.** $17.04 **13.** $99.40 **15.** $315.93 **17.** $729.01 **19.** $15,901.80

Page 73: **1.** $52.33; $104.66 **3.** $5.12; $26.88 **5.** $4.48; $51.52 **7.** $1.05; $13.90 **9.** $12.35; $64.85 **11.** $20; $60 **13.** $37.25, $149 **15.** $210; $1190

Page 74: **1.** 30% **3.** 14% **5.** $66\frac{2}{3}$% **7.** $4500 **9.** $63 **11.** $85 **13.** 5%

Page 75: **1.** $4.47 **3.** $10.54 **5.** $6.08 **7.** $9.69 **9.** $2.80 **11.** $17.43; $366.03 **13.** $4.98; $104.48 **15.** $13.99;$293.84 **17.** $11.40

Page 76: **1.** $120 **3.** $90 **5.** $261.90 **7.** $141.75 **9.** $19.60 **11.** $38.94 **13.** $367.62 **15.** $344

Page 77: **1.** 8% **3.** 15% **5.** 5% **7.** $225 **9.** $4050 **11.** $4550 **13.** $5000 **15.** 10%

Page 78: **1.** $480 **3.** $63 **5.** $307.20 **7.** $22.50 **9.** $113.40 **11.** $2194.80 **13.** $547.20

Page 79: **1.** I = $300; P = $5300; I = $318 **3.** Interest: $1515.75; Total: $9015.75 **5.** Mr. Mendoza ($50.31)

Page 80: **1.** $2.50 **3.** $.89 **5.** $1.95 **7.** $50 **9.** $25 **11.** $50 **13.** $12.50 **15.** $20 **17.** $183.63

Page 81: **1.** $\frac{1}{6}$ **3.** $\frac{1}{3}$ **5.** 0 **7.** $\frac{2}{3}$ **9.** $\frac{1}{6}$ **11.** $\frac{1}{8}$ **13.** $\frac{1}{8}$ **15.** 0 **17.** $\frac{1}{2}$ **19.** $\frac{1}{5}$ **21.** 0 **23.** $\frac{1}{2}$

Page 82: **1.** $\frac{1}{16}$ **3.** $\frac{1}{16}$ **5.** $\frac{1}{32}$ **7.** $\frac{1}{16}$ **9.** $\frac{1}{8}$ **11.** $\frac{1}{64}$; $\frac{1}{56}$ **13.** $\frac{1}{64}$; $\frac{1}{56}$ **15.** $\frac{1}{4}$; $\frac{2}{7}$ **17.** $\frac{1}{4}$; $\frac{3}{14}$ **19.** $\frac{1}{16}$; $\frac{1}{14}$

Page 83: **1.** 720 **3.** 40,320 **5.** 3,628,800 **7.** 40,314 **9.** 210 **11.** 24 **13.** 120, $\frac{1}{120}$

Page 84: **1.** 15; 25% **3.** 20; $33\frac{1}{3}$% **5.** 100 **7.** 150 **9.** 200 **11.** 22; 23% **13.** 31; 33% **15.** 18 **17.** 45 **19.** 69

Page 85: **1.** 600 **3.** hockey and soccer **5.** 7000 books **7.** 2500 books

Page 86: **1.** 11; 13; 8; 10; 7; 10

Page 87: **1.** 30 **3.** 94 **5.** 42 **7.** 70 **9.** 415

Page 89: **1.** 90° **3.** 120° **5.** 240° **7.** 216° **9.** $37\frac{1}{2}$; 25%; 25%; $12\frac{1}{2}$% **11.** 126; 86.4 (86); 64.8 (65); 43.2 (43); 14.4 (14); 8.28 (8); 7.56 (8); 4.68 (5); 4.68 (5)

Page 90: **1.** range = 72; median = $51; mean = $54.90; mode = none **3.** range = 36; median = 45; mean = 45.875; mode = none **5.** average = 0.313; range = 0.092; median = 0.308 **7.** mean = 9.34; mode = 5.6

Page 91: **1.** *a* **3.** *b* **5.** *c* **7.** *e* **15.** True **17.** False **19.** True **21.** False

Page 92: **1.** 50; acute **3.** 120; obtuse **9.** 2° **11.** 77° **13.** 166° **15.** 88° **17.** *a*

Page 94: **1.** $\overleftrightarrow{SW} \parallel \overleftrightarrow{TY}$ **3.** 90° **5.** 90° **7.** $\angle 1 - \angle 2$; $\angle 2 - \angle 4$; $\angle 3 - \angle 1$; $\angle 4 - \angle 3$; $\angle 5 - \angle 7$; $\angle 6 - \angle 5$; $\angle 7 - \angle 8$; $\angle 8 - \angle 6$ **9.** $\angle 2 - \angle 6$; $\angle 4 - \angle 8$; $\angle 1 - \angle 5$; $\angle 3 - \angle 7$ **11.** $\overleftrightarrow{AB} \parallel \overleftrightarrow{CD}$ **13.** $\angle CFH$ **15.** $\angle AEH$

Page 95: **1.** 70°; acute isosceles **3.** 61°; acute scalene **5.** 88; acute scalene **7.** 72°; acute scalene **9.** 65°; obtuse scalene **11.** 60°; acute equilateral **13.** 45°; right isosceles **15.** isosceles **17.** obtuse

Page 96: **1.** $\overline{XZ}$ **3.** $\overline{YZ}$ **5.** $\angle M$ **7.** ASA **9.** SAS

Page 97: **1.** 3 **3.** $1\frac{1}{2}$ **5.** 14 **7.** 6000 **9.** 7040 **11.** 10 lb **13.** 2 gal 2 qt **15.** 8 gal 2 qt **17.** 9 qt **19.** $69.36

Page 98: **1.** cm **3.** m **5.** cm **7.** 8.4 **9.** 0.0807 **11.** 36 **13.** 0.24 **15.** 24 **17.** 24 **19.** 400 **21.** 0.0005 **23.** 98 100 **25.** 0.026 **27.** 0.03 **29.** 0.091 **31.** 0.072 **33.** 600 000 **35.** 8100 **37.** 826 **39.** 16.047 **41.** 3.002 **43.** 80 005 **45.** 6019 **47.** 3.46

Page 99: **1.** 0.5; 500 **3.** 0.406; 40.6; 406; 40 600 **5.** 68; 6800; 68 000; 6 800 000 **7.** 1500 **9.** 25 000 **11.** 620 **13.** 0.0046 **15.** 0.3 **17.** = **19.** = **21.** $>$ **23.** Principal's office to library; 0.14 m

Page 100: **1.** 2.5 cm **3.** 48 mm **5.** 6.1 dm **7.** 7314 m **9.** 142 cm **11.** 0.1 cm; 0.05 cm; 16.1 ± 0.05 cm **13.** 1 dm; 0.5 dm; 7 ± 0.5 dm **15.** 0.1 m; 0.05 m; 2.7 ± 0.05 m **17.** 0.1 dam; 0.05 dam; 9.6 ± 0.05 dam **19.** 1 cm; 0.5 cm; 18 ± 0.5 cm

Page 101: **1.** 1 mi **3.** Town A: 62%; Town B: 39%; Both: 50% **5.** 16 students

Page 102: **7.** square 12 **9.** 90°; 22°; 68°

Page 103: **1.** 44.8 cm **3.** 25.41 m **5.** 30 m **7.** 25.2 cm **9.** 170.4 cm **11.** about 29 yd

Copyright © Sadlier-Oxford

Page 104: **1.** 240 cm² **3.** 69 $\frac{4}{9}$ in.²
5. 26.46 m² **7.** 44 $\frac{1}{3}$ ft² **9.** 213 m²
11. 0.72 m² or 72 dm² **13.** 20 yd² or 180 ft²
15. 20 containers **17.** 0.96 m² **19.** square: 144 ft²;
rectangle: 140 ft²; square

Page 105: **1.** 104 cm² **3.** 79.2 cm² **5.** 6 m²
7. 8.4 dm² **9.** 2340 cm² **11.** 47.5 yd²
13. 7.5 m² **15.** 165 ft²

Page 106: **1.** 36 cm² **3.** 32.76 m² **5.** 1 $\frac{1}{9}$
7. 1734 cm² **9.** 2200 cm² **11.** 76.5 ft² or 8 $\frac{1}{2}$ yd²

Page 107: **1.** 9.42 m **3.** 94.2 mm **5.** 5.024 km
7. 22 cm **9.** 132 dm **11.** 17.6 m **13.** 66 cm
15. 28.26 yd **17.** 13.2 m

Page 108: **1.** 154 **3.** 452.16
5. 218 $\frac{16}{63}$ or 218.06 **7.** 12.56 **9.** 615.44 mm²
11. 113.04 in.² **13.** 113.04 in.² **15.** 38.6851 m²
17. 0.2197 cm² **19.** 142 458.66 km²
21. 7234.56 m² **23.** 16 times **25.** 29.7083 m²

Page 109: **1.** 27.125 m² **3.** 625 cm²
5. 113.04 cm² **7.** 17.415 cm² **9.** 51.$\overline{3}$ cm²

Page 110: **1.** 12 m **3.** 1.5 ft **5.** 0.9 m
7. 6 $\frac{3}{4}$ ft **9.** 72.8 cm² **11.** 4 $\frac{1}{2}$ yd
13. 300 m **15.** 324 ft² **17.** 14 yd
19. 120.9 cm² **21.** 2 ft **23.** 3 yd
25. 0.9 m

Page 111: **1.** $\frac{71}{1}$ **3.** $\frac{14}{5}$ **5.** $\frac{-314}{1}$ **7.** $\frac{306}{100}$
or $\frac{153}{50}$ **9.** 100; 63.$\overline{63}$; 0.$\overline{63}$; 63.00; $\frac{63}{99} = \frac{7}{11}$
11. $\frac{16}{99}$ **13.** $\frac{1}{9}$ **15.** $\frac{79}{90}$ **17.** $\frac{5}{6}$ **19.** $\frac{7}{9}$ **21.** $\frac{5}{12}$

Page 112: **1.** 0.25 **3.** 0.0036 **5.** $\frac{4}{49}$
7. 0.81 **9.** $\frac{36}{49}$ **11.** 0.64 **13.** 0.0081
15. $\frac{4}{81}$ **17.** 0.0049 **19.** 0.0025 **21.** $\frac{7}{12}$
23. $\frac{9}{16}$ **25.** 1.9 **27.** 1.7 **29.** 1.5
31. $\frac{5}{11}$ **33.** 2 and 3

41. 10 and 11 **43.** 18 and 19 **45.** 8 and 9
47. 13 and 14 **49.** 12 and 13

Page 113: **1.** 4; 486; 46 **3.** 4; 486; 24.6 **5.** 48
7. 83 **9.** 235 **11.** 301 **13.** 6.04 **15.** 0.69
17. 44.6 **19.** 36.2

Page 114: **1.** rational **3.** irrational **5.** rational
7. rational **9.** rational **11.** ±4 **13.** ±8 **15.** ±7
17. 0.25 **19.** $\frac{11}{14}$ **21.** 0.0085

Page 115: **1.** {r: r > ⁻8} **3.** {x: x ≤ 5} **5.** {b: b ≥ 6}
7. {x: x ≤ 48} **9.** {t: t < 6} **11.** {y: y ≤ ⁻57}
13. {a: a < 21} **15.** {k: k ≤ 11.1} **17.** {a: a ≠ 4}
19. {n: n ≤ 1 $\frac{1}{5}$}

Page 116: **1.** 15 m **3.** 25 m **5.** 14 m **7.** 84 m
9. 200 m **11.** 20 m

Page 117: **1.** 304 in.² **3.** 115.2 m² **5.** 34.56 cm²
7. 864 cm² **9.** 1944 in.² **11.** 1536 ft²
13. 1940 cm² **15.** 4500 m² **17.** 12 304 cm²

Page 118: **1.** 336 in.² **3.** 152 ft² **5.** 336 ft²
7. 132 m² **9.** 14.7 m²

Page 119: **1.** 1280 m² **3.** 62.4 cm² **5.** 1372 in.²
7. 1112 cm² **9.** 3600 cm²

Page 120: **1.** 678.24 in.² **3.** 748 ft²
5. 244.92 yd² **7.** 1188 ft² **9.** 13 728 cm²
11. 785 ft² **13.** 179.3568 m² **15.** 31 550.72 cm²

Page 121: **1.** 266.9 cm² **3.** 5.495 m²
5. 113.04 m² **7.** 60.7904 cm² **9.** 21 703.68 cm²
11. 6600 cm² **13.** 5544 cm²

Page 122: **1.** 216 ft³ **3.** 1.728 m³ **5.** 54 m²
7. It is eight times greater. **9.** yes; no **11.** 5832
13. 0.216 m³

Page 123: **1.** 114.39 m³ **3.** 1092 in.³
5. 529 200 cm³ **7.** 9484.8 cm³ **9.** 28 800 cm³
11. 1 m³ (1.0944 m³)

Page 124: **1.** 206.64 cm³ **3.** 94.5 in.³
5. 906.36 m³ **7.** 360 yd³ **9.** 3 ft³

Page 125: **1.** 138.6 m³ **3.** 31 $\frac{2}{3}$ cm³ **5.** 14.7 cm³
7. 256 in.³ **9.** 36 cm³

Page 126: **1.** 86.24 m³ **3.** 125.6 dm³
5. 462 cm³ **7.** 8800 cm³ **9.** 282.6 in.³
11. 69.08 in.³ **13.** 33 264 cm³ **15.** cylindrical
container holds 66.6 yd³ more

Page 127: **1.** milliter **3.** kiloliter **5.** liter **7.** 8
9. 70 **11.** 6 **13.** 45 **15.** 30 **17.** 18 000
9. 3.4 **21.** 8.756 **23.** 531.441 **25.** 18.48 L
27. 565.2 kL

Page 128: **1.** grams **3.** kilograms **5.** grams
7. grams **9.** 6 **11.** 6 **13.** 25 **15.** 135 **17.** 2.5
19. 7 **21.** 1.8 kg

Page 129: **23.** e **25.** a **27.** d **29.** 5000
31. 6800 **33.** 4.9 **35.** 2900 **37.** 3800
39. 890 **41.** 11.3 **43.** 2 g **45.** 1000 kg
47. 10.5 dm³; 10.5 kg **49.** 35 kL; 35 000 kg
51. 10 L; 10 kg

Page 130: **1.** x = ⁻3 **3.** x = 4 **5.** x = ⁻3
7. x ≥ ⁻2 **9.** x ≤ ⁺2 **11.** x > ⁺2 **13.** x ≤ ⁺ $\frac{1}{2}$
15. x = ⁺2 **17.** x > 0 **19.** ⁻3 ≤ x ≤ ⁺2

Page 131: **21.** A, O, E, S **23.** C, T, P, G

Page 132: **1.** 3; 4; 5; 6; 7; 8; 9 **3.** 5; 6; 7; 8; 9; 10; 11
5. ⁻10; ⁻7; ⁻4; ⁻1; 2; 5; 8 **7.** 1; (⁻2, 1) **9.** 0 + 3; 3;
(0, 3) **11.** 2 + 3; 5; (2, 5) **13.** 3(⁻1); ⁻3; (⁻1, ⁻3)
15. 3(1); 3; (1, 3) **17.** 12; 11; 8; 7 **19.** ⁻5; ⁻6; ⁻7; ⁻8

Page 133: **1.** 1; 2; 3; 4; 5 **3.** 7; 5; 3; 1; ⁻1

Page 134: **1.** ⁻1; 0; 1; 2; 3; 4; 5; ⁻9; ⁻6; ⁻3; 0; 3; 6; 9;
(1,3) **3.** (⁻3, 5) **5.** (⁻2,⁻1)

Copyright © Sadlier-Oxford

Page 135: **1.** $(^-2, ^-12)$ **3.** $(^-4, ^-1)$ **5.** $(2, 7)$ **7.** $(2, ^-8)$ **9.** $(1, ^-1)$ **11.** $(^-1, 10)$ **13.** $(^-2, 2)$ **15.** $(11, 15)$

Page 136: **1.** $y > 3x - 5$; dotted **3.** $y < 3 - 2x$; dotted **5.** $y \le \frac{2}{3}x - \frac{1}{3}$; solid **7.** $y \ge \frac{-x}{2} + 3$; solid **11.** solid

Page 137: **1.** *a* **3.** *b*

Page 138: **1.** 10; 5; 2; 1; 2; 5; 10 **3.** 7; 2; $^-1$; $^-2$; $^-1$; 2; 7 **5.** $^-9$; $^-4$; $^-1$; 0; $^-1$; $^-4$; $^-9$

Page 139: **1.** *c* **3.** *a* **5.** *b* **7.** *a* **9.** *d* **11.** *a* **13.** *c* **15.** *c*

Page 140: **15.** *c* **17.** *b* **19.** *d* **21.** *d* **23.** *c* **25.** \$206.25 **27.** 90°; 37° **29.** 924 in.^{2}

Page 141: **1.** binomial; D = 4 **3.** trinomial; D = 3 **5.** monomial; D = 5 **7.** monomial; D = 0 **9.** trinomial; D = 3 **11.** trinomial; D = 6 **13.** -27 **15.** $\frac{-1}{81}$ **17.** 0 **19.** $\ell = 23$; $w = 8$; $A = 184$ **21.** height = 4; bases = 9; 5; area = 28

Page 142: **23.** edge = 10; volume = 1000 **25.** $\ell = 7$; $w = 3$; $h = 4$; $V = 84$ **27.** $r = 7$; $h = 17$; $V = 2618$ **29.** *c* **31.** *d*

Page 143: **1.** $35x^2y^3$ **3.** $6c - 8d$ **5.** $\frac{5}{8}pq - 1\frac{1}{9}cd$ **7.** $b^2 - 4.8n^2$ **9.** $-5a^2 + 28a - 1$ **11.** $63m^2 - 36mn + 2n^2$ **13.** $17d^2 - 9$ **15.** $74a^2 - 86b^2$ **17.** $35x^2y + 70xy^2 - 13xy$ **19.** y^2

Page 144: **21.** $20x - 8$ **23.** $24x - 2$ **25.** $10 + a - 3a^2$ **27.** $10 + 4ab - 7a^2b^2 + 9a^4b^3$ **29.** $-15x^5 - x^4y + x^3y^2 + x^2y + 3$ **31.** $5a^2 + 2b - 6$ **33.** $4x^2 + 11x - 31$

Page 145: **1.** a^{11} **3.** n^7 **5.** x^5 **7.** 1 **9.** m^{15} **11.** d^{36} **13.** x^7y^7 **15.** $81x^8y^{12}$ **17.** $1000a^{11}6b^{12}$ **19.** $a^8b^{10}c^{12}$ **21.** $x^{14}y^6z^{10}$ **23.** $32x^{20}y^5z^5$ **25.** 81 **27.** $\frac{1}{16}$ **29.** 49

Page 146: **1.** $60x^{11}$ **3.** $-206a^6$ **5.** $64x^9y^{12}$ **7.** $-80c^{12}$ **9.** $\frac{8}{27}a^{15}b^{12}c^6$ **11.** $-m^5n^5p^5$ **13.** $15a^3b^3 + 20a^5b^4 + 30a^6b^2$ **15.** $-63x^5y^7 + 42x^7y^5 - 49x^9y^3$ **17.** $-2m^6n^8 + 3m^7n^9 - 7m^5n^7$ **19.** $-2.38x^5y^3 - 3.06x^2y^5$ **21.** $8a^4b^3c^5$ **23.** $3a^2k$ **25.** $280xy$ cents **27.** $35a^5b^2$ cm^2

Page 147: **1.** $x^2 + 7x + 12$ **3.** $x^2 - 13x + 42$ **5.** $a^2 + 8a - 65$ **7.** $c^2 + 5c - 84$ **9.** $m^2 + 13m + 45$ **11.** $a^2 - 100$ **13.** $c^2 + 24c + 144$ **15.** $x^2 - 22x + 121$ **17.** $6x^2 + 19x + 15$ **19.** $6x^2 - 35x + 36$ **21.** $24x^2 + 47x - 21$ **23.** $4x^2 - 21x - 18$ **25.** $36x^2 - 121$ **27.** $49x^2 + 70x + 25$ **29.** $100x^2 - 20x + 1$ **31.** $77a^2 - ab - 6b^2$ **33.** $169a^2 - 25b^2$

Page 148: **35.** $48a^2 + 34ab - 105b^2$ **37.** $m^2 - 9n^2$ **39.** $121a^2 - 132ab + 36b^2$ **41.** $c^2 - 28cd + 196d^2$ **43.** $a^3 - 125$ **45.** $x^3 + 6x^2 + 12x + 8$ **47.** $a^3 + 3a^2 - 17a + 6$ **49.** $6 + a - 6a^2 - a^3$ **51.** $8x + 15$ **53.** $x^3 - 11x$ **55.** $(3x^2 + 20x - 63)$ in.^{2} **57.** $(121x^2 - 44x + 4)$ cm^2

Page 149: **1.** $3(2x + 3y)$ **3.** $a^2b^2c^3(ab - bc + ac)$ **5.** $5(r^6 + 2a^2)$ **7.** $5a^2(5a^4 + 2)$ **9.** $25x^2(5x^3 + 7x^2 + 8)$ **11.** $p^2q^3(pq - r)$ **13.** $12x^3y^2z^2(3x^3z^2 + 4x^2)$ **15.** $p^8(1 + p^4 + p^{12})$ **17.** $13a^4b^3(ab^2 - 13)$ **19.** $3(49 - 12x^5 + 96x^7)$ **21.** $9(21x^9 + 30x^4 + 16)$ **23.** $13ab(2a^2b + 3ac + 5bc^2)$ **25.** $8x^2y^3(4x^3 + 5xy + 6y^2)$

Page 150: **27.** $10cd2(4c3 - 5cd + d)$ **29.** $5x^3y(-2x^2 - 15xy - 9y^2)$ **31.** $11a^4bc^2(-3ab^2 - 4bc - 2ac^2)$ **33.** $0.2x^2y^2z^2(xy^3 - 4y^2z + 6x^2z^2)$ **35.** $0.3a^2b^2c(9ab + bc - 2a^2c)$ **37.** $2xy(x - y)$ **39.** $c^4 + 24$

Page 151: **1.** $(x + 5)(x + 1)$ **3.** $(y - 19)(y - 1)$ **5.** $(b - 16)(b - 4)$ **7.** $(y - 3)(y - 8)$ **9.** $(a + 16)(a + 1)$ **11.** $(x - 18)(x + 3)$ **13.** $(a - 5)(a + 2)$ **15.** $(x - 36)(x - 5)$ **17.** $(y + 10)(y + 12)$ **19.** $(m - 9)(m + 4)$ **21.** $(c - 4d)(c - 11d)$ **23.** $(y - 18)(y - 8)$ **25.** $(n - 9)(n - 1)$ **27.** $(m^2 - 7n^2)(m^2 + 15n^2)$ **29.** $(x + 15)(x + 8)$ **31.** $(d + 13)(d + 5)$ **33.** $(c^2 - 23d^2)(c^2 + d^2)$ **35.** $(x - 12)(x - 5)$

Page 152: **37.** $(a + 4b)(a + 2b)$ **39.** $(x - 4y)(x - 8y)$ **41.** $(b - 10c)(b + 2c)$ **43.** $(y + 16z)(y - 3z)$ **45.** $(m + 7n)(m + 2n)$ **47.** $(r - 5s)(r - 10s)$ **49.** $(a + 7b)(a + 9b)$ **51.** $(x - 4)(x - 3)$ **53.** $(x + 14)(x + 3)$

Page 153: **1.** $(3x + 1)(x + 1)$ **3.** $(12 - 7x)(5 + 2x)$ **5.** $(6x + 5)(x - 2)$ **7.** $(5a - 2)(3a - 1)$ **9.** $(4r + 3s)(6r + 5s)$ **11.** $(6a - 1)(5a - 2)$ **13.** $(7x + 2)(5x + 3)$ **15.** $(7a + 4b)(3a - 10b)$ **17.** $(3x - 4)(3x + 1)$ **19.** $(2x + 1)(8x - 1)$ **21.** $(8c - 9d)(3c + d)$ **23.** $(10x - 1)(2x - 3)$ **25.** $(5x - 1)(x + 1)$ **27.** $(9a - 5b)(5a + 9b)$ **29.** $(6x - 7)(2x - 1)$ **31.** $(5x - 2)(3x - 4)$ **33.** $(3x^3 + 11y)(2x^3 - 5y)$

Page 154: **35.** $(7x - 11y)(11x - 7y)$ **37.** $(2a + 3b)(3a - 2b)$ **39.** $(5x^2 - 4y)(3x^2 - 2y)$ **41.** $(19x^3 - 2y)(x^3 - 3y)$ **43.** $(6x^2 - 5y^2)(2x^2 - 5y^2)$ **45.** $(6x^3 - 5y^3)(x^3 + 2y^3)$ **47.** $(9h^2 - 2b^2)(2h^2 + 3b^2)$ **49.** $(5a^3 + b^3)(7a^3 - 8b^3)$ **51.** $(2x + 7)(x + 3)$

Page 155: **1.** $x^2 + 10x + 25$ **3.** $9a^2 - 12a + 4$ **5.** $m^2 + 4mn + 4n^2$ **7.** $4a^2 + 12a + 9$ **9.** $m^2 - 18mn + 81n^2$ **11.** $(x + 7)^2$ **13.** $(y - 10)^2$ **15.** $(2x - 7)^2$ **17.** $(3a - 11b)^2$ **19.** $(0.2x + 0.3y)^2$ **21.** $11x + 1$

Page 156: **1.** $x^2 - 25$ **3.** $196a^2 - 1$ **5.** $x^2 - 49y^2$ **7.** $9a^2 - 25b^2$ **9.** $\frac{16}{49}c^2 - \frac{4}{9}d^2$ **11.** $(x - 4)(x + 4)$ **13.** $(3 + 5a)(3 - 5a)$ **15.** $(\frac{1}{2}x + \frac{1}{3}y)(\frac{1}{2}x - \frac{1}{3}y)$ **17.** $(13x + 5y)(13x - 5y)$ **19.** $(ab + c)(ab - c)$ **21.** $(1.1c + 0.3d)$

Copyright © Sadlier-Oxford

$(1.1c - 0.3d)$ **23.** $(13x + 2y)(13x - 2y)$

Page 157: **1.** $7(x + 5y)$ **3.** $5b(3a + 7c)$
5. $5(x + 2y)(x - 2y)$ **7.** $m(m + n^2)(m - n^2)$
9. $4y(x - 1)^2$ **11.** $3x(x - 2)(x + 1)$
13. $5a(xy + z)(xy - z)$ **15.** $5(m - 3n)^2$
17. $a(2a + 1)(a - 1)$ **19.** $3b(3 + 2b)(2 + b)$
21. $4xy(2x - y)(3x - 2y)$

Page 158: **23.** $3(y^2 + 2)$
25. $m(x - 2)(x + 1)$
27. $mn(n - m)$
29. $x(x + 1)$
31. $\pi r(2 - r)$
33. $3x^2y^2(9 - y)^2$
35. $(6xy + 7z)^2$
37. Prime
39. $4(m^4 + 36n^6)$
41. $9(2a^2 + 5b^2)(2a^2 - 5b^2)$
43. $(11xy + 13z)(4xy - 5z)$
45. $(6ab + 7c)(7ab - 4c)$ **47.** Prime
49. $6a^3(rs + 3t^2)(rs - 3t^2)$ **51.** $6y(n^6 + 36)$

Page 159: **53.** $(y - 4)(y + 1)$
55. $(y + 4)(y - 1)$ **57.** $(x - 7)(x - 2)$
59. $(x + 7)(x - 2)$ **61.** $(x - 7)(x + 2)$
63. $(y + 50)(y - 2)$ **65.** $(x - 10)(x - 2)$
67. $(y + 25)(y + 4)$ **69.** $(2 + y)(1 - y)$
71. $(x^2 + 1)(x + 3)(x - 3)$ **73.** $a(3 - a)$
75. Prime **77.** $9x^2(x^3 + 3x - 5)$
79. $y(x^2y + 1)$ **81.** $x(3x^3 + 11x + 13)$
83. $(4n - r)(2n + r)$ **85.** $[(e + f) + 3]^2$
87. $9(r + m)(r - m)$

Page 160: **89.** $(x + 2)^2(3xy)$
91. $x(x + 2)(x + 1)$

Page 161: **1.** a^4 **3.** $3x^2$ **5.** $-4x$ **7.** $15m^3n$
9. $21c^3d^2$ **11.** $ab + 1$ **13.** $-8xy^2 + 11$
15. $-14a^2 + 9a$ **17.** $5x - 6x^3$ **19.** $-11r^2 + 5r^4$

Page 162: **21.** $2 - b$ **23.** $7 + 4m$
25. $m^2 + 7m + 5$ **27.** $r^2 - 7r + 4 + \frac{24}{r-3}$
29. $3x^2 - 2xy + 5y^2$ **31.** $2a^2 + 3ab - 4b^2$
33. $(x - 2)$ hours

Page 163:
1. $\frac{b}{4c}$ **3.** $\frac{5+x}{-2}$ **5.** $\frac{b+3}{-5}$ **7.** $\frac{4x-y}{x}$
9. $\frac{x-6}{x+1}$ **11.** $\frac{d}{d+2}$ **13.** 2 **15.** $\frac{a+2}{12}$ **17.** $\frac{5a+5}{a^3}$

Page 164:
19. $\frac{2}{x-2}$ **21.** 1 **23.** $\frac{8y}{5x^2}$ **25.** $\frac{xy}{30z}$ **27.** $2a - 2$
29. $\frac{a^2-5a}{3a-9}$ **31.** $\frac{-1}{4}$ **33.** $\frac{-1}{2}$ **35.** 7

Page 165: **1.** $\frac{7}{2x}$ **3.** 11 **5.** $\frac{1}{y}$ **7.** $\frac{x+2}{x-2}$
9. $x + y$ **11.** $\frac{2}{x+y}$ **13.** $\frac{a^2-2b^2+3y^2}{a^2+y^2}$

Page 166: **15.** $\frac{4}{a-3}$ **17.** $\frac{2x+9}{4x+3}$
19. 45 mph **21.** $\frac{3a-2}{6}$

Page 167: **1.** $4x$ **3.** $14x^2y^2$ **5.** $4x^2 - 28x + 49$
7. $(x - 3y)$ or $(3y - x)$ **9.** $x^2 - 5x$
11. $4x + 16$ **13.** $2ab + b^2$ **15.** $3x - 6$

Page 168: **1.** $\frac{3x}{8y}$ **3.** $\frac{4-7x}{x^2}$ **5.** $\frac{7c-9b}{abc}$
7. $\frac{4a+9}{4a}$ **9.** $\frac{9d^2-27d+4}{6d^2}$ **11.** $\frac{x^2+1}{x}$
13. $\frac{x^2-3x-8}{x+2}$ **15.** $\frac{-3}{3x-5y}$ **17.** $\frac{9}{4a-3}$

Page 169: **19.** $\frac{3y-75}{y^2-25}$ **21.** $\frac{7y+5x}{x^2y-xy^2}$
23. $\frac{-3x-29}{x^3-2x^2-9x+18}$ **25.** $\frac{4x-6}{3x^3-4x^2-5x+2}$
27. $\frac{3x^2-19}{x^3-19x+30}$

Page 170: **1.** 5 **3.** $\frac{-6}{13}$ **5.** $\frac{5}{4}$ **7.** $\frac{-3}{4}$ **9.** 2

Page 171: **11.** $\frac{-2}{3}$ **13.** -7 **15.** undefined
17. positive **19.** negative **21.** negative
23. $m(\overline{AB}) = \frac{-5}{3}$; $m(\overline{BC}) = \frac{1}{3}$; $m(\overline{AC}) = \frac{7}{3}$
25. b and c

Page 172: **1.** $m = \frac{2}{5}, b = \frac{-3}{5}$ **3.** $m = 4; b = 7$
5. $m = -2; b = 0$ **7.** $m = \frac{-4}{9}; b = \frac{2}{3}$
9. $m = \frac{-1}{8}; b = \frac{5}{2}$ **11.** $3y - x = 9$
13. $y + 4x = 5$ **15.** $y + 2x = 0$
17. parallel **19.** perpendicular

Page 173: **1.** $3x - 4y + 15 = 0$
3. $4x - 3y - 11 = 0$
5. $20x + 9y + 1 = 0$ **7.** $x - y = 0$
9. $3x - y - 11 = 0$ **11.** $x + 2y + 5 = 0$
13. $3x - 5y + 15 = 0$ **15.** $5x - y + 7 = 0$
17. $3x + 2y + 8 = 0$

Page 174: **17.** $x + y = 0$ **19.** $2x + y + 4 = 0$
21. $x + 2y - 4 = 0$ **23.** $y - 2 = 0$
25. $3x - 4y - 13 = 0$

Page 175: **1.** $\frac{-9}{4}$ **3.** -2 **5.** $x + 5y - 23 = 0$
7. $m = 1; b = \frac{4}{5}$ **9.** $2x + 5y - 19 = 0$
11. $13x - 9y + 8 = 0$ **13.** $\frac{-1}{3}; \frac{12}{5}$

Page 176: **1.** $4\sqrt{2}$ **3.** $8x\sqrt{2x}$ **5.** $12ab\sqrt{2a}$
7. $15x\sqrt{2}$ **9.** $16x\sqrt{2y}$ **11.** $\frac{\sqrt{2}}{2}$ **13.** $\frac{\sqrt{21xy}}{3y}$
15. $\frac{2a^3\sqrt{30ac}}{5c}$ **17.** $\frac{\sqrt{6a}}{22}$ **19.** $\frac{xy^2\sqrt{z}}{z^2}$
21. $\frac{4\sqrt{5a}}{5a}$ **23.** 8

Page 177: **25.** $\frac{5\sqrt{a+b}}{a+b}$ **27.** $\frac{3\sqrt{x-y}}{x-y}$
29. $x\sqrt{3x}$ **31.** $\frac{x\sqrt{xy}}{11y^2}$ **33.** $\frac{x\sqrt{5xy}}{5}$
35. $\frac{8a^2\sqrt{6b}}{3b}$ **37.** rational **39.** rational
41. rational **43.** irrational

Page 178: **1.** $11\sqrt{3}$ **3.** $2\sqrt{x}$ **5.** $4\sqrt{2}$
7. $5\sqrt{3}$ **9.** $2\sqrt{2}$ **11.** $-8x^2\sqrt{2}$ **13.** $7\sqrt{xy}$

Copyright © Sadlier-Oxford

15. $5b\sqrt{2ac}$ **17.** $\frac{2\sqrt{11}}{35}$ **19.** $\frac{3\sqrt{2}}{x^2}$

Page 179: **21.** $-7x\sqrt{2x}$ **23.** $30\sqrt{3}$ inches **25.** 15 meters **27.** 7 cm

Page 180: **1.** $30x$ **3.** $60x^2\sqrt{3}$ **5.** $-14a^4$ **7.** $25x\sqrt{2}$ **9.** $2\sqrt{6}$ **11.** $9x$ **13.** $2x^2yz^3$ **15.** 216 **17.** $140x^2\sqrt{3}$ **19.** $36a^2b^2\sqrt{c}$ **21.** $3\sqrt{2} - 3\sqrt{5}$

Page 181: **23.** 7 **25.** $\sqrt{3}$ **27.** $\frac{\sqrt{6x}}{2}$ **29.** $\frac{\sqrt{10y}}{2}$ **31.** $6\sqrt{2x}$ **33.** $\frac{\sqrt{15}+\sqrt{10}}{5}$ **35.** $54\sqrt{3xy}$ **37.** $11 - 5\sqrt{3}$ **39.** -67

Page 182: **1.** $\{-2, -7\}$ **3.** $\{6, 3\}$ **5.** $\{-7, 4\}$ **7.** $\{11, -5\}$ **9.** $\{0, -9\}$ **11.** $\{0, 15\}$ **13.** $\{8, 7\}$ **15.** $\{-12, -4\}$ **17.** $\left\{\frac{1}{2}, -\frac{1}{3}\right\}$ **19.** $\left\{\frac{3}{4}, -\frac{1}{8}\right\}$ **21.** $\{6, -9\}$ **23.** $\{-12, 5\}$

Page 183: **25.** $x^2 = 9x + 22$; $x = 11$ **27.** $w(w + 5) = 84$; width = 7 m; length = 12 m **29.** $n^2 - 27 = 6n$; $n = 9$ or -3

Page 184: **1.** $\frac{-1 \pm \sqrt{5}}{2}$ **3.** $-2 \pm \sqrt{10}$ **5.** $\frac{-3 \pm \sqrt{17}}{2}$ **7.** $\frac{6 \pm \sqrt{33}}{3}$ or $2 \pm \frac{\sqrt{33}}{3}$ **9.** $\frac{2 \pm \sqrt{5}}{2}$ or $1 \pm \frac{\sqrt{5}}{2}$ **11.** $\frac{3}{2}$ **13.** $h = 3\sqrt{2}$ cm; $b = 6\sqrt{2}$ cm

Page 185: **1.** $1 \pm \sqrt{11}$ **3.** $-3 \pm \sqrt{7}$ **5.** $\frac{-1 \pm \sqrt{2}}{2}$ **7.** $\frac{-2 \pm \sqrt{3}}{3}$ **9.** $\frac{3 \pm \sqrt{13}}{4}$ **11.** 7 and 17 **13.** 8 or -9

Page 186: **1.** $-3, 7$ **3.** $\frac{3}{5}, \frac{1}{2}$ **5.** $3 \pm \sqrt{14}$ **7.** $1, -\frac{2}{3}$ **9.** 6,0 **11.** 7,-4 **13.** $-\frac{3}{2}, -1$ **15.** $\frac{1 \pm \sqrt{5}}{4}$ **17.** ± 15

Page 187: **19.** $-5, 2$ **21.** $-\frac{1}{2}$ **23.** $\frac{2}{5}, -\frac{1}{6}$ **25.** $2 \pm 3\sqrt{2}$ **27.** $-\frac{3}{2}$ or 3 **29.** $\frac{1}{3}$ or 5 **31.** 8 in. and 15 in.

Page 188: **1.** c **3.** b **5.** b **7.** a **9.** b **11.** b **13.** a **15.** $x^2 + 15^2 = 25^2$; $x = 20$ ft

Page 189: **1.** 5 mi **3.** 951.39 mL or 950.5251 mL **5.** $w = 7$ ft; $\ell = 29$ ft

Page 190: **1.** c **3.** d **5.** d **7.** b **9.** d **11.** d **13.** a

Page 191: **15.** d **17.** c **19.** c **21.** b **23.** a

Page 192: **25.** d **27.** c **29.** d **31.** b **33.** a **35.** d

Page 193: **37.** *a* **39.** b **41.** $\frac{6y + 3x + 4xy}{x^2y^2}$ **43.** $\frac{2\sqrt{3x^3 + 9x}}{x^2 + 3}$ **45.** $\frac{-a^2 - 20a + 10}{(a+3)(a-5)(a-2)}$ or $\frac{-a^2 - 20a + 10}{a^3 - 4a^2 - 11a + 30}$ **47.** 14 dimes; 6 nickels **49.** 16 cm, 30 cm, 34 cm

Copyright © Sadlier-Oxford